From Sea to Shining Sea

FROM SEA TO SHINING SEA

A Treasury of American Folklore and Folk Songs

ILLUSTRATED BY ELEVEN CALDECOTT MEDAL AND FOUR CALDECOTT HONOR BOOK ARTISTS

Molly Bang   *Anita Lobel*

Marcia Brown   *Jerry Pinkney*

Barbara Cooney   *John Schoenherr*

Donald Crews   *Marc Simont*

Leo and Diane Dillon   *Chris Van Allsburg*

Richard Egielski   *David Wiesner*

Trina Schart Hyman   *Ed Young*

COMPILED BY AMY L. COHN

SCHOLASTIC HARDCOVER

SCHOLASTIC INC.,   NEW YORK

Library of Congress Cataloging-in-Publication Data
From sea to shining sea / selected by Amy L. Cohn;
illustrated by Molly Bang . . . et al.
p.   cm.
Includes bibliographical references.   Includes indexes.
Summary: A compilation of more than 140 folk songs, tales,
poems, and stories telling the history of America and reflecting
its multicultural society. Illustrated by eleven Caldecott
award-winning and four Caldecott Honor Book artists.
ISBN 0-590-42868-3
1. United States — Literary collections.   2. Children's
literature, American.   [1. United States — Literary
collections.]   I. Cohn, Amy L.   II. Bang, Molly, ill.
PZ5.F918   1993   810.8 — dc20   92-30598   CIP
AC
12 11 10 9 8 7 6 5 4 3 2 1   3 4 5 6 7 8/9
Printed in Italy
First Scholastic printing, October 1993

For my mother, who loves stories, and for my father,
who loves words. You gave them both to me.
— A.L.C.

A book as comprehensive as this one could not come to be without the help of many people. My thanks to:

Mary Ake, Walt Whitman Elementary School, Littleton, Colorado; Bridget Bennett, Memorial Hall Library, Andover, Massachusetts; Carol Birch, Chappaqua, New York, Public Library; Rita Butler, Alice Hoffman, Lucy Marx, and Sue Pile, Louisville, Kentucky, Public Library; Margaret Coughlan, The Library of Congress Center for Children's Books, Washington, D.C.; Ellin Greene, Consultant, Library Services for Children, Point Pleasant, New Jersey; Grace Greene, Vermont Department of Libraries, Montpelier, Vermont; Susan Hepler, Alexandria, Virginia; Marilyn Iarusso, New York, New York, Public Library; Eric A. Kimmel, Portland State University, Portland, Oregon; Carla Kozak and John Philbrook, San Francisco, California, Public Library; Koung Shin and Ming Hua Lee, Bayside, New York; Margaret Read MacDonald, King County Library System, Washington; Osee Mallio, formerly of Robbins Public Library, Arlington, Massachusetts; Donna Polhamus, Cary Memorial Library, Lexington, Massachusetts; Judith Rovenger, Westchester County Library System, New York; Terri Schmitz and Leo Landry, The Children's Book Shop, Brookline, Massachusetts; Leda Schubert, Vermont Department of Schools, Montpelier, Vermont; Suzanne Sigman, The Little Book Room, Milton, Massachusetts; the staff and librarians of the Beatley Library, Simmons College, Boston, Massachusetts; Charlotte Smutko, Washington, D.C., Public Library; Lynda Welborn, Colorado State Department of Education, Denver, Colorado; and Harriet Williams, formerly of Durham Academy, Durham, North Carolina.

With special thanks to Ellen Fader, Westport Public Library, Connecticut; Jean Feiwel, Dianne Hess, and the incredible professionals of Scholastic Inc., New York, New York; Ruth I. Gordon, Ph.D., Critical Reviewing Unltd., Cloverdale, California; John Langstaff, Revels, Inc., Cambridge, Massachusetts; Rachel Miller, New York, New York, who selected each song with taste, talent, tact, and an abiding respect for those young and not so young who would play and sing them; Carolyn Polese, Humboldt State University, Arcata, California; Lolly Robinson, Cambridge, Massachusetts; and finally, to Suzy Schmidt, Los Angeles, California. It is not often, E. B. White wrote, that someone comes along who is a true friend and a good writer. Suzy, like Charlotte, you're both.

— A.L.C.

CONTENTS

❧

THE SHOT HEARD 'ROUND THE WORLD
Illustrated by Anita Lobel

BRIDGING THE GAP
Illustrated by Molly Bang

WATER, WATER EVERYWHERE
Illustrated by Marcia Brown

LET MY PEOPLE GO
Illustrated by Jerry Pinkney

I'VE BEEN WORKING ON THE RAILROAD
Illustrated by David Wiesner

O PIONEERS!
Illustrated by Barbara Cooney

PART 3 ONLY IN AMERICA

TRICKSTERS, ON TWO FEET, FOUR — OR MORE
Illustrated by Trina Schart Hyman

NO-SENSE NONSENSE
Illustrated by Donald Crews

FEATHERS AND FUR, SCALES AND TAILS
Illustrated by John Schoenherr

AMERICAN GIANTS ON THE JOB
Illustrated by Chris Van Allsburg

TAKE ME OUT TO THE BALL GAME
Illustrated by Marc Simont

SCARY, CREEPY, SPOOKY GHOST STORIES
Illustrated by Ed Young

PART 4 IN OUR TIME

IN OUR TIME

*I*NTRODUCTION

❧

The book you are about to begin is filled with American folklore. Just what is folklore? Simply, folklore is a story, a rhyme, a song, a saying passed down orally through the generations. In some ways folklore is a lot like the popular party game, telephone. Each time someone hears a story or song and repeats it, he or she changes it slightly. A gray dress becomes a blue blouse, a woman who lives in a shack in the woods suddenly moves to a cabin on a hill, a boy who owns a spotted dog gives him up for a black one. And other changes occur as a story is passed from person to person. Each teller infuses in the tale a part of himself or herself, filling it with his or her ideas about the world, its people, and its creatures.

Just what is American folklore? Like our country American folklore is big and bold, full of life and full of humor. It also reflects the experiences of hundreds of groups who came from distant shores to make this land their home. Like our country, American folklore molds and blends different cultures without destroying their essences. It's a story from Portugal found in Puerto Rico told by a Mexican living in California. It's a lament sung by Chinese workers completing our nation's first transcontinental railroad system. And it's a tale told by Africans enslaved in the American South about a feisty fellow named Brer Rabbit, kin to the West African spider-man Anansi. American folklore, it seems to me, is both cultural *and* historical. Our stories and songs don't exist in a vacuum. They can, along with tales that interpret the past from a contemporary perspective, help us understand who we are as a people and what we have accomplished as a nation.

As I began work on the book that eventually became *From Sea to Shining Sea,* I wanted more than anything to capture and to celebrate the ideas I've just described. This desire guided me as I searched through hundreds of sources and spoke with countless librarians, storytellers, academics, and booksellers. And it also made me think about being an American. How do I fit in, I wondered? What do I think about when I think about my country, about its people, about its history, about its stories?

I grew up in New York City in the borough of Queens where everyone I knew — or at least everyone's parents, grandparents, or great-grandparents — came from some place else: Italy or Ireland, Poland or Puerto Rico, China, Japan, India, or Africa.

I read a lot as a kid, mostly historical fiction. Elizabeth George Speare and Laura Ingalls Wilder were particular favorites. In their books I met people — regular, ordinary people — who built boats and pushed plows, who tended gardens and raised children, people in whose lives, I now realize, the story of a nation is told.

When I reached junior high school my seventh-grade social studies teacher, Mrs. Louise Burke, introduced me to the idea that understanding a nation and its past requires more than memorizing the date of a battle or the names of successive presidents. Compare different interpretations of the same event and put them into a context that makes sense in terms of historical inquiry and personal perspective, she instructed. Draw your own conclusions, but only after you've explored all the angles.

Later on, I spent my junior year of college in Aberdeen, Scotland, where my fellow exchange students and I talked a lot about what it might mean to be an American. America, we concluded, meant opportunity. No barrier would stand between us and the future we chose if we were willing to work hard to realize our dreams. Many of the young people we met at the university, from Britain and from nations around the world, did not share the same sense of expectation and confidence.

A diverse neighborhood — a love of history and of story — an appreciation for the value of an individual point of view about the past — optimism about the future — faith in the rewards that come from work: The experiences and ideas that have shaped my view of my country and of myself have formed *From Sea to Shining Sea*.

The book begins — where else? — in the beginning. American folklore, history, and culture first meet in the soil. The United States may have declared itself an independent country one hot July day in Philadelphia in 1776, but the land preceded that announcement by more generations than we can count. Next, the American story is told through each successive wave of immigrants to find their way here.

Thousands of years ago the first of these immigrants walked across an ancient land bridge between Asia and Alaska, following the animals that provided them with food, clothing, and shelter. Centuries later more people arrived in wooden ships from the other side of the Atlantic Ocean. Some came by choice. Others were forced to endure in chains the misery and horror of the Middle Passage. In the early part of this century, the United States welcomed millions, mostly immigrants from Eastern and Southern Europe, who took the courageous step away from all they knew to seek a better life for themselves and their children. Still more arrive daily. From the islands of the Caribbean, from ancient Asian nations, from all corners of the earth, people come to our country to pursue their dreams. And they bring their stories with them.

From Sea to Shining Sea follows this historical progression. The book is divided into four parts. First comes "In the Beginning." It celebrates the traditional American Indian view of our vast continent and how it came to be. Next is "From Sea to Shining Sea," which describes through story and song and an occasional historical essay some of the ways the United States grew into a westernized nation. The third part is called "Only in America." Here's a place to kick back and have fun. These stories and songs about tricksters, animals, ghosts, and buried treasure reflect some of the characteristics of folklore the world over. At the same time they provide clues to our unique American character. "In Our Time" concludes *From Sea to Shining Sea*. It tells the story of our century, the twentieth century. Pivotal events, such as immigration, economic depression, and war, have inspired many to create work that is now part of our collective national experience.

Do the selections have anything in common? I chose stories that I found a joy to read aloud and a pleasure to listen to; songs that anyone, of any age and ability, might sing and play. As I researched and read, listened and learned, I became determined to strike a balance between what might be familiar to many and what might be new.

Familiar to the Plains Indians is this belief: *Miakuye oyasin*. It means "we are all related." The phrase refers specifically to the common bond between human beings and animals, but it also describes what being an American has come to mean to me and what I hope this book comes to mean to its readers.

Despite different backgrounds and experiences, Americans share a single nation that stretches from sea to shining sea. Our history, our stories, and our songs belong, like the nation, to us all.

— AMY L. COHN
New York, New York

Part 1

⤙

In the

Beginning

Where did our country begin? It began
with the land. It began with the animals.
It began with the first people.

⤙

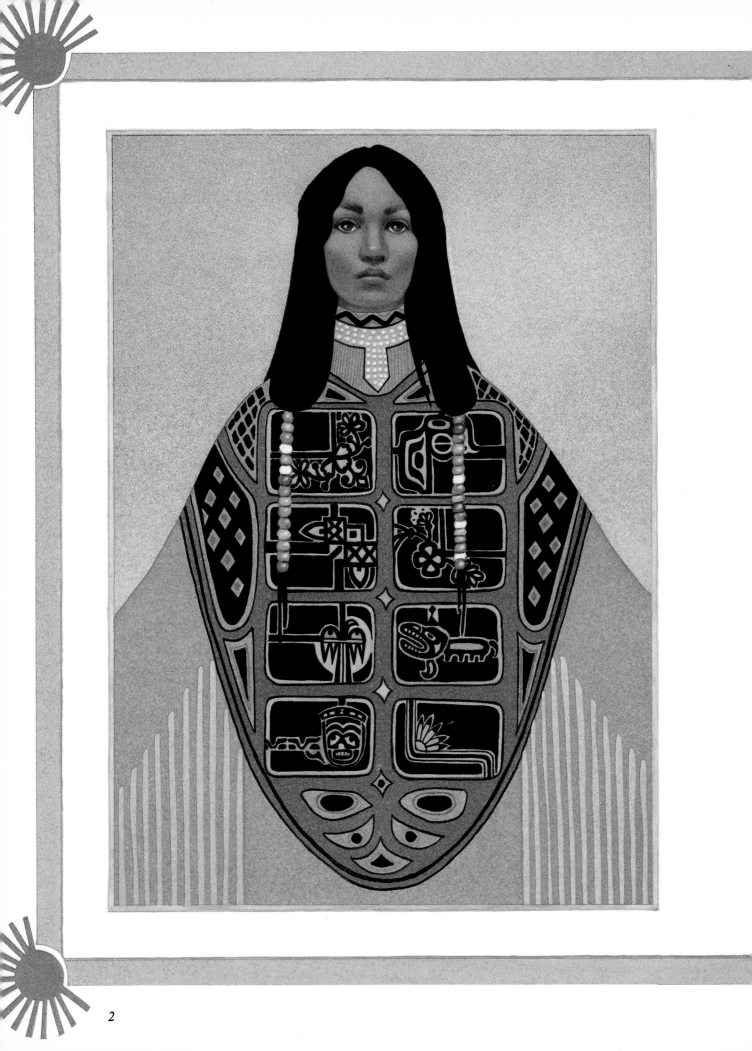

Leo and Diane Dillon

IN THE BEGINNING

The Creation

RETOLD BY JOSEPH BRUCHAC

*How was the earth formed? The Iroquois people of the Northeast Woodlands
say our land began when Muskrat placed a speck of earth on Turtle's back.*

Before this world came to be,
there lived in the Sky-World
an ancient chief.
In the center of his land
grew a beautiful tree
which had four white roots
stretching to each
of the four directions:
North, South, East, and West.
From that beautiful tree,
all good things grew.

Then it came to be
that the beautiful tree
was uprooted and through
the hole it made in the Sky-World
fell the youthful wife
of the ancient chief,
a handful of seeds,
which she grabbed from the tree
as she fell, clutched in her hand.

Far below there were only water
and water creatures
who looked up as they swam.

"Someone comes," said the duck.
"We must make room for her."

The great turtle swam up
from his place in the depths.
"There is room on my back,"
the great turtle said.

"But there must be earth
where she can stand," said the duck.
And so he dove beneath the waters,
but he could not reach the bottom.

"I shall bring up earth,"
the loon then said and he dove,
too,
but could not reach the bottom.

"I shall try," said the beaver
and he, too, dove but
could not reach the bottom.

Finally the muskrat tried.
He dove as deeply as he could,
swimming until his lungs almost burst.
With one paw he touched the bottom
and came up with a tiny speck
of earth clutched in his paw.

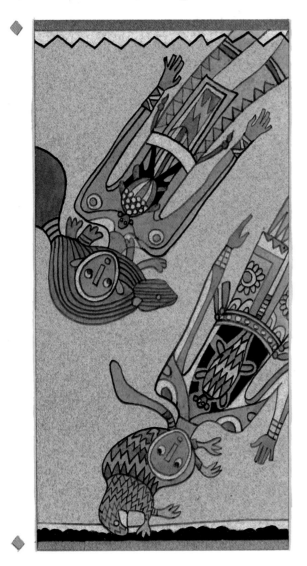

"Place the earth on my back,"
the great turtle said,
and as they spread
the tiny speck of earth, it grew
larger and larger and larger
until it became the whole world.

Then it was that the first plants grew and life on this new earth began.

Then two swans flew up
and between their wings
they caught the woman
who fell from the sky.
They brought her gently
down to the earth
where she dropped her handful
of seeds from the Sky-World.

Raven Brings Fresh Water

RETOLD BY FRAN MARTIN

All the indigenous people of the Pacific Northwest tell tales about Raven, who is sometimes a trickster and sometimes a good friend to humankind. Here, he brings fresh water to the thirsty people who lived along that rock-strewn, fogbound coast.

In the beginning there was nothing but soft darkness, and Raven beat and beat with his wings until the darkness packed itself down into solid earth. Then there was only the icy black ocean and a narrow strip of shoreline. But people came soon to live along the coast. And Raven felt sorry for them, poor, sickly things, who never had any sunshine. They lived by chewing on nuts and leaves, and crushed the roots of the alder trees for something to drink.

I must help them, thought Raven, and he flew down to earth, calling, *"Ga, ga, ga!"* and gathered the people together.

Like ghosts they were, shadowy and pale in the misty darkness.

"Raven has come!" they told each other. "It is Raven-Who-Sets-Things-Right."

The poor things were encouraged, and they gathered round to see what he would do.

Raven plucked a branch from an alder, and scattered the leaves on the surface of a pool. At once the leaves were sucked under, and the water started to bubble. After the pool had boiled for a moment, the surface cleared and fish began to jump there. So that was how Raven gave the people fish.

But now that they had fish to eat, they were thirstier than ever. They called on Raven, and down he came, and the people said, "Here is Raven-Who-Sets-Things-Right."

Raven knew that there was only one spring of fresh water in all the world. A man named Ganook had built his house around it, and refused to give any away.

Maybe, thought Raven, I can drink enough to carry some back to the people.

So he went to the house and asked to come in, and Ganook was very glad to have his company. Raven sat down and made polite conversation, and pretty soon he asked for a drink of water.

"Very well," said Ganook grudgingly, and showed him the spring, a crystal pool welling up in a basin of rock.

"Don't drink it all!" Ganook warned him. "You know that's the only fresh water in all the world."

Raven knew it well; that was what he had come for. But he said, "Just a sip!" and drank until he staggered.

"Hold on there, Raven!" cried Ganook. "Are you trying to drink the well dry?"

That was just what Raven was trying to do, but he passed it off lightly. He made himself comfortable close to the fire and said, "Ganook, let me tell you a story."

Then Raven started out on a long, dull

9

story about four dull brothers who went on a long, dull journey. As he went along he made up dull things to add to it, and Ganook's eyelids drooped, and Raven spoke softly, and more and more slowly, and Ganook's chin dropped upon his chest.

"So then," said Raven gently, with his eyes on Ganook, "on and on through the long, gray valley through the soft, gray fog went the four tall, gray brothers. And now, snore!" And Ganook began to snore.

Quick as a thought, Raven darted to the spring and stuck his beak into the water. But no sooner had he lifted his head to swallow than Ganook started up with a terrible snort, and said, "Go on, go on, I'm listening! I'm not asleep." Then he shook his head and blinked his eyes and said, "Where are you, Raven? What are you doing?"

"Just walking around for exercise," Raven assured him, and back he went, and in a low, unchanging voice he went on with the long, dull story of the four brothers. No sooner had he started than Ganook began to nod, and his chin dropped down, and he jerked it back and opened his eyes and scowled at Raven, and nodded his head and said, "Go on! What next?" and his head dropped down upon his chest.

"So on and on," said Raven slowly, "over the hills, went the four tall, gray brothers. The air was thick and gray around them. Fog was stealing softly over the mountains. Fog before them, fog behind them, soft, cloudy fog. And now, snore!" And Ganook began to snore.

Quietly Raven slipped to the spring and, *glub, glub, glub,* he drank up the water until the pool was dry. But as he lifted his head for a last, long gulp, Ganook leapt up and saw what he was doing.

"So, Raven!" shouted Ganook. "You think you can lull me to sleep and steal my water!"

He picked up his club and started to chase Raven round and round the fire. Raven would run a few steps and flap his big wings and rise a few inches off the floor. Then with a last tremendous flap he went sailing toward the open smoke hole. But he had swallowed so much water that he stuck fast in the opening, and there he struggled, while Ganook shouted, "You squint-eyed Raven, I've got you now, Raven! You miserable thief!" And Ganook threw green alder logs on the fire and made a great smoke that came billowing up and almost choked Raven to death.

Raven hung there, strangling and struggling, until at last he pulled free with a mighty wrench and went wobbling heavily off across the sky. He was so heavy he flew in a crooked line, and as he flew he spurted little streams of water from his bill. These became rivers, first the Nass and the Sitka, then the Taku and the Iskut and the Stikine. Since Raven flew in a crooked line, all the rivers are crooked as snakes. Here and there he scattered single drops, and these became narrow creeks and salmon pools.

And so Raven brought fresh water to the people — but he bore the mark of that smoke hole ever after. He had gone to Ganook as a great, white, snowy creature, but from that day on, Raven was black, as black as the endless sky of the endless night.

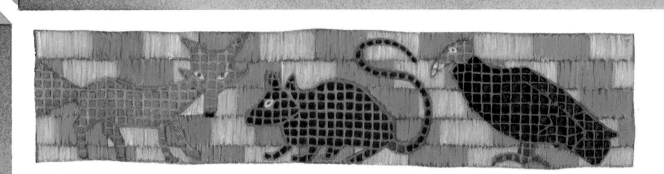

Grandmother Spider Steals the Sun

RETOLD BY JAMES MOONEY

Possum has a tail without fur. Buzzard has a head without feathers. Why? Because both tried to steal the sun — and failed. Can quick-witted, fast-moving Grandmother Spider succeed?

In the beginning there was only blackness, and nobody could see anything. People kept bumping into each other and groping blindly. They said, "What this world needs is light."

Fox said he knew some people on the other side of the world who had plenty of light, but they were too greedy to share it with others. Possum said he would be glad to steal a little of it. "I have a bushy tail," he said. "I can hide the light inside all that fur." Then he set out for the other side of the world. There he found the sun hanging in a tree and lighting up everything. He sneaked over to the sun, picked out a tiny piece of light, and stuffed it into his tail. But the light was hot and burned all the fur off. The people discovered his theft and took back the light, and ever since, Possum's tail has been bald.

"Let me try," said Buzzard. "I know better than to hide a piece of stolen light in my tail. I'll put it on my head." He flew to the other side of the world and, diving straight into the sun, seized it in his claws. He put it on his head, but it burned his head feathers off. The people grabbed the sun away from him, and ever since that time Buzzard's head has remained bald.

Then Grandmother Spider said, "Let me try!" First she made a thick-walled pot out of clay. Next she spun a web reaching all the way to the other side of the world. She was so small that none of the people there noticed her coming. Quickly Grandmother Spider snatched up the sun, put it in the bowl of clay, and scrambled back home along one of the strands of her web. Now her side of the world had light, and everyone rejoiced.

Spider Woman brought not only the sun to the Cherokee, but fire with it. And besides that, she taught the Cherokee people the art of pottery making.

Dream Song

TRADITIONAL

The Chippewa believed that a dream — or a vision — could reveal some-thing about the dreamer and about his life.

With a steady beat   *Arranged by John Bierhorst*

High in the sky I go, walk-ing in the sky I go, high a-bove the way be-low,_____ way be-low. By my side a bird will go, bird and I a-bove the way be - low,_____ way be - low.

High a-cross the sky I go, walk-ing with a bird I go, all a-round the sky we go,———— all a-round we go, in the sky we go, bird and I.————

Coyote Helps Decorate the Night

RETOLD BY HAROLD COURLANDER

The Hopi have lived for centuries in the American Southwest, where vast night skies sparkle because of Coyote's handiwork.

I n the beginning, before people came, there were only animals on the earth. It was the animals who arranged things. They all worked except Coyote. He was lazy. He merely watched. The other animals put the rivers where they are now, so that there would be water to drink. They put mountains here and there for beauty. They made trees and forests for shade. They made grass grow. They created the desert, putting down sand and all kinds of rocks, and then to make the desert attractive to look at, they painted the rocks pink and yellow and other colors. They caused cactus to grow, and put lakes in different places.

They looked at what they had done and said, "It is not enough." So they made mesas and canyons. They went on decorating the earth every way they could think of. And finally, when things were nearly finished, they did one more thing. They made hundreds and hundreds of small, shiny objects with which they planned to complete their work. But they didn't know what to do with them. Some said, "Put them on the mountains." Some said, "Sprinkle them around the desert." Some said, "Hang them in the trees." They could not agree. So they left the pile of shiny objects on the ground and went home to sleep.

While they slept, Coyote came to see what they had been doing all day. He sniffed at the objects. He picked one up and examined it closely. "What is this?" he said. And seeing no use for it, he tossed it into the air. He picked up another and looked at it. "What is this good for?" he said. And he tossed it over his shoulder. Again he picked up one of the objects. "What is this supposed to be?" He threw it away in disgust. One by one he examined the shiny things, and finding them not good to eat nor useful in any way, he threw them into the air, until at last they were all gone.

Then he looked up into the sky and saw them where he had thrown them, tiny spots of light in the darkness. This is how the stars came to be where they are. Coyote the busybody is responsible.

Sedna, the Sea Goddess

RETOLD BY HELEN CASWELL

For food, for materials to make clothes and to build shelters, and for fuel to create heat and light, the people of the Arctic turned to the animals of the sea. Here's how these sea creatures came to the icy waters of the Far North.

The petrels, proud birds that they are, live on the highest parts of the cliffs. From their peaks they swirl out like snowflakes, looking down on the rolling noisiness of razorbills, who build their nests halfway up, and the gulls and the little kittiwakes, who are content to nest at the bottom.

Once, long, long ago, there was a petrel who was so proud that he could find no mate that pleased him among his own kind, so he decided he would marry a human being.

With a little magic, the petrel gave himself a human form. Then, wanting to look his best, he got some fine sealskins and made a beautiful parka. Now he looked very handsome, but his eyes were still the eyes of a bird, so he made some spectacles from thin pieces of walrus tusk. These spectacles had only narrow slits to look through, and hid the petrel's eyes completely.

In this disguise, he went out in his kayak to find a wife.

In a skin-covered tent beside the sea

there lived a beautiful girl named Sedna, who had many brothers but no sisters, and her father was a widower. Many men had come to her to ask her to marry them — men from her own tribe and other tribes — but Sedna refused to marry. She was as proud in her way as the petrel, and could find no man who pleased her.

Then the petrel came, appearing as a handsome stranger in a beautiful sealskin parka. Instead of bringing his kayak up onto the beach, he stayed in it at the edge of the surf and called out to Sedna to come to him. This interested Sedna, as no other suitor had done such a thing, but she would not go to him.

Then he began to sing to her:

"Come to me,
  Come into the land of the birds
  Where there is never hunger,
  Where my tent is made of beautiful skins.
  You will have a necklace of ivory
  And sleep on the skins of bears.
  Your lamps will be always filled with
    oil
  And your pot with meat."

The song was so beautiful that Sedna could not refuse. She packed her belongings in a bag, she stepped out of the tent, and she walked down across the beach and got into the stranger's kayak. They sailed out over the sea, away from Sedna's home and her father and brothers.

The petrel made a home for Sedna on the rocky cliff. Every day he caught fish for her, telling her that they were young seals, and for a while Sedna was happy,

because the petrel had enchanted her. But one day the petrel's spectacles fell off, and for the first time Sedna looked into her husband's eyes. In that moment the spell was broken. She realized all at once that she was married to a bird, and she saw that her home was a nest on a barren cliff. For the first time she felt the sting of the sea spray and the lashing winds.

Sedna wept with grief and despair, and the petrel, although he loved her, could not console her.

In the meantime, Sedna's father and brothers had grown more and more lonely, with no woman to cook their meat and sew their clothing and keep the oil burning in their lamps. They set out in their boat in the direction that the stranger had taken Sedna.

When they came to the cliff where Sedna lived, the petrel was away hunting, and Sedna was alone. When she saw her family, she went running down to them, weeping, and in a rush told them all that had happened to her. Her brothers immediately lifted her into the boat, and they began paddling as rapidly as possible back toward their own coast.

They had not been gone long when the petrel returned to the nest. He looked everywhere for Sedna, and he called for her, his cry a long and lonely sound that was lost in the wind and the sound of the sea.

Other petrels answered him; they told him where Sedna had gone. Spreading his wings, he soared out over the sea and was soon flying over the boat that was carrying Sedna back to her home. This made the brothers nervous, and they paddled faster. As they skimmed over the water, the petrel became angry. He began to beat his wings against the wind, making it whirl and shriek, and making the waves leap higher and higher. In minutes the sea was black with storm, and the waves so wild that the boat was in danger of turning over. Then Sedna's brothers and father realized that the petrel was such a powerful spirit that even the sea was angry because his bride was being taken from him. They decided that they must sacrifice Sedna to the sea in order to save their own lives. They picked her up and threw her into the icy water.

Sedna, blue with cold, came to the surface and grabbed at the side of the boat with fingers that were turning to ice. Her brothers, out of their minds with fear, hit at her hands with a paddle, and her fingertips broke off like icicles and fell back into the sea, where they turned into seals and swam away. Coming up again, Sedna tried once more to catch hold of the boat, and again her brothers hit at her hands with the paddle. The second joints of her fingers broke off and fell into the water, turning into *ojuk*, into ground seals. Two more times Sedna tried to take hold of the side of the boat, and each time her terrified brothers hit her hands, and the third joints of her fingers turned into walrus and the thumbs became whales. Then Sedna sank to the bottom of the sea. The storm died down, and the brothers finally brought their boat to land, but a great wave followed them and drowned them all.

Sedna became a powerful spirit, in control of the sea creatures who sprang from her fingers. Sometimes she sends storms and wrecks kayaks. The people fear her and hold ceremonies in her honor, and on especially serious occasions — as when she causes famines by keeping the seals from being caught by the hunters — the *angakok,* the conjurer, goes on a spirit journey to Sedna's home at the bottom of the sea, to arrange her hair.

Sedna wears her hair in two braids, each as thick as an arm, but since she has no fingers, she cannot plait her own hair, and this is the service she appreciates most of all. So when the *angakok* comes to her and arranges her hair for her, she is so grateful that she sends some of the seals and other animals to the hunters so that they may have food.

Song for Smooth Waters

TRADITIONAL

Ocean Spirit
calm the waves for me
get close to me, my power
my heart is tired
make the sea like milk for me
yeho
yehólo

HAIDA

The Gods Made Man

BY NATALIA BELTING

Many of the Navajo myths about the creation of man reflect the rugged beauty of the Southwest and the importance the cultivation of corn played in the lives of the people.

The gods made man
Of turquoise and white shell,
Striped corn and blue corn,
Red corn and black;

Made his feet of the earth,
His legs and his tongue
From the lightning, his voice
From the thunder;

They made him,
Sang over him through the night,
So that breath entered his body,
So that he moved,
So that his feet danced with the wind.

The gods sang,
And man had life.
They gave him songs,
And he had power.

Made him of pollen
And rainwater, lake water,
And mountain springwater;

Made his arms from the rainbow,
His hair from black night,
His face from the dawn sky,

And they named him
Created-from-Everything.

Song of Happiness

TRADITIONAL

For the Navajo people, music has long played a central role in community rituals. This is a song for feasts and other joyous occasions.

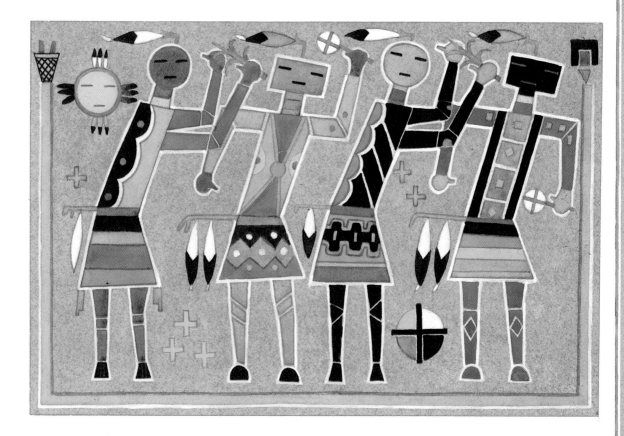

With strong rhythm

Arranged by Janet E. Tobitt

Hi yo hi yo ip si ni yah, Hi yo

hi yo ip si ni —— yah, Hi —— yo hi yo ip si

ni yah, Hi —— yo hi yo ip si ni yah. Ip si ni YAH!

Part 2

❧

FROM SEA TO SHINING SEA

From the moment Columbus arrived on the shores of what he called San Salvador, the future of the North American continent changed irrevocably. Here are some of the ways our country grew from a tiny consortium of settlements into a westernized nation stretching from sea to shining sea.

❧

Richard Egielski

COMING TO AMERICA

Centuries after the Native Americans established homes
on this continent, Europeans and Africans began to arrive.

The Mezcla Man

RETOLD BY J. FRANK DOBIE

The search for gold by the conquistadores, *the Spanish conquerors, began the moment Christopher Columbus stepped onto the soil of the Americas in 1492 and claimed the land for Spain. Wherever the* conquistadores *explored in the New World, they hunted for gold. They had heard stories about fabulous treasures, and they wanted desperately to claim the riches for themselves. The decades passed. But these legendary treasures were never found. So other legends, and other treasures, took their places.*

There were no banks in the Spanish Southwest, so when the *rancheros*, the ranchers, sold their wool and sheep, they brought their gold and silver home with them. Often they hid it in holes in the rock walls of their houses or buried it in their floors.

Now, one *ranchero* had more sheep and wool than any other. He lived in the high hills of the Casa Blanca country west of San Diego, near the Nueces River. His house was a kind of fort, with walls higher than the flat roof, and loopholes in the walls to shoot through.

One time, after he had sold thousands of sheep and had conducted a caravan of carts loaded with wool to San Antonio, he brought home more gold than he had ever had before. Instead of hiding it in his house he carried it to the highest hill on his ranch. There, black chaparral and catsclaw and other thorned brush grew so dense a *jabalina*, a wild pig, could hardly squeeze through. The top of the hill was flat, and in the middle of the thicket was a small natural clearing. The trail to it was dim and thorny.

The cunning old *rico*, the rich man, knew that. There, in the middle of the clearing, he made a man out of *mezcla*, a mixture of mud and straw or little sticks. The *mezcla* man was as big as a giant. His head was thrown back, and his mouth was wide open. He stood with his arms stretched to the east and to the west and across his chest was written these words: *Excava hacia el este y después hacia el oeste de la forma que mis manos están apuntando, y tú encontrarás el oro.* Dig to the east and then to the west the way my hands are pointing, and you will find the gold.

After the cunning old *rico* had finished making the *mezcla* man there in the middle of the thicket on top of the hill where nobody ever went, and had written on his chest the waybill to the gold, he kept his secret. He raised more sheep and his shearers sheared more wool for him and he got more gold and he hid it.

Then one night, some *bandidos*, some bandits, came as quietly as the owl flies. They stole into the *rico*'s room, tied his hands behind him, and noosed him by the neck. Then they drew the other end of the rope over a beam and pulled the rope until the *rico*'s feet were kicking nothing but air. When he began breathing like a lassoed wild horse, they lowered him. The *bandidos* asked again and again, but the *rico* refused to tell where the gold was. So

they hung him up again and again, pulling the rope tighter and tighter until the *rico*'s legs finally made their last jerk.

Then they all went to searching. They looked in the bed and under the bed and under all the other beds. They got bars and dug into the floors and pried up rocks set into the fireplaces. They found candles and lit up all the rooms while they tapped and hammered on the walls searching for secret little holes fitted with money boxes. They pried up the lid of a big leather chest. They looked everywhere there was

to look inside the house and found not one piece of gold.

When daylight came, they began digging holes under mesquite trees and around the big corral. One found the trail going up through the brush on the hill, followed it, and came to the *mezcla* man. He could not read the writing on the *mezcla* man's chest, but he knew it meant something. He came back yelling, "Now it is found!"

All the *bandidos* went up the hill. The leader read out the words and quickly they dug under the hands of the *mezcla* man. Nothing.

For two days the *bandidos* ran east and west the way the hands pointed, looking for likely places to dig. They were in a hurry, not only from eagerness for the gold, but also because they knew that, before long, honest people would find out about the murder of the *rico* and begin tracking them down.

With all that scrambling up and down the hill, the trail became as plain as the road to Laredo. On the afternoon of the second day, the *bandidos* heard horses galloping, so they fled.

The *rancheros* who were after the bandits came to the thicket and saw the strange *mezcla* man. They read the writing on his breast and forgot all about murder and justice. They thought only about gold. Nobody was after them, so they could dig as deep and as far out as they wanted to. They followed the imaginary lines extending from the *mezcla* man's shoulders, his arms, his forefingers, and out his middle fingers, trying, trying to locate the right place to dig. They even dug a hole on a hill five miles away. They cut paths through the brush east and west. But after they had dug and dug and found nothing, they got disgusted and quit.

Then the *pastores*, the shepherds, began grazing their sheep up to the *Cerro del Rico*, up to the Hill of the Rich One. These *pastores* left their dogs to care for the sheep so they could dig all day long. They dug new holes and they dug the old holes deeper.

But they did not find anything, and after a while they got disgusted and quit.

One old *pastor* did not quit. Every morning he took his grubbing hoe and spade, and dug, dug, dug. One day, after he had been working very hard and was thirsty and tired, the *pastor* looked at the writing for a long time. At last he spoke to the man of mud and sticks.

"*Bandidos* came here and found you and read your message, but they did not find gold. Then all the rich and important *rancheros* came. They dug out to the east and the west, but they did not find gold. Then, after they quit, the *pastores* dug more holes and still found no gold. And I? I have been digging my arms off for over a year and have never found so much as a copper *centavo*, so much as a penny." Enraged, the *pastor* slapped the *mezcla* man on his mouth and then seized his spade and hacked off his head. Then he chopped off the right arm, which pointed to the east, and then the left arm, which pointed to the west. And then, with all his might, the *pastor* brought his spade down through the words on the *mezcla* man's chest and into his enormous stomach.

And when he did, gold coins (and some silver coins, too) poured out onto the ground. You see, the cunning old *ranchero* had built the man to hold plenty and then fed him through his open mouth until he was full. The *pastor* gave his master some of the money, but he kept the rest. He never again herded sheep or anything else. He lived *muy contento*, quite happily, all the rest of his life.

The Other 1492

BY NORMAN H. FINKELSTEIN

The conquistadores *who followed Columbus to the New World did so by choice. Other Spaniards, Jewish Spaniards, were not so fortunate.*

I n the spring of 1492, King Ferdinand and Queen Isabella of Spain issued two seemingly unrelated decrees. On March 31, they ordered all Jews to leave Spanish soil, taking nothing of value with them, within four months. Because they had decided to impose one national religion, the king and queen wanted anyone who did not practice Catholicism expelled from their country. And on April 17, they bestowed the exalted title Admiral of the Ocean Sea upon a persistent Genoese sailor named Christopher Columbus. It directed him to undertake an expedition in search of a new route to the rich Indies.

Throughout Spain that spring and summer, Jewish families busily made plans for their departures. Even Columbus began the diary of his momentous journey by noting what was happening to the Jews.

Jews streamed toward the port cities of Spain to begin their uncertain futures as exiles, and as far as anyone knows, the last Jew left Spain on August 2, 1492. A day later Columbus and his hardy crew sailed out of the harbor at Palos.

Some of the Jewish refugees turned to neighboring Portugal as a temporary haven. Others fled to Italy, Holland, and Turkey. Many ultimately made their way to South America, but the Inquisition followed them, and Jews again found themselves forced to move on.

By 1654, most of the Jewish population of Recife, Brazil, chose to return to their first home of exile, Holland. One small group never made it. Storms forced them ashore on Spanish territory in Jamaica. They immediately made plans to leave.

But nearly all their funds were used up. Even so, they booked passage on a French ship bound for New Amsterdam, a Dutch West India Company colony today called New York City. There, they expected money from relatives and friends in Amsterdam to reach them with which to pay the captain.

In early September 1654, the *Sainte Catherine* entered New Amsterdam's harbor. Uncertain of their welcome in this new land, the twenty-three Jewish passengers stepped hesitantly onto Dutch territory. The history of the Jewish people in what would become the United States had begun.

The Debate in Sign Language

RETOLD BY SYD LIEBERMAN

Although centuries old and recorded in many lands, this tale puts a humorous face on the experiences the Jews from Spain had at the time of the Inquisition.

Once there was an evil king who decided he wanted to throw the Jews out of his land. And the way he would do it was this: He would have a debate with one of them — in sign language.

He said to the Jewish community, "I will give you three signs. If someone can read my three signs and answer me correctly, all of you can stay here for the rest of your days. But if not, all of your people will have to go."

Well, the Jewish community was up in arms. No one knew what to do. There were arguments and discussions but no volunteers. After all, who could debate a king, let alone debate a king in sign language?

So, finally, after days of arguments going up and back, Yankel, a little chicken man, said, "Look, if no one will do it, I'll do it." And so the Jews agreed. Off went Yankel to the debate.

A huge platform had been set up in the center of town. Everybody surrounded it. The king stood on one side, little Yankel on the other. The king said, "Okay, I will give you three signs. If you get them all correct, you can stay with your people in this land. If you don't, all of you will have to leave.

"Here is the first sign."

The king threw an arm in the air and stretched out the fingers of his hand. Yankel looked at the king and put a fist in front of his face.

The king said, "Correct. I'm amazed. Here is the second sign."

He threw his arm toward Yankel with two fingers straight out, and Yankel put one finger up in front of his nose.

The king said, "Correct again. If you get the third sign right, you and all of your people will be able to remain." And he reached into the folds of his robe and pulled out a piece of cheese. Yankel looked at the king, shrugged, and pulled out an egg from his pouch.

The king gasped. "Correct again. The Jews can stay!"

That night in the castle the whole court gathered around the king and asked, "What was the debate about?"

The king replied, "It was astonishing that the Jews had a little chicken man who could read my signs. I put out my hand with my fingers spread to show him that Jews were scattered all over the world. But he put up a fist to show me that they were one in the hand of God.

"Then I held up two fingers to show him that there were two kings, one in heaven and one on the earth. But he held up one finger to show me there was only one king, the king in heaven.

"So I brought out a piece of cheese to show him that the Jewish religion had grown old and moldy, but he brought out an egg to show me that it was fresh and whole.

"It was amazing."

Meanwhile, at Yankel's, everybody crowded into the chicken store and asked, "What was the debate about?"

Yankel replied, "I don't know! It wasn't much of a debate. I mean, the king reached out to grab me so I put up a fist to show him I'd punch him if he touched me. Then the king held up two fingers to poke out my eyes, so I held up one to block him. I guess he knew I was going to stand up to him, so he brought out his lunch and I brought out mine!"

The First Thanksgiving

BY MARCIA SEWALL

The English men, women, and children who established Plymouth Colony were indeed Pilgrims — wandering refugees seeking a place where they could practice their religion without fear or persecution. At the first Thanksgiving, they celebrated the survival of their fledgling community with those who had helped them most.

How we feared those unclothed and painted savages when we first came to America. Indians are so unlike Englishmen! They move about the woods as specks of light and shadow. They are as silent as snow. No loud conversation or clanking armor or musket fire can be heard from them, just an arrow from nowhere! In March of our first year of settlement, a tall sagamore named Samoset surprised us with a friendly visit. He told us that his tribe came not from here. That the Indians hereabouts were called Patuxets, but a deadly plague had destroyed them four years before our arrival. All but one, named Squanto, who was elsewhere in the world as a captive of Englishmen.

Squanto became our helpful friend. Aye, our language he knew and so could interpret for us Indian affairs. He was the pilot of our shallop as we explored the coast of America. He understood the ways of nature and taught us to plant corn when the oak bud had burst and the leaves were as big as a mouse's ear. He taught us how to catch herring and how to fertilize our harsh soil with them when we planted corn seed. He taught us to tread eels out of the river mud in warm seasons and to catch them by hand. And he taught us how to catch them through winter's ice.

Samoset and Squanto also introduced us to a great *sachem*, a great chief, of these parts named Massasoit. And in our first year of settlement we made a peace treaty with him. We agreed that his people must not hurt our people, or might bear punishment; we agreed not to steal from each other, and to leave our weapons behind when we came to each other upon any occasion; and we agreed to help each other if we should suffer attack. Aye, we have respected and honored that treaty. Now we walk "as peacefully and safely in the woods as in the highways of England."

Our first wondrous harvest called for celebration. We sang psalms and played games. We rejoiced and fired our noisy muskets into the air. And the Indians came and joined in the feasting; not just an Indian or two, but Massasoit arrived with more than ninety braves who stayed among us for three festive days. We prayed and gave thanks for such a harvest and our survival.

Simple Gifts

TRADITIONAL

Almost two centuries after the Pilgrims founded Plymouth Colony in the name of religious freedom, a woman named Ann Lee traveled to America from England to establish an unorthodox Christian sect commonly called the Shakers. Like the Pilgrims, the Shakers were able to worship freely and without interference from the government. Based on an English folk tune, this hymn celebrates the Shaker commitment to a simple, nonmaterialistic way of life.

Arranged by Marilyn Davidson and Nathaniel Fenmore

'Tis the gift to be sim - ple, 'Tis the gift to be free. 'Tis the gift to come down where we ought to be, And when we find our - selves— in the place just right, 'Twill be in the val - ley of love and de - light. When true sim-

plic - i - ty is gained, To bow and to bend we— shan't be a - shamed, to turn, turn will

be our de - light, Till by turn - ing, turn - ing we come 'round right.

39

Sarasponda

TRADITIONAL

In 1624, a Dutchman named Peter Minuit bought Manhattan Island for approximately twenty-four dollars' worth of beads and baubles from a group of native people whose culture did not recognize private property. New Amsterdam was born.

Settlement spread along the winding, hilly land bordering the majestic Hudson River, which Washington Irving would immortalize centuries later in his stories about Rip Van Winkle and Ichabod Crane. Although New Amsterdam fell to the British in 1664 and became New York, the Dutch left their mark all over the area — in roofs with gables, in street names like the Bowery, and in songs like this.

With a strong pulse   *Arranged by Rachel Miller*

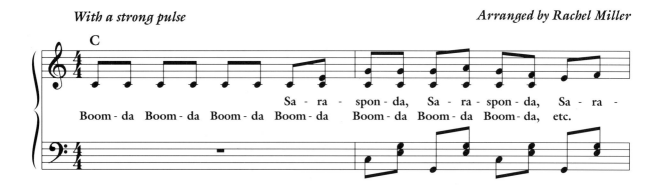

Sa - ra - spon - da, Sa - ra - spon - da, Sa - ra -
Boom - da Boom - da Boom - da Boom - da   Boom - da Boom - da Boom - da,   etc.

spon - da, Ret - set - set. Sa - ra - spon - da, Sa - ra - spon - da, Sa - ra -

spon - da, Ret - set - set. Ah - do - ray - oh, Ah - do - ray - boom - day - oh. Ah -

do - ray - boom - day, Ret - set - set, Ah - say - pa - say - oh.

When Africans were brought to the Americas against their will, they brought with them the songs, rhythms, and chants of their faraway homes. And those chants have lived on in America for centuries. Two of the best known are "Juba This and Juba That" and "Hambone." Both chants have hand motions that go with them. (See page 376.)

Juba This and Juba That

TRADITIONAL

Juba, Juba
Juba this and Juba that
And Juba killed a yellow cat
And get over double trouble, Juba.

You sift-a the meal,
you give me the husk,
You cook-a the bread,
you give me the crust.
You fry the meat,
you give me the skin,
And that's where my mama's trouble begin.
And then you Juba,
You just Juba.

Say, Juba up, Juba down,
Juba all around the town.
Juba for Ma, Juba for Pa,
Juba for your brother-in-law.
You just Juba, Juba.

Hambone

TRADITIONAL

Hambone, Hambone, pat him on the shoulder,
If you get a pretty girl,
I'll show you how to hold her.
Hambone, Hambone, where have you been?
All 'round the world and back again.

Hambone, Hambone, what did you do?
I got a train and I fairly flew.
Hambone, Hambone, where did you go?

I hopped up to Miss Lucy's door.
I asked Miss Lucy would she marry me
"Well, I don't care if Papa don't care!"

First come in was Mister Snake,
He crawled all over that wedding cake.
Next walked in was Mister Tick,
He ate so much that it made him sick.
Next walked in was Mister Coon,
We asked him to sing us a wedding tune.
Now Ham!
Now Ham!

Three Pennsylvania Dutch Riddles

TRADITIONAL

On October 8, 1737, the ship Charming Nancy *arrived in Philadelphia. On board was a group of Amish from the Palatinate, an area in Europe where Switzerland, Germany, and France come together. Persecuted in their own country because they would not affiliate with a church other than their own, the Amish came in response to an offer made decades earlier by William Penn. He had promised them religious freedom in Penn Sylvania, the new colony bearing his name. Most of the new immigrants moved west from Philadelphia to what was then the frontier: present-day Berks and Lancaster counties, where their descendants still speak a form of German and practice the centuries-old traditions of their people.*

En eisner Gaul,
Un en flache Schwantzel.
Wie de starker das des Gauliche springt
We kurtzer das sei Schwantzel werd.

(Nodle un Fadem)

An iron horse,
With a flaxen tail.
The faster that the horse does run,
The shorter does his tail become.

(Needle and thread)

Wer es macht, der sagt es net,
Wer es nehmt der kent es net,
Wer es kent der will es net.

(Falsh Geld)

Whoever makes it, tells it not,
And whoever takes it, recognizes it not,
And whoever recognizes it, wants it not.

(Counterfeit money)

Was geht zu der Deer rei un glemt sich net?
Was geht uf der Ofa un brent sich net?
Was geht uf der Disch un shamt sich net?

(Die Sonn)

What goes through the door without pinching itself?
What sits on the stove without burning itself?
What sits on the table and is not ashamed?

(The sun)

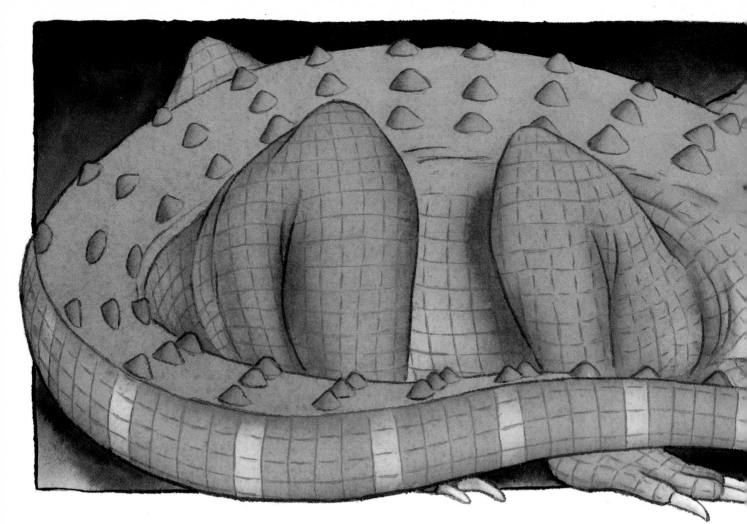

Why Alligator Hates Dog

RETOLD BY J. J. RENEAUX

The people who live in the bayous, or swamps, south and west of New Orleans, are descended from the French people of Acadie (now Nova Scotia) in Canada. The Acadians were forced by the British, following their victory in the French and Indian War, to leave their homes and relocate in another part of French North America. Known now as Cajuns, many continue to speak the language of their ancestors.

M'sieur Cocodril, the alligator, was once king of all the swamp and the bayou. All the critters cut a wide circle 'round ol' Cocodril lest they wind up in his belly. Even Man, with his traps and guns, was wary of M'sieur Cocodril. One

snap of those jaws and a fella could lose an arm, a leg, or even his life! M'sieur Cocodril enjoyed the respect and fear of everybody, everybody, that is, except for *les chiens*, the dogs. How those dogs loved to tease and mock him — from a safe distance, of course.

Back in those days, M'sieur Cocodril lived in a deep, dark, muddy hole in the bank of the bayou, not far from the *cabane*, the cabin, of Man and his pesky dogs. In the evening he loved to curl up in his hole and take a little nap before he went hunting for his supper. But just as he was dozing off, those dogs up at the

cabane would start carryin' on — howlin', whinin', barkin', teasin' — 'til he thought he'd go mad.

They'd howl out, "M'sieur Cocodril, M'sieur Cocodril! Come and get us if you dare!" And, ooowheee! Alligator couldn't even do a thing about it, 'cept gnash those big ol' sharp teeth, thump his tail, and wait for one of those dogs to get just a little too close.

"One of these days I'm gonna get them dogs," he'd hiss. "I'll teach them to mock me, the King o' the Swamp."

Now one day, Hound Dog came running down the bank of the bayou. I mean he was hot on the trail of Lapin, the rabbit. Thumpity, thumpity, thump. But that rabbit was too *smart-smart*! He led that dog right up to Alligator's hole. Well, Lapin easily jumped across, but Dog fell

straight down that hole and found himself snout to snout with M'sieur Cocodril. Hound Dog knew he was trapped. He better do some fast talkin' if he was gonna get out of there alive.

"Arrhoooo," howled Hound Dog. *"Comment ça va?* How's it goin'?"

"Soooo, at last you come to pay me a visit, hmmmm," hissed M'sieur Cocodril. "Every evenin' you dogs call out, 'M'sieur Cocodril, come and get us!' Well, now, that's exactly what I'm gonna do. I'm gonna get you. I'm gonna grind you into mincemeat, you miserable, mangy mutt!"

"Oh, *mais non, mon ami,* but no, my friend," whined Dog. "Surely you did not think that my friends and I would insult you, the mighty King o' the Swamp! Oh, *mais non, pas du tout,* but no, not at all. We were only calling you to join us for supper. We did not call 'come and get us.' We called 'come and get *it,* come and get *it*!' You see, every evenin' our master brings us a big bowl filled with delicious scraps of meat and bones. We call for you to come and get it, to come and join us for supper. But you never come, *mon ami,* you never come."

"Hmmmm, is that so?" asked M'sieur Cocodril.

"Oh, *mais oui*! Come this very evenin' and dine with us. For you, we will save the very best!" said *le chien.*

"Hmmmm," said M'sieur Cocodril. "But what of your master, the Man?"

"Oh, do not worry about him, M'sieur. Us dogs will keep watch. If we see our master comin', we'll warn you in plenty of time, and you can escape. Come and join us. We will save the very best scraps for you. After all, *mon ami,* shouldn't the King o' the Swamp eat as good as us poor dogs?"

Now, M'sieur Cocodril was a powerful and fearsome creature, for sure. But he wasn't overly blessed with what you call the smarts. He thought with his stomach and he acted on the advice of his mighty appetite. So he agreed to come for supper and he let that rascal dog escape the crush of his jaws.

That evening, Alligator crawled up the bank of the bayou all the way to the *cabane.* When he got to the steps of the *galerie,* the porch, he stopped and looked around. He feared the master might be

somewhere about. But the dogs started whining, "Come up, come up, M'sieur Cocodril. Our master is not here. Do you see our master? Do you hear our master? It is safe, M'sieur Cocodril. You can have your pick o' the scraps. Come up and get it, M'sieur, come up and get it!"

M'sieur Cocodril looked, for sure. He didn't see a thing. He listened, and all was quiet. So he climbed up the steps to the *galerie,* dragging that big, heavy tail behind him. But no sooner had he tasted one bit of those juicy scraps than the dogs started carryin' on — howlin', whinin', barkin', teasin' — and their master came running out to see what all the ruckus was about. When Man saw M'sieur Cocodril on his *galerie,* he took a club and started beating him on the snout, yelling for his wife to fetch his gun. And if that wasn't bad enough, those snarling dogs leapt on M'sieur Cocodril and began to bite him on his tail. That poor alligator was lucky to escape back down his hole with his life!

Well, ever since that time, Alligator hates Dog. He floats in the water like a half-sunk log with only those big eyes peering out. He's waitin' and watchin' for one of those dogs to come just a little too close. This time, Dog won't be able to trick M'sieur Cocodril. These days, ol' Alligator is a whole lot smarter. He's learned his lesson. And if M'sieur Cocodril was here today, why, he'd tell you himself, for true.

"Believe nothin' you hear, *mon ami,* and only half of what you see. Hmmmmm?"

'Tit Galop pour Mamou

WORDS AND MUSIC BY DEWEY BALFA

Here's a nonsense song that has been sung in the bayous for generations.

Arranged by Randa Kirshbaum

Quickly

'Tit ga-lop,— 'tit ga-lop, pour Ma-mou,— J'ai ven-du mon 'tit mu-
Tee gah-lohp,— tee gah-lohp, pohr Mah-moo, Zhay vahn-doo mohn tee moo-

let, pour quinze sous,— J'ai ache-té du can-dy
lay, pohr kehnz soo,— Zhay ahsh-tay doo kahn-dee

English translation:

2. 'Tit galop, 'tit galop pour Mamou
   J'ai vendu mon 'tit wagon pour quinze sous,
   J'ai acheté du candy rouge pour les petits
   Et une yard du ruban pour la vieille.

   (Tee gah-lohp, tee gah-lohp pohr Mah-moo
   Zhay vahn-doo mohn tee wah-gohn pohr kehnz soo,
   Zhay ahsh-tay doo kahn-dee roozh pohr layp tee
   Ay uhn yahrd doo roo-bahn pohr la vyay.)

1. Canter, canter to Mamou
   I sold my little mule for fifteen cents,
   I bought some red candy for the little ones
   And some sugar and coffee for the old ones.

2. Canter, canter to Mamou
   I sold my little wagon for fifteen cents,
   I bought some red candy for the little ones
   And a yard of red ribbon for the old lady.

51

Anita Lobel

THE SHOT HEARD 'ROUND THE WORLD

When the American Revolution began in 1776, no one suspected
that the men and women of the thirteen colonies could drive
the British Army from their soil.

Revolutionary Tea

TRADITIONAL

This allegorical song about a rich lady "over the sea" and her rebellious daughter "off in a new countrie" was one of the many songs inspired by the Boston Tea Party and sung throughout the colonies during the Revolutionary War period.

Arranged by Ruth and Norman Lloyd

1. There was an old la-dy lived o-ver the sea, And she was an Is-land Queen; Her daugh-ter lived off in a new coun-trie, With an o-cean of wa-ter be-tween. The old la-dy's pock-ets were full of gold. But ne-ver con-tent-ed was

2. "Now, Moth-er, dear Moth-er," the daugh-ter re-plied, "I shan't do the thing you ax; I'm will-ing to pay a fair price for the tea, But never the three-pen-ny tax." "You shall," quoth the moth-er, and red-den'd with rage, "For you're my own daugh-ter, you

she,_____ So she called on her daugh-ter to pay her a tax Of
see._____ And— sure, 'tis quite pro-per the daugh-ter should pay Her

three pence a pound on her tea, Of three pence a pound on her tea.____
moth-er a tax on her tea. Her moth-er a tax on her tea."____

3. The tea was conveyed to the daughter's door,
   All down by the ocean's side;
   And the bouncing girl pour'd out ev'ry pound,
   In the dark and boiling tide.
   And then she called out to the Island Queen,
   "Oh, Mother, dear Mother," quoth she,
   "Your tea you may have when 'tis steep'd enough,
   But never a tax from me,
   But never a tax from me."

Paul Revere's Ride

BY HENRY WADSWORTH LONGFELLOW

If you ever visit Massachusetts, you can ride along State Route 60, the same road Paul Revere galloped down more than two hundred years ago shouting, "The British are coming! The British are coming!"

In truth, Paul Revere never reached Concord. He was captured just after leaving Lexington.

Listen, my children, and you shall hear
Of the midnight ride of Paul Revere,
On the eighteenth of April, in Seventy-five;
Hardly a man is now alive
Who remembers that famous day and year.

He said to his friend, "If the British march
By land or sea from the town tonight,
Hang a lantern aloft in the belfry arch
Of the North Church tower as a signal light, —
One, if by land, and two, if by sea;
And I on the opposite shore will be,
Ready to ride and spread the alarm
Through every Middlesex village and farm,
For the country folk to be up and to arm."

Then he said, "Good night!" and with muffled oar
Silently rowed to the Charlestown shore,
Just as the moon rose over the bay,
Where swinging wide at her moorings lay
The *Somerset,* British man-of-war;
A phantom ship, with each mast and spar
Across the moon like a prison bar,
And a huge black hulk, that was magnified
By its own reflection in the tide.

Meanwhile, his friend, through alley and street,
Wanders and watches with eager ears,
Till in the silence around him he hears

The muster of men at the barrack door,
The sound of arms, and the tramp of feet,
And the measured tread of the grenadiers,
Marching down to their boats on the shore.

Then he climbed the tower of the Old
  North Church,
By the wooden stairs, with stealthy tread,
To the belfry-chamber overhead,
And startled the pigeons from their perch
On the somber rafters, that 'round him made
Masses and moving shapes of shade, —
By the trembling ladder, steep and tall,
To the highest window in the wall,
Where he paused to listen and look down
A moment on the roofs of the town,
And the moonlight flowing over all.

Beneath, in the churchyard, lay the dead,
In their night-encampment on the hill,
Wrapped in silence so deep and still

That he could hear, like a sentinel's tread,
The watchful night-wind, as it went
Creeping along from tent to tent,
And seeming to whisper, "All is well!"
A moment only he feels the spell
Of the place and the hour, and the secret dread
Of the lonely belfry and the dead;
For suddenly all his thoughts are bent
On a shadowy something far away,
Where the river widens to meet the bay, —
A line of black that bends and floats
On the rising tide, like a bridge of boats.

Meanwhile, impatient to mount and ride,
Booted and spurred, with a heavy stride
On the opposite shore walked Paul Revere.
Now he patted his horse's side,
Now gazed at the landscape far and near,
Then, impetuous, stamped the earth,
And turned and tightened his saddle-girth;
But mostly he watched with eager search
The belfry-tower of the Old North Church,
As it rose above the graves on the hill,
Lonely and spectral and somber and still.
And lo! as he looks, on the belfry's height
A glimmer, and then a gleam of light!
He springs to the saddle, the bridle he turns,
But lingers and gazes, till full on his sight
A second lamp in the belfry burns!

A hurry of hoofs in a village street,
A shape in the moonlight, a bulk in the dark,
And beneath, from the pebbles, in passing, a spark
Struck out by a steed flying fearless and fleet;
That was all! And yet, through the gloom
   and the light,
The fate of a nation was riding that night;
And the spark struck out by that steed in his flight,
Kindled the land into flame with its heat.

He has left the village and mounted the steep,
And beneath him, tranquil and broad and deep,
Is the Mystic, meeting the ocean tides;
And under the alders, that skirt its edge,
Now soft on the sand, now loud on the ledge,
Is heard the tramp of his steed as he rides.

It was twelve by the village clock
When he crossed the bridge into Medford town.
He heard the crowing of the cock,
And the barking of the farmer's dog,
And felt the damp of the river fog,
That rises after the sun goes down.

It was one by the village clock,
When he galloped into Lexington.
He saw the gilded weathercock
Swim in the moonlight as he passed,
And the meeting-house windows, blank and bare,
Gaze at him with a spectral glare,
As if they already stood aghast
At the bloody work they would look upon.

It was two by the village clock,
When he came to the bridge in Concord town.
He heard the bleating of the flock,
And the twitter of birds among the trees,
And felt the breath of the morning breeze
Blowing over the meadows brown.
And one was safe and asleep in his bed
Who at the bridge would be first to fall,
Who at the bridge would be lying dead,
Pierced by a British musket-ball.

You know the rest. In the books you have read,
How the British Regulars fired and fled, —
How the farmers gave them ball for ball,
From behind each fence and farmyard wall,
Chasing the redcoats down the lane,

Then crossing the fields to emerge again
Under the trees at the turn of the road,
And only pausing to fire and load.

So through the night rode Paul Revere;
And so through the night went his cry of alarm
To every Middlesex village and farm, —
A cry of defiance, and not of fear,
A voice in the darkness, a knock at the door,
And a word that shall echo forevermore!
For, borne on the night-wind of the Past,
Through all our history, to the last,
In the hour of darkness and peril and need,
The people will waken and listen to hear
The hurrying hoofbeats of that steed,
And the midnight message of Paul Revere.

Yankee Doodle

WORDS BY DR. RICHARD SHUCKBURGH
TRADITIONAL MUSIC

Although the expression Yankee Doodle *was meant by the British Regulars to mock the Continental soldiers, it quickly became a rallying cry and badge of honor.*

2. Father and I went down to camp,
Along with Captain Gooding,
And there we saw the men and boys
As thick as hasty pudding.

Chorus

3. And there was Captain Washington
Upon a slapping stallion,
A-giving orders to his men,
I guess there was a million.

Chorus

The Tory's Conversion

TRADITIONAL

In every American conflict, families have been torn apart by differing loyalties, as the Kuchs were so many years ago.

Old Michael Kuch sat with his daughter in the firelit parlor of their little house at Valley Forge, Pennsylvania. It was Christmas Eve, 1777, but their conversation had little cheer. When the clock struck twelve, the man prepared to offer his evening prayer for the safety of his son, one of Washington's troops.

Suddenly, the two heard hurried steps in the snow. There was a fumbling at the latch. The door flew open, and in burst a haggard, panting man. He hastily closed the door and fell into a seat, shaking from head to foot.

"John!" Jennie Kuch cried, for the man was her fiancé.

"What is wrong with thee, John Blake?" asked her father. "What is wrong?"

In a broken voice the trembling man confessed that he had tried to shoot General Washington, but the bullet missed the commander-in-chief. Instead it struck and killed the general's only guard.

"I ran, but they followed my footprints through the snow," Blake whispered. "I came here for shelter."

"Thou know'st I am neutral in this war, John Blake, although I have a boy down yonder in the camp," said the farmer. "You ask me for a hiding place, and I shall give it, but know that it is more on the girl's account than yours. Out — this way — to the springhouse."

Before old Michael had time to return to his chair, the door again flew open, and men in blue and buff entered. They demanded the assassin be turned over.

When Michael didn't answer, they moved toward him. Just as they were about to strike, General Washington came through the door. In his arms he carried a drooping form splashed with blood. He placed it on the hearth as gently as a mother lays a babe in its cradle. As the firelight fell on the still face, the farmer's eyes grew round and big. His son was lying there.

Kuch grabbed the pistol the Tory had dropped. He leapt to his feet and rushed to the springhouse where Blake crouched.

Jennie was there as soon as her father. She knocked his arm aside so the bullet meant for her beloved lodged in the springhouse wall. Kuch then drew his knife. Before he could use it, the soldiers burst in and dragged Blake back to the house. They placed the culprit before General Washington.

"What harm," asked the general, "have you suffered from your fellow countrymen that you turn against them this way?"

"I am willing to die," Blake replied.

Suddenly, the figure near the fire called out. Both father and sister rushed over, and Blake's face flushed with hope.

Washington turned to the captive. "I will put you under guard until you are needed. Take him into custody, my dear young lady, and try to make an American of him." Beckoning to his men, he left the house and rode away.

When young Kuch recovered, he returned to his regiment. John Blake was with him. Blake joined the Continental forces, and no soldier ever served the Stars and Stripes more honorably.

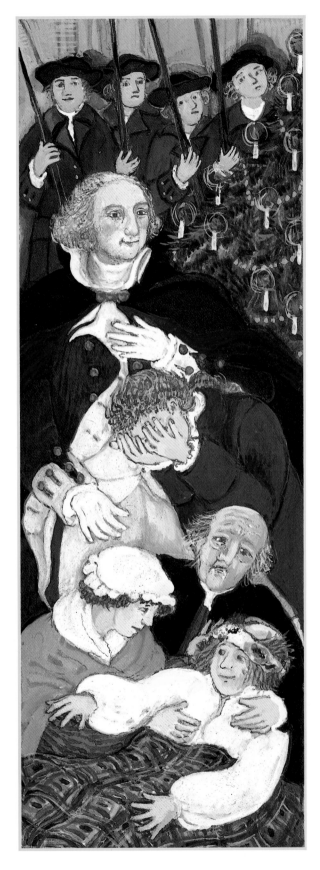

Johnny Has Gone for a Soldier

TRADITIONAL

This melancholy lament is based on the old Irish tune "Shule Aroon," which was first sung about 1691.

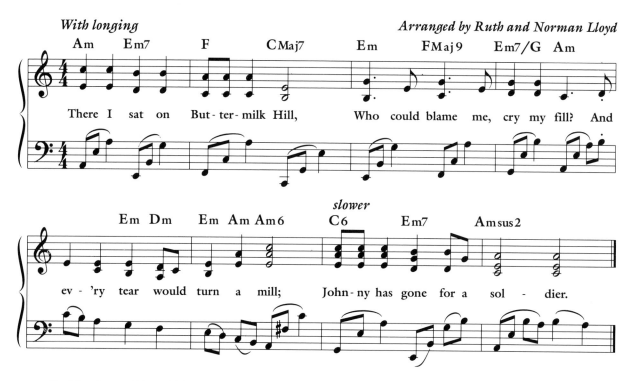

With longing   *Arranged by Ruth and Norman Lloyd*

There I sat on But-ter-milk Hill, Who could blame me, cry my fill? And

ev-'ry tear would turn a mill; John-ny has gone for a sol - dier.

2. Me oh my, I loved him so,
Broke my heart to see him go.
And only time will heal my woe;
Johnny has gone for a soldier.

3. I'll sell my flax, I'll sell my wheel,
Buy my love a sword of steel,
So it in battle he may wield;
Johnny has gone for a soldier.

Clever Mistress Murray

RETOLD BY M. A. JAGENDORF

Here's a historical folktale about the woman who saved four thousand American patriots from capture by the English redcoats. For many years a painting commemorating her quick thinking hung at The New-York Historical Society.

Mistress Robert Murray and her husband, who was one of the richest merchants in New York City in the days of George Washington, had a beautiful summer home at what is now Fifth Avenue and Thirty-seventh Street.

Master Murray was a very clever Quaker merchant, and Mistress Murray was a very clever lady, with a quick wit and a quick mind. There was one giant disagreement between them. Master Murray believed in the British cause, and Mistress Murray and her beautiful daughters were heart and soul with the men who were fighting to make America independent. And so men from both sides visited their lovely country home.

Came the day when the British landed in Kips Bay, which is on the east side of Manhattan, to capture General Washington and his army. The British outnumbered the Americans and so the Americans were in retreat. All but four thousand men, under the command of General Putnam, had gotten well away on the Bloomingdale Road. Now the Americans needed time to move the rest.

That very day, General Washington was visiting Mistress Murray and her lovely daughters at their summer home. Master Murray was away on business.

"The British are on the march," said Mistress Murray.

"I know that well, madame. But we'll escape and we'll win. At the moment, we need just a few more hours. Old Putnam and his men are hard on the march to join the army that's up on the shores of the Hudson River. When he joins them, all will be safe."

"True indeed, General. Thee knowest well, he who fights and retreats a way, lives to fight another day." They all laughed.

"Well said, Mistress Murray, and I thank you from my very heart for a few happy and restful hours. Now I must be off to my men. You can hear the thunder of the cannons."

They all said good-bye and good luck, and off went the general and two officers over the hills and heights.

The British were indeed on the march, headed by General William Howe and his officers. These men rode ahead of their troops and were approaching the home of the Murrays. General Howe and Master Robert Murray were staunch friends, and so the British general decided to stop off for a little time at the Murrays' home.

Mistress Murray and her beautiful daughters were out listening to the sound of the approaching troops. Suddenly in the distance they saw a group of brightly dressed officers approaching.

"They are coming this way, Mother."

"Yes, methinks it is General Howe and his staff. Daughters, we must do our best to keep General Howe here as long as possible so General Putnam and his men can escape. Remember, General Washington said he needs a few more hours."

"We will do our best — here they are, Mother."

And so they all went out on the green, sweet smiles of welcome on their lips.

Soon the British general and a large number of his staff rode up on prancing horses.

"Good day to you, beautiful Mistress Murray, and to your lovely daughters," said General Howe.

"Welcome to our home, General. Thee and thy officers must alight and refresh yourselves awhile. There is good cake and repast and you must taste the wines my daughters and I have made from berries. I have just brought up some five-year-old mulberry wine. And we also have good Madeira from England."

"Nothing will give me greater pleasure. A happy hour with you, Mistress, will shorten a whole week's hard work."

The general and his officers dismounted.

General Howe continued, "I'll get that ragtail, bobtail mob that calls itself an army and their misguided officers when I'm ready. For the present, it will be a great joy to be in such charming company."

The girls curtsied and smiled at the red-coated officers.

"Sir," said the eldest of the girls, "I helped Mother make the mulberry wine — it is truly delicious. And you must try the fine Madeira of which Mother spoke."

The table was richly set with fine cakes and dainties; decanters gleamed with golden yellow and dark ruby wines. Howe and his officers forgot all about battles and soldiers, even though they could hear now and then the cannons thundering. They ate freely and drank deeply and discussed the fire that had just swept through the city.

The hours went by. Well fed, richly entertained by good conversation, the men slowly began to get ready to leave.

"We must keep them longer," Mistress Murray whispered to her eldest daughter.

The Murrays had an unusually beautiful young serving girl, and Mistress Murray had noticed that the younger officers had paid considerable attention to her.

"Gentlemen," said Mistress Murray gaily, "I know it's time to go, but what is a fine repast without a fine song? Young Daisy, my little maid, besides being so pretty has a charming voice."

"Yes, and we have just received some tuneful songs from London," said the eldest daughter. "Why not have her sing for us?"

"Aye, come, gentlemen, just a little longer. You must listen to Daisy's singing," said Mistress Murray.

"I'll fetch more mulberry wine and more cold meats and cakes. These should go well with the songs," said the youngest daughter.

The men felt warm and happy and were only too glad to stay. Daisy sang "Sally in Our Alley" and many others, and the men

drank more while the hands on the clock moved steadily.

Finally, the men reluctantly went out to mount their horses. Mistress Murray and her daughters were on the steps. The roaring of the cannons had died down and there was no more smoke in the blue air.

A young officer came dashing up to the mounting officers.

"Sir," he spoke quickly to General Howe, "sir, the rebels have escaped through McGowan's Pass. All of 'em, with their leader, Putnam. . . . Perhaps if we had left early . . ."

General Howe was too comfortable with food and wine to be bothered.

"Young man, the fine feast and good wines and the entertainment served by these lovely, loyal ladies are of much greater importance than that riffraff mob of rebels. We can catch them anytime. We don't find such entertainment every day. Thank you, lovely Mistress and lovely girls, and you, sweet little Daisy."

The officers joined in the thanks and the red-coated officers rode away.

Mistress Murray stood on the steps, radiant and smiling. Her daughters, their faces flushed and their eyes shining, stood with her.

"The entertainment was successful indeed," said Mistress Murray. "General Putnam and his four thousand men had plenty of time to join General Washington's army up the Hudson. 'He who fights and retreats a way, lives to fight another day.'" And her daughters smiled knowingly.

Jennie Jenkins

TRADITIONAL

This nonsense song dates back to the Revolutionary War, and even before.
It could be one that Daisy sang to General Howe and his men.

Simply

Arranged by Darrell Peter

Will you wear white, O my dear, O my dear? Oh, will you wear white, Jen - nie Jen - kins? I won't wear white, for the col - or's too bright. I'll buy me a fol - de - rol - dy, til - dy - tol - dy, seek - a - dou - ble roll, Jen - nie Jen - kins, roll.

2. Will you wear red, O my dear, O my dear?
   Oh, will you wear red, Jennie Jenkins?
   I won't wear red, it's the color of my head.

   Chorus

3. Will you wear blue, O my dear, O my dear?
   Oh, will you wear blue, Jennie Jenkins?
   I won't wear blue, for it isn't very true.

   Chorus

Concord Hymn

BY RALPH WALDO EMERSON

*Fifty-one years after the Battle of Concord, in 1826, a monument
was raised and a poem written in honor of those who died.*

By the rude bridge that arched the flood,
　　Their flag to April's breeze unfurled,
Here once the embattled farmers stood,
　　And fired the shot heard 'round the world.

The foe long since in silence slept;
　　Alike the conqueror silent sleeps;
And Time the ruined bridge has swept
　　Down the dark stream which seaward creeps.

On this green bank, by this soft stream,
　　We set today a votive stone;
That memory may their deed redeem,
　　When, like our sires, our sons are gone.

Spirit, that made those heroes dare
　　To die, and leave their children free,
Bid Time and Nature gently spare
　　The shaft we raise to them and thee.

Molly Bang

BRIDGING THE GAP

*Once the Revolutionary War was won, it was off to the west
to settle the region we now call Appalachia.*

The Wilderness Road

BY MERIDEL LeSUEUR

O nce this was a country with tall forests standing in gloom, and the mountains to cross to the broad sun prairie of the middle country. There the land was free, with wild turkeys in the blue grass asking to be popped into the pot. Clear mountain streams ran from the earth to the green meadows where the light struck in the timber openings, and the paths of Daniel Boone were beckoning, leading down the Shenandoah

Valley to Lexington, around the Cumberland Gap in the Tennessee Mountains, and northwest into Kentucky.

There was a great green valley across the Appalachians going west. The deer, raccoons, all the glowworms and the wolves, the canaries and the eagles, and rabbits, oxen, babies, men in leather stockings and coonskin hats, and sunbonneted women with little children dressed in squirrel coats and bearskin moccasins — all pressed against the ridge of mountains that made a bowl of the western prairie. The many feet and hoofs made an opening in the Cumberland Mountains and a trail, beat wide from deer and buffalo; and feet of oxen and horses and cows and barefoot children — thousands of feet going yonder — beat out a great road, which came to be called the Wilderness Road.

Cumberland Gap

TRADITIONAL

*In the late eighteenth and early nineteenth centuries the Cumberland
Gap provided a natural passage in the mountains for settlers to stream
through on their way to new land in the west.*

Fast and with gusto

Arranged by Rachel Miller

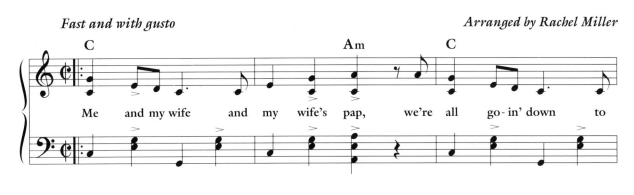

Me and my wife and my wife's pap, we're all go- in' down to

Cum- ber- land Gap. Cum- ber- land Gap, Cum- ber- land Gap,

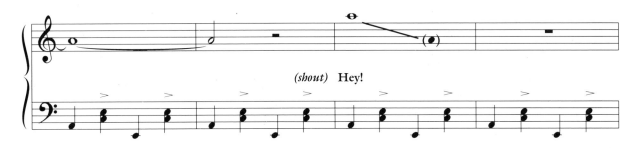

(shout) Hey!

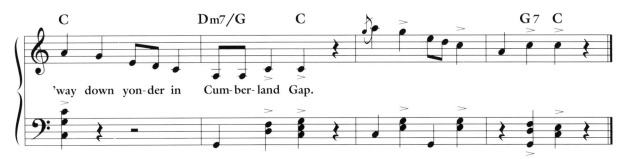

'way down yon- der in Cum- ber- land Gap.

2. Cumberland Gap with its cliffs and rocks,
   Home of panther, bear, and fox.

   Chorus

3. Daniel Boone on Pinnacle Rock
   Had a coonskin hat and an old flintlock.

   Chorus

4. Cumberland Gap is a mighty fine place,
   Three kinds of water to wash your face.

   Chorus

5. Lay down, boys, an' take a little nap,
   Fourteen miles to Cumberland Gap.

   Chorus

Bewildered Boone

TRADITIONAL

Of all the countless yarns told about Daniel Boone, the pathfinder and wilderness hero, this is the shortest — and one of the best.

A fter coming back from many months in the forests of Kentucky, Daniel Boone was talking one time with some settlers. "Daniel, did you ever get lost?" they asked the great explorer. "Lost?" said Boone. "No, I can't say I was ever lost, but I was bewildered once for three days."

Strong but Quirky:
The Birth of Davy Crockett

RETOLD BY IRWIN SHAPIRO

*Davy Crockett, pathfinder, explorer, and United States congressman, was
always up to something or other, right from the start.*

The morning Davy Crockett was born Davy's pa came busting out of his cabin in Tennessee alongside the Nolachucky River. He fired three shots into the air, gave a whoop, and said, "I've got me a son. His name is Davy Crockett, and he'll be the greatest hunter in all creation."

When he said that, the sun rose up in the sky like a ball of fire. The wind howled riproariously. Thunder boomed, and all the critters and varmints of the forest let out a moan.

Then Davy's pa went back into the cabin. Little Davy was stretched out in a cradle made of a snapping turtle's shell. There was a pair of elk horns over the top, and over the elk horns was the skin of a wildcat. The cradle was run by water power, and it was rocking away — *rockety-whump, rockety-whump.*

Now all the Crocketts were big, but Davy was big even for a Crockett. He weighed two hundred pounds, fourteen ounces, and he was as frisky as a wildcat. His ma and his aunt Ketinah stood over Davy, trying to get him to sleep.

"Sing somethin' to quiet the boy," said Aunt Ketinah to his uncle Roarious, who was standing in a corner combing his hair with a rake.

Uncle Roarious opened his mouth and sang a bit of "Over the River to Charley." That is, it was meant for singing. It sounded worse than a nor'easter howling around a country barn at midnight.

"Hmmm," said Uncle Roarious. He reached for a jug and took him a sip of kerosene oil to loosen up his pipes.

Davy was sitting up in his cradle. He kept his peepers on his uncle, watching him pull at the jug.

"I'll have a sip o' the same," said Davy, as loud as you please.

That kerosene jug slipped right out of Uncle Roarious's hand. Davy's ma and his aunt Ketinah let out a shriek.

"Why, the little shaver can talk!" said Davy's pa.

"We-ell," said Davy, talking slow and easylike, "maybe I don't jabber good enough to make a speech in Congress, but I reckon I got the hang of 'er. It's nothin' to Davy Crockett."

"That's mighty big talk, son," said Davy's pa.

"It ought to be," said Davy. "It's comin' from a big man."

And with that he leapt out of his cradle, kicked his heels together, and crowed like a rooster. He flapped his arms and he bellowed, "I'm Davy Crockett, fresh from the backwoods! I'm half horse, half alligator, with a little touch o' snappin' turtle! I can wade the Mississippi, ride a streak o' lightnin', hug a bear too close for comfort, and whip my weight in wildcats! I can outeat, outsleep, outfight, outshoot, outrun, outjump, and outsquat any man in these here United States! And I will!"

Aunt Ketinah eyed him as if he was a little bit of a mosquito making a buzz.

"That'll be enough o' your sass," said she, kind of sharplike. "Now get back into your cradle and behave."

"Yes, ma'am," said Davy. He was always polite to the ladies.

"No such thing!" said Uncle Roarious. "Settin' in the cradle won't grow him none! We've got to plant him in the earth and water him with wild buffalo's milk, with boiled corncobs and tobacco leaves mixed in."

"Can't do any harm," said Davy's ma.

"Might do good," said Davy's pa.

"Suits me," said Davy. "Let's give 'er a try."

So they took Davy out to Thunder Shower Hill and planted him in the earth. They watered him with wild buffalo's milk, with boiled corncobs and tobacco leaves mixed in. The sun shone on him by day, and the moon beamed down on him by night. The wind cooled him and the rain freshened him. And Davy Crockett began to grow proper.

One morning Davy's pa got up as usual and looked out the window. Instead of the sun shining, it was like a cloudy night with fog and no moon. Davy's pa had never seen it so dark in all his born days.

"Hurricane's comin' up," he said to Uncle Roarious, who was standing in a corner buttoning up his cast-iron shirt.

"We'd better water Davy before she breaks," said Uncle Roarious.

Davy's pa and Uncle Roarious each picked up a barrel of wild buffalo's milk, with boiled corncobs and tobacco leaves mixed in. Davy's ma and Aunt Ketinah followed along, carrying another barrel between them.

But when they got outside there wasn't a sign of a hurricane. There wasn't a hurricane coming up, going down, or standing still. There wasn't any hurricane at all. The sky was blue with little white clouds, and the sun was shining just as pretty. Only reason it was so dark was that Davy's shadow was falling over the cabin.

"Davy must have growed some," said Davy's ma, and they all hurried over to Thunder Shower Hill. Davy was standing on tiptoe with his head poked through a cloud. He was taller than the tallest tree, and a sight friskier.

Uncle Roarious let out a yip and Davy leaned down. Davy wiped a bit of cloud out of his eye and said, "I've been lookin' over the country. She's right pretty, and I think I'm goin' to like 'er."

"You'd better," said Aunt Ketinah, kind of snappylike. "She's the only one you've got."

"Yes, ma'am!" roared out Davy. His voice was so loud it started an avalanche at Whangdoodle Knob, thirty miles away. The trees all around flattened out, and Aunt Ketinah, Uncle Roarious, and Davy's ma and pa fell over from the force of it.

Davy's pa picked himself up and shook his head.

"He's too big," he said.

"Oh, I don't know," said Uncle Roarious. "He'll settle some."

"No," said Davy's pa, "he's too big for a hunter. It wouldn't be fair and square."

"What are we goin' to do?" asked Uncle Roarious.

"Only one thing *to* do," said Davy's pa. "We've got to uproot him and let him grow down to man-size."

So Davy's ma and pa, his aunt Ketinah and his uncle Roarious uprooted Davy. Soon as his feet were free, Davy leapt high into the air. He kicked his heels together, flapped his arms, and he bellowed, "Look out, all you critters and varmints o' the forest! For here comes Davy Crockett, fresh from the backwoods! I'm half horse, half alligator, with a little touch o' snappin' turtle! I can run faster, jump higher, squat lower, dive deeper, stay under water longer, and come up drier than any man in these here United States! *Who-o-o-o-p!*"

Uncle Roarious listened to Davy and he looked at Davy. Then he said, "He's strong, but he's quirky."

Davy's pa looked at Davy and he listened to Davy.

"He'll do," he said. "He'll do for a Crockett till a better one comes along."

And when Davy's pa said that, lightning flashed and thunder boomed. The wind howled riproariously, and all the critters and varmints of the forest let out a moan.

Ol' Dan Tucker

WORDS AND MUSIC BY DANIEL EMMETT

Rollicking   *Arranged by Randa Kirshbaum*

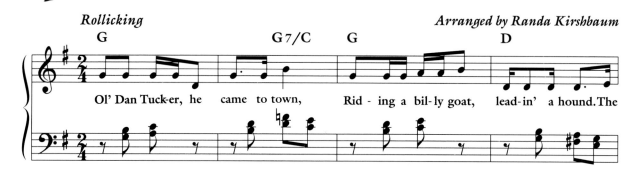

Ol' Dan Tuck-er, he came to town, Rid-ing a bil-ly goat, lead-in' a hound. The

hound gave a yelp, the goat gave a jump And threw ol' Dan a-strad-dle of a stump, so —

Get out' the way for ol' Dan Tuck-er! He's too late to get his sup-per.

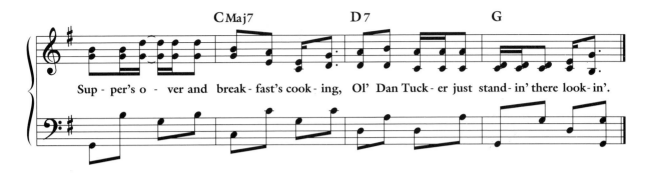

CMaj7   D7   G

Sup - per's o - ver and break - fast's cook - ing, Ol' Dan Tuck - er just stand - in' there look - in'.

2. Ol' Dan Tucker was a fine old man,
He washed his face in a frying pan.
He combed his hair with a wagon wheel
And died with a toothache in his heel, so —

Chorus

3. When at night he went to bed,
He pulled a nightcap over his head.
He tried to sleep but it wasn't any use
'Cause his legs hung out for the chickens to roost, so —

Chorus

4. Dan wore his shirttails outside his coat,
Buttoned his breeches up round his throat.
His nose stuck out, his eyes stuck in,
And his beard grew out all over his chin, so —

Chorus

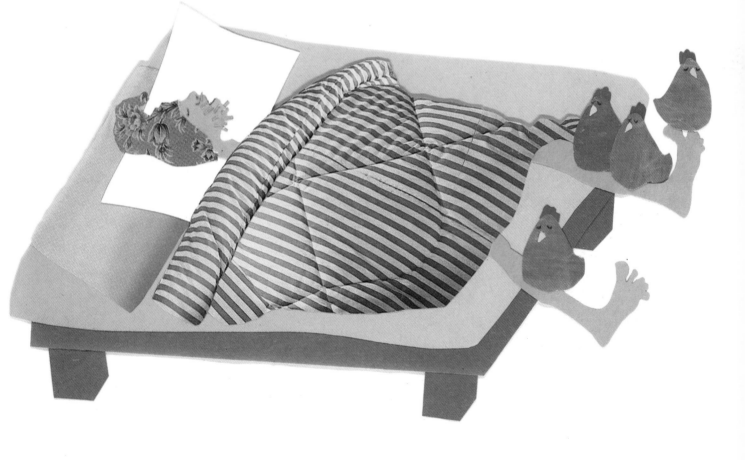

Jack and the Two-Bullet Hunt

RETOLD BY AMY L. COHN AND SUZY SCHMIDT

Tales about a lazy — but lucky — fellow named Jack are told all over the southern Appalachian Mountains.

One time away back years ago, there was a boy named Jack. He and his folk lived off in the mountains and they were awful poor, just didn't have a thing. Jack had two brothers, Will and Tom, and they are in some of the Jack Tales, but this one, there's mostly just Jack in it.

Jack was awful lazy sometimes, just wouldn't do ary lick of work. His mother and his daddy kept tryin' to get him to help, but they couldn't do a thing with him when he took a lazy spell. But they kept tryin'.

So one cold December morning Jack's daddy stood beside Jack in the yard. Looked at rabbit tracks in the snow, looked at Jack, and said, "Son, at the end of them tracks is your breakfast."

Jack got his old single-barrel and the only two shells he had and started out. Jack walked on, walked on. After following the tracks around the hill apiece, he started gettin' tired and stopped to rest. Just then he heard a fluttering sound above him. He looked up and saw nine wild turkeys land on a tree limb in a big sweetgum.

"Can't pass them up," said Jack and fired away. Jack was so close that the charge split the tree limb and the turkeys caught their toes in the crack and beat each other to death flapping their wings. All Jack had to do was climb up and get 'em.

"I got nine turkeys," said Jack, "but I still don't have that rabbit." So he traveled on, traveled on. The tracks led him down the hill, and he stepped along after 'em.

"Whoa," cried Jack, sliding down through the snow, "what's that?" A big grizzly bear and a wild boar came tumbling toward him, fighting for dear life.

Well, Jack didn't think he had a chance. He just threw his gun down, closed his eyes, and threw out his arms hopin' to protect himself. The bear ran right into one of 'em, and Jack's hand went down its throat and out the other end. So Jack grabbed the bear's tail and turned him inside out.

When the old boar saw there wasn't anything else around to fight, he started butting Jack from behind with his six-inch tusks. Jack got so tired of landing flat on his rear that he gave up. "I'll just hide behind this tree," said Jack, " 'til it's all over." But the boar kept comin'. When that boar rammed his six-inch tusks into the five-inch tree, Jack bent down, picked up a rock, and bashed 'im down with it. "Yer caught," said Jack. "Now I got nine turkeys and two flavors of big game, but I still don't have that rabbit."

So Jack ambled on, ambled on, along after those rabbit tracks 'til he got to the creek bank. He looked on up the creek, and there, flying right close together, were nine wild ducks. Jack looked on down the creek. "Whoa," he said, "there's nine wild geese." Then Jack heard a buzzing sound. He turned and stood face to face with a coiled up rattlesnake. Hadn't more than a second to think what to do so he just fired away, and Jack's old gun blew right up.

Well, the barrel went up the creek and killed the nine wild ducks. The stock went down the creek and killed the nine wild geese. The bullet ricocheted off a stone and hit the rattlesnake between the eyes. The kick of the gun knocked Jack head over heels backward right into the creek.

"Whoa," said Jack, wiping his eyes, "there's that durn rabbit." He paddled out of the cold water, intent on catchin' it. But when he came out on land his pockets were so full of fish he couldn't hardly

move. The weight of those fish made a button pop off Jack's overalls. "Whoa," said Jack, and watched the button fly over and kill that rabbit.

Well, Jack took the rabbit, the fish, the rattlesnake, the geese, the ducks, the boar, the bear, and the turkeys and put out for home to cook his breakfast. And the last time I went to see him, he was a-doin' real well.

Groundhog

TRADITIONAL

With vigor

Arranged by Rachel Miller

Call up your hounds and whis - tle up your dogs, Call up your hounds and

whis - tle up your dogs, We're off to the woods to hunt a ground-hog. Ground -

2. Too many rocks and too many logs,
   Too many rocks to hunt a groundhog.
   Groundhog! Groundhog!

3. Here comes Sam with a ten-foot pole
   To roust that groundhog out of his hole.
   Groundhog! Groundhog!

4. Stand back, boys, and let's be wise,
   I think I see his beady eyes.
   Groundhog! Groundhog!

5. The meat'll do to eat and the hide'll do to wear,
   If that ain't groundhog, I'll declare.
   Groundhog! Groundhog!

6. I like my groundhog stewed and fried,
   Little piece of bacon by the side.
   Groundhog! Groundhog!

7. Little piece of cornbread sitting on the shelf,
   If you want any more you can sing it yourself.
   Groundhog! Groundhog!

Gol' in the Chimley

TRADITIONAL

Once upon a time there was two girls. They were sisters, and one went to a witch's house to get a place to stay. Well, the witch said, "All right, you can stay, but I'm going to the store and don't you look up the chimley while I'm gone."

While the witch was gone the girl looked up the chimley. There hung a bag of gold. She got this gold and started, and come to a cow. The cow says, "Please milk me, little girl, I hain't been milked in several long years."

She says, "I hain't got time."

She went on to a sheep and the sheep said, "Please shear me, little girl, I hain't been sheared in several long years."

She says, "I hain't got time."

She went on to a horse, and the horse said, "Please ride me, little girl, I hain't been rode in several long years."

She said, "I hain't got time."

She went on and come to a mill. The mill said, "Please turn me, little girl, I hain't been turned in several long years."

The little girl said, "I hain't got time." She went over and laid down behind the door and went to sleep.

Well, the old witch came back and her gold was gone. She started and come to the cow and said:

"Cowel o' mine, cowel o' mine,
  Have you ever seen a maid o' mine,
  With a wig and a wag and a long
    leather bag,
  Who stold all the money I ever had?"

The cow said, "Yeaw, she just passed." She went on to the sheep and said:

"Sheep o' mine, sheep o' mine,
  Have you ever seen a maid o' mine,
  With a wig and a wag and a long
    leather bag,
  Who stold all the money I ever had?"

The sheep said, "Yeaw, she just passed." She went on to the horse and said:

"Horse o' mine, horse o' mine,
  Have you ever seen a maid o' mine,
  With a wig and a wag and a long
    leather bag,
  Who stold all the money I ever had?"

The horse said, "Yeaw, she just passed." She went on to the mill and said:

"Mill o' mine, mill o' mine,
  Have you ever seen a maid o' mine,
  With a wig and a wag and a long
    leather bag,
  Who stold all the money I ever had?"

It said, "She's layin' over there behind the door."

She went over there and turned that girl into a stone. She got her gold and went on back home.

Well, the next girl come along and said, "Can I get to stay here?"

The witch said, "Yeaw, but I'm going to the store. Don't look up the chimley while I'm gone."

When she got gone the girl looked up the chimley. There hung this bag of gold. She got it and started. Come to this cow, and the cow said, "Please milk me, little girl, I hain't been milked in several long years."

She milked the cow. Went on to the sheep. The sheep says, "Please shear me, little girl, I hain't been sheared in several long years."

She sheared the sheep. Went on to the horse. The horse said, "Please ride me, little girl, I hain't been rode in several long years."

So she rode the horse. Come to the mill. The mill says, "Please turn me, little girl, I hain't been turned in several long years."

She turned the mill and then she hid.

Well, the old witch come back, and her gold was gone. She started. She come to the cow and said:

"Cowel o' mine, cowel o' mine,
 Have you ever seen a maid o' mine,
 With a wig and a wag and a long
     leather bag,
 Who stold all the money I ever had?"

The cow said, "No."
She went to the sheep and said:

"Sheep o' mine, sheep o' mine,
 Have you ever seen a maid o' mine,
 With a wig and a wag and a long
     leather bag,
 Who stold all the money I ever had?"

The sheep said, "No, I hain't never seen her."
She went on to the horse and said:

"Horse o' mine, horse o' mine,
 Have you ever seen a maid o' mine,
 With a wig and a wag and a long
     leather bag,
 Who stold all the money I ever had?"

The horse said, "No, I hain't never seen her."
She went on to the mill and said:

"Mill o' mine, mill o' mine,
 Have you ever seen a maid o' mine,
 With a wig and a wag and a long
     leather bag,
 Who stold all the money I ever had?"

It said, "Get up in my hopper. I can't hear good."

She got up in the hopper and shouted:

"Mill o' mine, mill o' mine,
Have you ever seen a maid o' mine,
With a wig and a wag and a long
leather bag,
Who stold all the money I ever had?"

The mill started grinding and ground her up.

The little girl she came out, turned the stone back into her sister, and they lived happily ever after.

Hush, Little Baby

TRADITIONAL

Tenderly

Arranged by Allan Miller

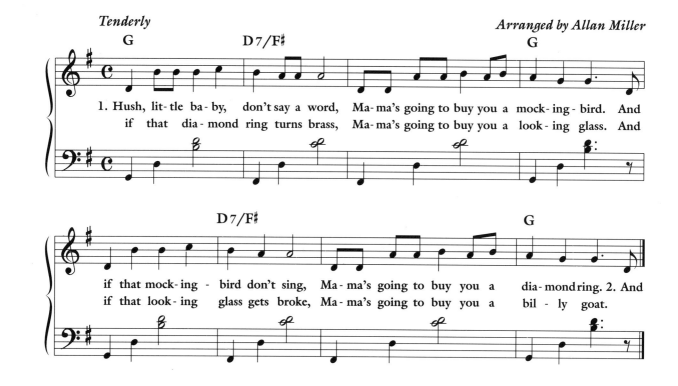

1. Hush, lit-tle ba-by, don't say a word, Ma-ma's going to buy you a mock-ing-bird. And
if that dia-mond ring turns brass, Ma-ma's going to buy you a look-ing glass. And

if that mock-ing - bird don't sing, Ma-ma's going to buy you a dia-mond ring. 2. And
if that look-ing glass gets broke, Ma-ma's going to buy you a bil-ly goat.

3. And if that billy goat won't pull,
   Mama's going to buy you a cart and bull.
   And if that cart and bull turn over,
   Mama's going to buy you a dog named Rover.

4. And if that dog named Rover won't bark,
   Mama's going to buy you a horse and cart.
   And if that horse and cart fall down,
   You'll still be the sweetest little baby in town.

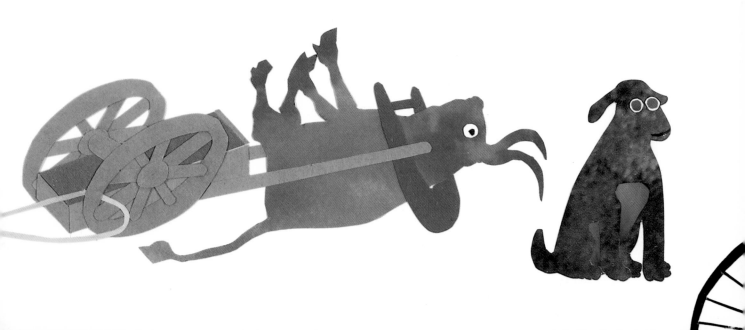

Marcia Brown

WATER, WATER EVERYWHERE

*In the early nineteenth century, Americans living
along the Atlantic seaboard set their sails
to bring goods to every corner of the earth.*

Blow, Ye Winds, in the Morning

TRADITIONAL

Arranged by Jerome Epstein

'Tis ad - ver - tised in Bos - ton, New York, and Buf - fa - lo, Five hun - dred brave A - mer - i - cans a - whal - ing for to go— sing - in',

Chorus

"Blow, ye winds, in the morn – ing— Blow, ye winds, high - O! Clear a - way the run - ning gear and blow, boys, blow!"

2. They send you to New Bedford, that famous whaling port, And give you to some land sharks to board and fit you out — singin',

Chorus

3. They tell you of the clipper ships a-going in and out, And say you'll take five hundred sperm, before you're six months out — singin',

Chorus

With a Way, Hey, Mister Stormalong

RETOLD BY AMY L. COHN AND SUZY SCHMIDT

No one knows exactly where he came from, but most agree it was one of those New England towns hard by the sea, one of those towns ending in "nuck" or "nocket" or "tucket." Old Stormalong, they called him, or Stormy for short, but his real name was Alfred Bulltop Stormalong. And though he wasn't very old, he sure was tall — four fathoms tall. When he signed onto the *Lady of the Sea,* the captain nearly lost his eyesight looking up at him. But he let Stormy sign on all the same. "Stormalong, A. B.," wrote the new hand. The captain looked at the ledger and said, "You're able-bodied, all right." Well, all the first-class seamen standing in line behind Stormalong put A. B. after their names, too, and right there on the Boston waterfront a new tradition started.

Now the *Lady of the Sea* was one of the largest ships ever built, but Stormalong still had to be careful not to step too heavily or pull too hard. Fact was, he could rig sails to the highest mast without leaving the deck, so the captain couldn't help but promote him to bos'n right away. (For you landlubbers, that's boatswain, meaning Stormy took charge of the rigging and cables and such like.)

But, like I said, those four fathoms could sure cause trouble, especially around mealtime. Only ostrich eggs could fill Stormy at breakfast, and he drank whale soup from a dory for lunch. Feeding Stormy was a full-time job in itself and many a worn-out cook handed in his apron in disgust. But Mister Stormalong was too valuable a hand to dismiss on account of his prodigious appetite.

One time when the *Lady of the Sea* was in the northern Atlantic, the lookout spotted a good-sized whale to starboard. All free hands went to crank in the mudhook, but even with Stormy heave-hoing, it wouldn't budge. Stormalong didn't bother to call the captain. He stripped to the waist and dove overboard. The men waited and waited — and waited.

Turns out that at the bottom of the anchor chain Stormalong met an enormous octopus who had wrapped his tenta-

cles around the anchor and wouldn't let go. Stormy grabbed the octopus and swiftly tied each arm into a double carrick bend. He made the knots so tight that the beast turned scarlet and scurried off on tiptoe. At last Old Stormy came back upside and gulped a breath of air. The sailors whistled and stomped, and the captain gave the bos'n the rest of the day off.

Eventually even Stormy got tired of salt pork and hardtack and cramped quarters on the ship. When the *Lady of the Sea* pulled into Long Wharf he quit, hoofing it inland to try his hand at potato farming. Wasn't but a year or two later he appeared at the wharf, peaked and dispirited, his eyes gazing hungrily out to sea. Sure he'd been a successful farmer, but as he himself said, "All my muscles were made for pulling, and on a farm there's nothing to do but push."

His timing was perfect, for the largest ship ever built was taking on crew. She was so big she couldn't enter Boston Harbor. Her mast was so tall it pierced the clouds, and she was so long from stem to stern that it took a man on horseback twenty-four hours to make the trip.

Stormy swam ten miles to get to the *Courser*, signed on, and was soon happier than a porpoise. Before the ship headed for the high seas, the captain did the only right thing and bowed out, letting the big man take his place.

The *Courser* could ride out a storm like a bobber on a pond. 'Course, there was no telling where it might end up, and once, on the way back from Norway with a hold full of pickled herring, she was swept into the English Channel. Directly ahead loomed the narrow Straits of Dover.

The *Courser* had no room to come about. She'd have to go through. Stormalong directed the crew to gather up all the soap on board. What they found didn't amount to a barrelful, but Stormy wasn't stumped. He dispatched a party ashore, telling the men to trade the herring for as much of that slick stuff as they could get. Before too long Cap'n Stormy sent his able-bodied seamen over the deck rails in bos'ns' chairs to swab the *Courser*'s sides with soap. The men spread the greasy soap so good and thick that even the barnacles lost their grip and slid off. Working in two shifts, the sailors finished in just three days, and they were all cleaner than a whistle when they got through.

Sober sailor faces watched as Stormy squeezed the mighty clipper through the gap. The ship scraped and rubbed and strained against the north shore, but, thanks to the soap, she made it. Most of it rubbed off, though, and that's why they call 'em the White Cliffs of Dover.

Now, you would think a man as mighty as Stormalong would live forever. But he died, that's sure. Not a soul knows how, but everyone knows when. They laid Stormy's body to rest about the time those newfangled steamships challenged the graceful old clippers for control of the seas. Stormalong and his mates were iron men who went to sea in wooden ships, and it broke the big man's heart to see iron ships crewed by wooden men.

"I'd rather be found dead than aboard a steamboat," he vowed. And sure enough, the salt spray splashed atop his grave before the last Yankee clipper furled her silver sails.

The Sailor's Alphabet

TRADITIONAL

Oh, **A** is the anchor and that you all know,
B is the bowsprit that's over the bow,
C is the capstan with which we heave 'round,
And **D** are the decks where our sailors are found.

Oh, **E** is the ensign our mizzen peak flew,
F is the fo'c'sle where we muster our crew,
G are the guns, sir, by which we all stand,
And **H** are the halyards that ofttimes are manned.

Oh, **I** is the iron of our stunsail boom sheet,
J is the jib that oft weathers the bleat,
K is the keelson away down below,
And **L** are the lanyards that give us good hold.

M is our mainmast so stout and so strong,
N is the needle that never points wrong,
O are the oars of our jolly boat's crew,
And **P** is the pennant of red, white, and blue.

Q is the quarterdeck where our captain oft stood,
R is the rigging that ever holds good,
S are the stilliards that weigh out our beef,
And **T** are the topsails we ofttimes do reef.

Oh, **U** is the Union at which none dare laugh,
V are the vangs that steady the gaff,
W's the wheel that we all take in time,
And **X** is the letter for which we've no rhyme.

Oh, **Y** are the yards that we ofttimes do brace,
Z is the letter for which we've no place,
The bos'n pipes grog, so we'll all go below,
My song it is finished, I'm glad that it's so.

Blow, Boys, Blow

TRADITIONAL

This is a halyard shanty, sung by sailors as they performed tasks requiring strength and teamwork.

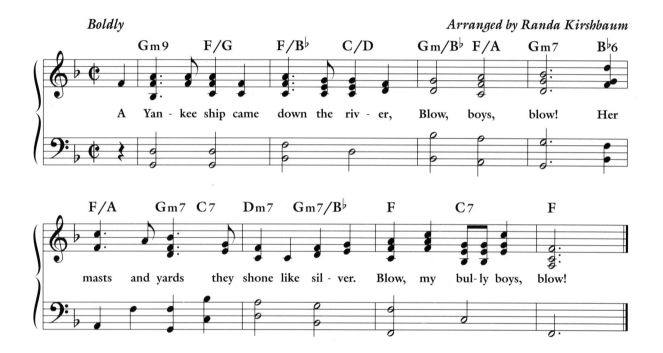

2. How do you know she's a Yankee liner?
Blow, boys, blow!
The Stars and Stripes float out behind her.
Blow, my bully boys, blow!

3. And who d'you think is the captain of her?
Blow, boys, blow!
Why, Bully Hayes is the captain of her.
Blow, my bully boys, blow!

4. And what do you think they've got for dinner?
Blow, boys, blow!
Pickled eels' feet and bullock's liver.
Blow, my bully boys, blow!

5. Blow, boys, blow, the sun's drawing water.
Blow, boys, blow!
Three cheers for the cook and one for his daughter.
Blow, my bully boys, blow!

The Salem Ghost Ship

RETOLD BY FRANK SHAY

Wherever men have gone to sea in ships, there are stories about phantom ships — ghost ships that appear suddenly only to vanish again.

We were all Salem men aboard the brig *Neptune* and we were ending a sixteen months' voyage on the shortest day of the year. We'd be home in Salem in time for Christmas. Salem's a town that holds its people wherever they roam. Although many of us travel far and long, we remain Salem men until death. There's even an old legend that says no matter where his body dies, the spirit of a true Salem man always returns.

Captain Abner Low had taken Jack Somers and me along with him. We were fourteen and had taken a year out of school to see what we were made of. Jack was in the captain's watch, the starboard. And I was in the second watch, the larboard, under the mate.

We had started out with the usual Yankee cargo of rum, Lowell cottons, codfish, cheese, clocks, furniture, and shoes. Our run took us first to Madeira for wine. Then we traded along Africa's west coast, sailing around the Cape to Madagascar. We pushed on to the Arabian ports for coffees and then to the Indian ports. From India, we headed for China for teas, silks, and nankeens. In Sumatra we traded for pepper, and finally we reached Manila where we took on cigars. Then we beat across the Pacific to Juan Fernandez for water and fresh provisions. We doubled the Cape and crossed the Atlantic to Antwerp, and now we were returning, returning home to Salem, with a rich haul from Europe, Africa, and Asia.

Each Tuesday and Friday night us boys went to the captain's cabin. There, he instructed us in arithmetic and the simple problems of navigation. That was our book learning. Our more practical education was in the hands of "Sails," the elderly sailmaker. It was this character who taught us to knot, reeve, and splice, to hand, reef, and steer. And he counseled us not to run when an officer gave an order, but jump. From old Sails we learned the lore of the sea, the legends, superstitions, and the salty speech. Sails loved talking about the ghost ships. He had seen them all, he said — the *Flying Dutchman* in the Hudson River, the *Dead Ship* of Orr's Island up Maine way, the *Palatine* over to Block Island.

Even though we were sure Sails was pulling our legs, we loved hearing the stories as much as he loved telling them. Before we'd put the first patches on our sea breeches, we were sneaking peeks at the horizon, hoping to catch a glimpse of a phantom ship. We hadn't seen a one.

And now the trip was over. We were entering Salem Harbor under reefed topsails, riding a following easterly of moderate gale strength. It was the first dog of the watch. Darkness had already fallen. Mr. Cates, the pilot, was beside me. Sails stood with Jack just below.

We passed Peach's Point and were inside Kettle Bottom. The pilot gave orders in his quiet voice, and I repeated them loud and strong with the added "sir." In a few moments, the bell would be struck and Jack would sound off briskly.

"Ease her a bit to port, lad," said Mr. Cates.

"To port, sir!" I snapped, and then two bells were struck. I listened for Jack Somers's cry, and it came promptly.

"Two bells, sir, and all the lights are burning brightly!" Then he screamed, "Astern! Look astern! Ship ho!"

I turned and looked aft. A great ship under full sail, four times the size of the *Neptune,* was bearing down on us. For a moment I wondered what maniac was her master. Then, quickly, I threw the helm over hard to port, believing I could throw the brig over enough to ease a dead-on crash. But the wheel was taken roughly from my hands, and I was crowded off the grating.

The wheel spun back to its old position, and Mr. Cates's calm voice said, "Steady, lad, steady!"

I must have been cringing, waiting for the crash. She'll strike us starboard, I thought, and we'll find ourselves swimming for the Triangles, our ship at the bottom.

The crash didn't come. Lifting my head, I saw the giant vessel tack slightly and come along starboard, crowding us. But there was no splintering of wood, no rush of water. There was no creaking and straining of ropes and canvas, only a grim and glowing silence. Every sail was set, every rope taut or coiled on her deck. Her anchor was stowed for a long voyage. I thought I could see her masts through her sails, as though they were cobwebs; I could see her stout frames through the hull. But she carried no cargo, there were no men in her fo'c'sle, and there was no one at her helm. And, as we all looked at her, she faded away, as though she'd entered a dense fogbank.

Jack and I looked to each other and then to Sails. His jaw hung open and his eyes stared straight ahead, fixed on the now-vanished ship.

"It's the Ghost Ship," Mr. Cates said in his quiet voice. "A proper Salem man has died somewhere, and the ship is bringing his spirit home to Salem, home for Christmas."

Clinton's Ditch: Digging the Erie Canal

BY SUZY SCHMIDT

America needed more than the world's oceans to grow into a strong nation. It needed inland waterways — rivers, lakes, and even canals.

In the early nineteenth century, citizens of the brand-new United States turned, with their hopes and dreams, to the fertile farmlands and new towns of the region we now call the Midwest. But the Appalachian Mountains stood in the way. Saddled with belongings, settlers leaving from New York City found no easy route to get beyond that barrier.

Could a canal be the answer? Many laughed at the proposal, but De Witt Clinton, a future governor of New York, realized the possibilities. In 1817, the state assembly and senate approved the plans. De Witt Clinton would oversee from start to finish the construction of what adversaries called "Clinton's Ditch."

To connect the Atlantic with the Great Lakes, the 363-mile canal would run from Albany, where the Hudson River came up from New York City, west to the city of Buffalo on Lake Erie. Before digging, local laborers cut down trees, then burned and cleared the land. Then they dug the canal forty feet wide and four feet deep at the center, with sloping sides. A path was prepared alongside on which mule teams pulled boats using 100-foot-long towropes.

Troubles dogged the project from the start. One of the worst disasters came in the Montezuma swamp west of Syracuse. Standing in water above their knees, the workers' feet swelled and leeches fed gluttonously on their blood. But though no one knew it at the time, it was the anopheles mosquito that brought the fevers and chills and death of what everyone called "the ague." Doctors tried bleeding, snakeroot, green pigweed, and kerosene before they discovered that Jesuit's bark from Peru seemed to help. The bark contained a crude form of quinine, which is still used to treat "ague" or malaria.

In an attempt to assuage people's disappointment in the tragic epidemic and the canal's slow progress, De Witt Clinton opened fifteen miles of the waterway in October 1819. People found so many unforeseen uses for the canal, from living on it to racing horses on its track, that a commission adopted rules to reserve the canal strictly for freight and passenger transport. Even speed limits were imposed. No one could travel faster than four miles per hour!

The canal inspired all kinds of enterprises. As sections were completed, gamblers, thieves, and fortune-tellers, even entertainers with dancing bears, opened lucrative operations. Others set up floating groceries, tinkers' shops, penny museums, bookstores, and libraries. And these entrepreneurs stayed in business for many years.

The Erie Canal

TRADITIONAL

Robustly

Arranged by Denes Agay

1. I've got a mule, her name is Sal, Fif - teen miles on the E - rie Ca - nal. She's a
2. We bet - ter get on our way, old pal, Fif - teen miles on the E - rie Ca - nal. 'Cause you

good ol' wor - ker and a good ol' pal, Fif - teen miles on the E - rie Ca - nal. We've
bet your life I'd ne - ver part with Sal, Fif - teen miles on the E - rie Ca - nal. Get

hauled some bar - ges in our day, Filled with lum - ber, coal, and hay, And
up there, mule, here comes a lock, We'll make Rome 'bout six o' - clock,

we know ev - 'ry inch of the way From Al - ba - ny to— Buf - fa - lo.—
One more trip and back we'll go, Right back home to— Buf - fa - lo.—

Sally Ann Thunder Ann Whirlwind Crockett Meets Mike Fink, Snappin' Turkle

RETOLD BY CARON LEE COHEN

In the early part of the nineteenth century, a man named Mike Fink lived along the Mississippi River. In fact, he made his living along it. Fink was a keelboatman, one of the strong-armed, strong-backed, bull-headed fellows who floated flatboats down the river to New Orleans. At the mouth of the Mississippi, Fink and his mates would reload the keelboat with cargo and bring it up to St. Louis and beyond, propelling the boat forward against the current by pushing down with all their might on long poles.

Life along the river was rough. And tough. And Mike Fink was one of the roughest, toughest parts about it. To make sure everyone knew just how tough he was, he always wore a red turkey feather stuck in the brim of his hat. "Half of me is wild horse and half is alligator. And the rest is crooked nails and red-hot snappin' turkles," he'd shout, whenever and wherever he had the chance.

They say Fink never lost a fight. But then, he hadn't ever met up with Sally Ann Thunder Ann Whirlwind Crockett.

S ally Ann Thunder Ann Whirlwind Crockett lived long ago near the Mississippi River. Her husband was Davy Crockett.

Now that lady was made of thunder with a little dash of whirlwind. She wore a beehive for a bonnet and a bearskin for a dress. Her toothpick was a bowie knife.

She could stomp a litter of wildcats and smash a band of starving wolves. She could outscream an eagle and outclaw a mountain lion.

She could skin a bear faster than an alligator swallows a fish.

She walked like an ox and ran like a fox.

She could wade the wide Mississippi without getting wet.

And she could jump over the Grand Canyon with both eyes shut.

She could do just about anything. And nothing on earth scared her. Nothing!

But she never bragged. And she never fought a man, woman, or critter for no good reason.

Now Mike Fink lived along the Mississippi, too. He was a bad man, always looking for a fight. He could beat any man except his enemy, Davy Crockett. Their fights ended in a draw. And when Mike Fink wasn't fighting, he was bragging!

One day, Mike walked into a tavern. He jumped on a table and roared, "Half of me is wild horse and half is alligator. And

the rest is crooked nails and red-hot snappin' turkles. I can outrun, outshoot, outfight any man! If any man says that's not true, let him step up and fight."

No man dared to fight bad man Mike Fink. But Davy Crockett was in that tavern. And he was sick of hearing Mike Fink brag. "You don't scare me," Davy said. "And you couldn't even scare my sweet little wife, Sally Ann Thunder Ann Whirlwind Crockett."

Mike roared, "I'll bet you a dozen wildcats I can SCARE HER TEETH LOOSE!" And the bet was made.

So one evening, by the river, Mike found an alligator. He skinned it and crept inside the skin.

Then he crawled along the river. And there was Sally Ann Thunder Ann Whirlwind Crockett out for her nightly walk.

Mike crawled toward Sally Ann. He poked the alligator's head here and there. He opened its jaws big and wide. He let out a horrible cry.

He nearly scared himself out of the alligator's skin. But Sally Ann wasn't scared. Not one little bit. She just stepped aside as if that alligator were a dead stump.

So Mike crawled closer and stood up on his hind legs. Then he threw his front paws around Sally Ann.

Sally Ann Thunder Ann Whirlwind Crockett didn't let just any critter hug her. Her rage rose higher than a Mississippi flood.

Her eyes flashed lightning. The night sky lit up like day. Mike was scareder than a raccoon looking down a rifle barrel. But he thought of his bet with Davy Crockett.

He kept circling Sally Ann and wagging his tail.

"That's enough, you worm!" said Sally Ann Thunder Ann Whirlwind Crockett. And she pulled out her toothpick.

With one swing, she cut off the head of that alligator. It flew fifty feet into the Mississippi River. Then she could see it was just bad man Mike Fink playing a trick.

"You lowly skunk!" she said. "Trying to scare a lady out on her nightly walk. Now stand up and fight like a man." She threw down her toothpick and rolled up her sleeves. She battered poor Mike till he fainted. She was still in a rage, but she wouldn't touch a man who was down. So she just walked off.

Mike didn't wake up till the next day. He couldn't tell his friends he had been beaten by a woman. Instead he bragged! "I got swallowed by an alligator. But I was chock full of fight and cut my way out. And here I am."

Still, a bet was a bet.

So he caught a dozen wildcats and gave them to Davy Crockett.

But that wasn't the end of it.

One night by the river, Sally Ann Thunder Ann Whirlwind Crockett met bad man Mike Fink.

Her rage rose higher than a Mississippi flood. She lit the sky with lightning from her eyes.

And this time it scared Mike Fink's teeth loose.

From then on, bad man Mike Fink had a mouth full of loose teeth. And every time he bragged, those teeth rattled!

Steamboats on the Mississippi: Sounding Calls

TRADITIONAL

Often the only way to safely navigate a river was to "heave the lead": drop a rope overboard with a lead pipe attached to the end, the rope marked along its length to indicate the water's depth. The soundings were called out in a rhythmic chant to the pilot and could be heard, often in fog or darkness, up and down the river. These melodious leadsmen were said to have inspired the young Samuel Clemens in his search for a writing name. Listen to them now as they call out shallower and shallower water to the pilot.

No bottom,

Mark four,

Quarter less four,

Quarter less five,

Half twain,

Quarter twain,

Quarter less four,

Half twain,

Quarter twain,

Mark twain,

Quarter less twain,

Nine-and-a-half feet,

Nine feet,

Eight-and-a-half feet.

Shenandoah

TRADITIONAL

This river shanty, with its haunting melody, was sung to pass the time as sailors weighed anchor or loaded and unloaded cargo.

Slowly and freely

Arranged by Denes Agay

Oh, Shen-an-doah, I long to hear you, A way, you rol-ling riv-er! Oh, Shen-an-doah, I long to hear you, A- way, I'm bound a-way, 'Cross the wide Mis-sour-i.

2. Oh, Shenandoah, I love your daughter,
   Away, you rolling river!
   For her I've crossed the stormy water,
   Away, I'm bound away,
   'Cross the wide Missouri.

3. Farewell, my dear, I'm bound to leave you,
   Away, you rolling river!
   Oh, Shenandoah, I'll not deceive you,
   Away, I'm bound away,
   'Cross the wide Missouri.

HARRIET TUBMAN

FREEDOM'

" RIGHTEOUSNESS

NEW-YORK, FRIDA

works of trivial importance, we shall conside
a part of our duty to recommend to our youn
readers, such authors as will not only enlarg
their stock of useful knowledge, but such
will also serve to stimulate them to higher a
tainments in science.

We trust also . . . through the [colum
. . . the P

Jerry Pinkney

LET MY PEOPLE GO

For generations, the African men, women, and children held in bondage in America longed to be free.

Go Down, Moses

TRADITIONAL

*The enslaved Africans living in the American South often used Biblical tales
and images to describe their own heartache and suffering.*

Dramatically

Arranged by Theodore Raph

When Is-rael was in E-gypt's land, Let my peo-ple go, Op-
pressed so hard they could not stand, Let my peo-ple go.

Chorus

Go down, Mo-ses, way down in E-gypt land

Tell ol' Phar-aoh, let my peo-ple go.

2. The Lord told Moses what to do,
   Let my people go,
   To lead his people right on through,
   Let my people go.

   Chorus

3. 'Twas on a dark and dismal night,
   Let my people go,
   When Moses led the Israelites,
   Let my people go.

   Chorus

4. When Israel reached the water side,
   Let my people go,
   Commanded God, "It shall divide,"
   Let my people go.

   Chorus

5. When they had reached the other shore,
   Let my people go,
   They sang a song of triumph o'er,
   Let my people go.

   Chorus

How the Slaves Helped Each Other

RETOLD BY WILLIAM J. FAULKNER

H ere's a story Simon Brown told me when I was a little boy. He said, "Willie, we slaves had to make our own way in this old world. We didn't have any church in those days, or hospital or doctors or nurses, either. We had to fend for ourselves if sickness came.

"In slavery time only white folks had doctors or nurses to care for them. Still, if a slave became ill, he wasn't left alone to suffer unattended. In time of illness or other trouble, fellow slaves would 'turn in and help out.'

"After the field work was done for the day, men would cut wood for the sick person and pile it up near his fireplace. Since the slaves did not have stoves, their fireplaces kept the cabins warm and also served for cooking. Usually the chimneys were wide and built of mud and sticks, interlocked at the four corners, and the hearths were big enough to hold three-foot logs.

"If the woman of a slave family fell ill, other black women came to tend the children, cook the meals, wash the clothes, and do other necessary chores. Women would come over just to sit a spell and sing and pray around the sick bed. Nobody was left to suffer alone. Sometimes a man or woman with a healing touch would brew an herb tea, mix a poultice, or apply peach tree leaves to a fevered brow, to help the sick get well. And all this loving care cheered up the troubled soul, whether he got well or died.

"Here's what happened to an old slave woman named Dicey and how much her friends cared about her."

Sister Dicey was as good a soul as ever lived. She was the friend of all the folks, black and white. One day she passed away in her sleep. Now, the slaves had no undertakers, so the womenfolk came in and prepared her body for burial, which had to be done in twenty-four hours. After bathing her, they put on her the best dress they could find and laid her out in a homemade coffin, resting on two chairs. Somebody pinned a flower on her bosom.

Later that night slaves from all about came to the cabin and sat around while they sang and prayed. People kept coming and going all night long. The singing was mostly sad songs with happy endings, because the folks felt that now Sister Dicey was freed from all the trials and tribulations of slavery and was safe in heaven, at rest and in peace forevermore. She wouldn't be a barefoot slave dressed in rags anymore. In God's heaven, she would have shoes, a robe, a crown, a harp, and the wings of an angel — she'd have everything she needed to make her happy.

The next morning old Master John Brown came over to the cabin to pay his last respects to Sister Dicey, his faithful servant, and to tell the people that he would let them off from work to go to the funeral. They could use a pair of mules and his best farm wagon to carry the coffin to the graveyard.

After the coffin was lowered into the grave, the slave preacher said words of comfort over the body — something like this: "Sister Dicey, since God in His mercy has taken your soul from earth to heaven and out of your misery, I commit your body to the ground, earth to earth, ashes to ashes, dust to dust, where it will rest in peace. But on that Great Getting Up Morning, when the trumpet of God shall sound to wake up all the dead, we will meet you in the skies and join the hosts of saints who will go marching in. Yes, we want to be in that number, Sister Dicey, when the saints go marching in."

Before the preacher could finish his benediction, some of the women got so happy that they drowned him out with their singing and hand clapping and shouting. Then some men and boys began to fill up the grave. When it was full, they rounded it up real prettylike and put one wood shingle at the head and another at the foot of the grave. The womenfolk laid some flowers and ribbon grass on top and put colored bottles, broken glass, and seashells all around the grave of Sister Dicey.

In that way, they showed their love for her. It was the best that slaves could do in those days, when everybody was poor and owned by their masters. But no man could own their souls or keep them from loving one another. These gifts came only from God.

I Got Shoes

TRADITIONAL

With spirit

Arranged by Darrell Peter

High John the Conqueror

BY STEVE SANFIELD

It's said that High John came across the water from Africa. Some people remember him as a big man. Others remember him as a small man. I myself don't rightly know, but I do know he was a *Be-Man*. He *be* there when the trouble come, and he *be* there when the trouble go.

Even though John was a slave, he hated slaving and loved living, and he tried to do as much living and as little slaving as possible. I mean, he'd pick up a shovel, and the shovel would break — accidentally, of course. He'd go out to the toolshed, and the toolshed would burn down — accidentally, of course. If he ever did get to the fields with the mules, the mules would tromp down four rows of cotton — accidentally, of course.

But some years he'd do the work of four or five men. When he picked cotton and was half trying, he could pick a thousand pounds a day, and when he was really trying, those cotton bolls flew so fast you would've thought you were in the middle of a blizzard.

Of course, Old Master could never quite figure out whether John was working for him or against him, and believe me, that's just the way John wanted it.

High John was, among other things, a fine fisherman. He knew where the fish lay, and he knew what had to be done to catch them.

Even Old Master liked to go fishing with John now and then. They'd go down to the big pond under the live oaks, and Master would try to catch a few catfish himself.

John and Master had planned to meet early one bright summer morning. John was already there behind the barn when along came Master. Of course he had his fishing pole with him, but he was also carrying a brand-new walking stick. The stick was polished almost as bright as a mirror. It had a shiny silver handle on one end and a shiny silver tip on the other.

From the way he was swinging and flashing it about, you could tell Master was very proud of his new stick. John, however, didn't make any mention of it, at least not until they were settled on the bank of the pond with their lines in the water.

"Say, Massa," said John, "that's a mighty fine-looking walking stick you've got there."

"Why, thank you, John. I was beginning to wonder if you were going to take any notice of it."

"Oh, Massa, I noticed it right off. I mean it's the only walking stick I've ever seen with three ends."

"Three ends?" asked Master. "What are you talking about, John?"

"Well, I ain't talking about anything but the three ends of that stick," John answered.

"John, are you drunk or have you gone crazy?"

"I'm not drunk and I'm not crazy,

Massa, but I can see as clear as the nose on my face that your stick's got three ends."

"John, no stick's got three ends."

"Well, that one does," said John, "and I'd be willing to bet you a big, fat hen that it does."

Old Master took a careful look at his walking stick just to be sure. After all, John had been playing tricks on him for years. This time, though, he was certain John was wrong.

"Agreed," he said. "I'll bet you a hen that this stick has only two ends."

With that, John took the stick and held it out in front of him. He pointed to the silver handle and said, "That's one end, right?"

"Right," answered Master.

He pointed to the silver tip and said, "That's two ends, right?"

"Right," answered Master again.

Then John raised the stick over his head and threw it directly into the center of the pond, where it sank without a trace.

"And that's the third end of that stick, right?" said John with a twinkle in his eye.

Old Master didn't answer this time. He knew John had fooled him again, and that when they got back home he'd have to give him a nice, plump hen.

It was the custom of Old Master and his family to have a turkey dinner every Christmas, and it was John's responsibility to get the turkey ready for the oven.

Thinking he might have some fun at John's expense, Master called him to the Big House just before the holiday.

"John," he said, "you know tomorrow is Christmas."

"Yes, I know," responded John.

"And you know," Master continued, "you take care of the turkey every year."

"Yes, Massa, I know that, too."

"Well, John, I've decided that this year whatever you do to that turkey we're going to do to you."

John went back to his cabin with a worried mind. He knew he had a serious problem. If he cut off the turkey's head, then Master would cut off his head. If he shot the turkey, he himself would be shot. And if he plucked off all its feathers, Master would probably skin him alive.

John spent most of the night tossing and turning, trying to find a way to save himself. Just before the sun rose on Christmas morning, he got a splendid idea.

When John appeared at the Big House, Old Master and his entire family were waiting on the veranda. They were all looking forward to making a fool of him.

But when he showed up he wasn't carrying a dead and plucked bird. This tom turkey was alive and well and gobbling for the whole world to hear, and John was leading it on a long, red string.

"Merry Christmas to you, Massa," said John.

"And Merry Christmas to you, John. Remember now, whatever you do to that turkey we're going to do to you," laughed Master, and everyone laughed with him.

"Yes, Massa," said John.

Just as if he didn't have a care in the world, John led the big bird right to the edge of the veranda. Then he stepped behind it, dropped to his knees, lifted up its tail feathers, and kissed it right on its butt.

No one said a word, but High John stood up, turned his back on Old Master and his family, lifted his own coattails, and said, "Take your time, folks. Take your time. I've got all day."

Long John

TRADITIONAL

Syncopated

Arranged by James Rooker

The Sad Tale of Three Slavers

RETOLD BY M. A. JAGENDORF

Slave owners had the right to pursue and capture runaways even if they already had made their way to the North and freedom. But the pursuers were not always successful.

There came riding into Bloomfield, Ohio, just as the sun was setting one Sunday, three men out on the hunt for fleeing slaves. They asked this one and that one and everyone if they hadn't seen a young black man and his family, running from their rightful owners.

Folks in Bloomfield had little love for slave owners and slave hunters and said they hadn't seen the family — even though most of them had. But at the inn the slave owners heard a different tale. The innkeeper, Joshua, loved slavers as snakes love boiling water, and he was a mighty smart fellow who always liked a clever trick.

"Bless ye, gentlemen," he said, sugar on his face, "bless ye. 'Deed I saw the four fleeing slaves. They were on the road to Ashtabula. They were crawlin' sore-footed like snails and they can't be far. Might as well stay in my inn, enjoy a good meal, and take a well-needed rest. Ye'll get those runaways tomorrow."

The host was so honey-kind, and the slavers were so tired and hungry, they decided to stay.

The three ate well, drank well, and soon were dreaming. But the host was wide awake and at work. First thing he did was call his staff and tell 'em to sleep a little later the next morning.

"Just don't get up till ye hear me," he said. Some looked puzzled, some knowing, but all promised faithfully to oblige.

Then he ran to the house of his friend Barnes, the blacksmith, and told him what he had in mind. Barnes roared at the scheme, slapped his thighs, and cried he was with it body, boots, and britches.

Next Joshua ran to his neighbor Squire Brown. Squire Brown laughed with glee and swore he'd do all he could to help.

As soon as Joshua left, Squire Brown hitched up his wagon and went where he believed the slaves had gone. Bloomfield and all the towns nearby were honeycombed with homes where slaves were hidden. He rode until he came to a house where he knew slaves often found refuge.

He knocked, then told his errand, but it took heaps of talk before he could take the runaways with him. He soon had the family safe in a barn not far from Bloomfield.

The morning came warm and sunny, pigeons were cooing and hens were scratching, but the inn was quiet as a mole run.

The sun kept on shining stronger and was beating in the room where the slavers were sleeping. In the end it woke 'em, and they leapt out o' bed, for they could tell by the sun it was late. They roared for the innkeeper and shouted at him why hadn't he awakened 'em early as he said he would. Joshua ran in half-dressed, cried in distress, begged to be forgiven, and swore at his help who were lazy and ever oversleeping. But soon the morning meal was on the table and a good meal it was. The coffee smelled strong, and the mistress of the inn was very pleasant, urging the three gentlemen slavers to eat and drink. Soon they forgot their anger. There were second helpings and second cups of coffee. At last they were done.

The slavers smiled and went out to the stable, where they found Joshua ranting and roaring.

"Where's the key! Where is that key? Where is it? Ye see, gentlemen, I always lock the stable door at night for fear o' thieves. Now I can't find the key. Maybe I dropped it."

He bent down, looking in the dirt and in the grass. So did the help and the hostess and the slavers.

Suddenly Joshua leapt and shouted, "Shucks creation! Now I remember. I left the key over the fireplace."

He ran into the inn and soon came out. The door was unlocked, and there they found that each horse wanted a shoe and one of the animals had a cracked hoof.

"Everything's gone wrong," cried the innkeeper. "Gentlemen, I must beg yer forgiveness. Come, let's rush to Barnes, the smith. He's a friend o' mine, and I'll make 'im stop all work and tend to yer horses."

He rushed off, the slavers following. Soon they got to the smith, and the door was locked! Joshua banged, shouted, used strong words, but it didn't bring Barnes.

A crowd gathered around 'em, but not a one knew where the blacksmith was.

"I'll run and find that nimshi," cried Joshua, and off he went.

The horses pawed the ground, and the slavers swore and walked up and down, while folks smiled and said little. They kind of guessed what the game was.

It took near half an hour until Joshua returned with Barnes, and then — the smith found something had gone wrong with the lock. It took a long time before that door was opened.

Now there was new trouble: making a fire. "It's the first time in my life such a thing's happened to me," the smith kept on mumbling.

At last the fire was ready, and now Barnes found there wasn't a single horseshoe and not a nail in the smithy. So he set to work making both.

The hours dragged on, and the slavers were soon wild as a hurricane on Lake Erie. But the folks standing around smiled and kept their mouths buttoned up.

The sun was standing in the middle o' the sky, but Barnes was still hammering and pounding. His hands seemed made o' bullet lead that day. At last the horses were ready and the slavers rode off wilder than hungry wolves.

They rushed in the direction Joshua told them, passing right alongside the barn where the slaves were hiding.

When they were gone, Squire Brown put the fugitives in a hut on his own grounds where they would be safe until the catawampus was over.

Three days later, three tired slavers came back to Bloomfield, without any slaves. At once the sheriff told 'em they hadn't paid the right toll when they passed through town and they'd have to pay a fine.

The slavers cried and shouted, but to the judge they had to go. No innkeeper would lodge their horses, so they tied 'em to a signpost and went to pay the fine.

While they were gone, some folks full of old scratch cut off chunks from the horses' manes and tails so they looked silly 'nuf to stop a clock.

When the slavers saw that, they called Bloomfield the devil's own pasture and ran off as quick as they could.

All the folks laughed at this. All except Squire Brown, who held out that there was no sense in punishing fine animals for the misdeeds of their masters — and I say the same.

Follow the Drinkin' Gourd

TRADITIONAL

The words of this song provide disguised directions for those escaping north toward the Big Dipper — "the drinkin' gourd."

Resolutely

Arranged by Carl Miller

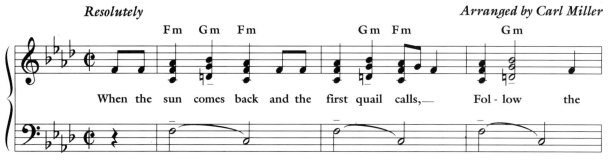

When the sun comes back and the first quail calls,— Fol-low the

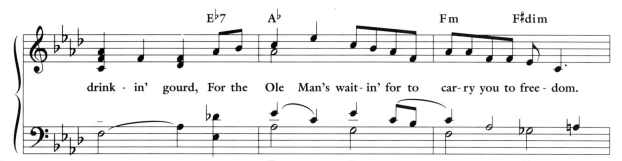

drink-in' gourd, For the Ole Man's wait-in' for to car-ry you to free-dom.

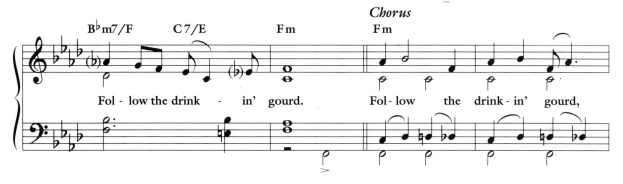

Chorus

Fol-low the drink - in' gourd. Fol-low the drink-in' gourd,

2. Oh, the riverbank makes a very true road.
   Dead trees will mark the way.
   The left foot, pegfoot, travelin' on.
   Follow the drinkin' gourd.

   Chorus

3. Where the river ends in between two hills,
   Follow the drinkin' gourd.
   There the Ole Man's waitin' for to carry you to freedom.
   Follow the drinkin' gourd.

   Chorus

Harriet Tubman

BY ELOISE GREENFIELD

*Conductors on the Underground Railroad didn't take tickets for passengers
riding on trains that ran on iron tracks. Instead, they "conducted," or led,
on foot or in wagons, slaves escaping north to freedom. Harriet Tubman was
the most famous conductor of all.*

Harriet Tubman didn't take no stuff
Wasn't scared of nothing neither
Didn't come in this world to be no slave
And wasn't going to stay one either

"Farewell!" she sang to her friends one night
She was mighty sad to leave 'em
But she ran away that dark, hot night
Ran looking for her freedom

She ran to the woods and she ran through the woods
With the slave catchers right behind her
And she kept on going till she got to the North
Where those mean men couldn't find her

Nineteen times she went back South
To get three hundred others
She ran for her freedom nineteen times
To save black sisters and brothers

Harriet Tubman didn't take no stuff
Wasn't scared of nothing neither
Didn't come in this world to be no slave
And didn't stay one either

And didn't stay one either

The People Could Fly

RETOLD BY VIRGINIA HAMILTON

" 'The People Could Fly' was first told and retold by those who had only their imaginations to set them free." —Virginia Hamilton

hey say the people could fly. Say that long ago in Africa, some of the people knew magic. And they would walk up on the air like climbin up on a gate. And they flew like blackbirds over the fields. Black, shiny wings flappin against the blue up there.

Then, many of the people were captured for Slavery. The ones that could fly shed their wings. They couldn't take their wings across the water on the slave ships. Too crowded, don't you know.

The folks were full of misery, then. Got sick with the up and down of the sea. So they forgot about flyin when they could no longer breathe the sweet scent of Africa.

Say the people who could fly kept their power, although they shed their wings. They kept their secret magic in the land of slavery. They looked the same as the other people from Africa who had been coming over, who had dark skin. Say you couldn't tell anymore one who could fly from one who couldn't.

One such who could was an old man, call him Toby. And standin tall, yet afraid, was a young woman who once had wings. Call her Sarah. Now Sarah carried a babe tied to her back. She trembled to be so hard worked and scorned.

The slaves labored in the fields from sunup to sundown. The owner of the slaves callin himself their Master. Say he was a hard lump of clay. A hard, glinty coal. A hard rock pile, wouldn't be moved. His Overseer on horseback pointed out the slaves who were slowin down. So the one called Driver cracked his whip over the slow ones to make them move faster. That whip was a slice-open cut of pain. So they did move faster. Had to.

Sarah hoed and chopped the row as the babe on her back slept.

Say the child grew hungry. That babe started up bawling too loud. Sarah couldn't stop to feed it. Couldn't stop to soothe and quiet it down. She let it cry. She didn't want to. She had no heart to croon to it.

"Keep that thing quiet," called the Overseer. He pointed his finger at the babe. The woman scrunched low. The Driver cracked his whip across the babe anyhow. The babe hollered like any hurt child, and the woman fell to the earth.

The old man that was there, Toby, came and helped her to her feet.

"I must go soon," she told him.

"Soon," he said.

Sarah couldn't stand up straight any

longer. She was too weak. The sun burned her face. The babe cried and cried. "Pity me, oh, pity me," say it sounded like. Sarah was so sad and starvin, she sat down in the row.

"Get up, you black cow," called the Overseer. He pointed his hand, and the Driver's whip snarled around Sarah's legs. Her sack dress tore into rags. Her legs bled onto the earth. She couldn't get up.

Toby was there where there was no one to help her and the babe.

"Now, before it's too late," panted Sarah. "Now, Father!"

"Yes, Daughter, the time is come," Toby answered. "Go, as you know how to go!"

He raised his arms, holding them out to her. *"Kum . . . yali, kum buba tambe,"* and more magic words, said so quickly, they sounded like whispers and sighs.

The young woman lifted one foot on the air. Then the other. She flew clumsily at first, with the child now held tightly in her arms. Then she felt the magic, the African mystery. Say she rose just as free as a bird. As light as a feather.

The Overseer rode after her, hollerin. Sarah flew over the fences. She flew over the woods. Tall trees could not snag her. Nor could the Overseer. She flew like an eagle now, until she was gone from sight. No one dared speak about it. Couldn't believe it. But it was, because they that was there saw that it was.

Say the next day was dead hot in the fields. A young man slave fell from the heat. The Driver come and whipped him. Toby come over and spoke words to the fallen one. The words of ancient Africa once heard are never remembered completely. The young man forgot them as soon as he heard them. They went way inside him. He got up and rolled over on the air. He rode it awhile. And he flew away.

Another and another fell from the heat. Toby was there. He cried out to the fallen and reached his arms out to them. *"Kum kunka yali, kum . . . tambe!"* Whispers and sighs. And they, too, rose on the air. They rode the hot breezes. The ones flyin were black and shinin sticks, wheelin above the head of the Overseer. They crossed the

146

rows, the fields, the fences, the streams, and were away.

"Seize the old man!" cried the Overseer. "I heard him say the magic *words*. Seize him!"

The one callin himself Master come runnin. The Driver got his whip ready to curl around old Toby and tie him up. The slave owner took his hip gun from its place. He meant to kill old, black Toby.

But Toby just laughed. Say he threw back his head and said, "Hee, hee! Don't you know who I am? Don't you know some of us in this field?" He said it to their faces. "We are ones who fly!"

And he sighed the ancient words that were a dark promise. He said them all around to the others in the field under the whip, "*. . . buba yali . . . buba tambe. . . .*"

There was a great outcryin. The bent backs straighted up. Old and young who were called slaves and could fly joined hands. Say like they would ring-sing. But they didn't shuffle in a circle. They didn't sing. They rose on the air. They flew in a flock that was black against the heavenly blue. Black crows or black shadows. It didn't matter, they went so high. Way

above the plantation, way over the slavery land. Say they flew away to *Free-dom*.

And the old man, old Toby, flew behind them, takin care of them. He wasn't cryin. He wasn't laughin. He was the seer. His gaze fell on the plantation where the slaves who could not fly waited.

"Take us with you!" Their looks spoke it but they were afraid to shout it. Toby couldn't take them with him. Hadn't the time to teach them to fly. They must wait for a chance to run.

"Goodie-bye!" The old man called Toby spoke to them, poor souls! And he was flyin gone.

So they say. The Overseer told it. The one called Master said it was a lie, a trick of the light. The Driver kept his mouth shut.

The slaves who could not fly told about the people who could fly to their children. When they were free. When they sat close before the fire in the free land, they told it. They did so love firelight and *Free-dom*, and tellin.

They say that the children of the ones who could not fly told their children. And now, me, I have told it to you.

Swing Low, Sweet Chariot

TRADITIONAL

This plaintive lament implies that death may provide, for some, the only deliverance from slavery.

Expressively

Arranged by Theodore Raph

Swing low, sweet char - i - ot, ⎯ Com - in' for to car - ry me

home. Swing ⎯ low, sweet char - i - ot, ⎯

Com - in' for to car - ry me home. I

looked o - ver Jor - dan and what did I see, ⎯ Com - in' for to car - ry me

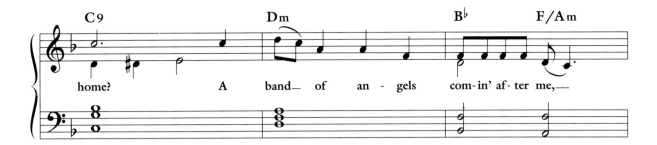

home? A band— of an-gels com-in' af-ter me,—

Com-in' for to car-ry me home. Swing low, sweet

char - i - ot,— Com-in' for to car-ry me home.

Swing low, sweet char - i - ot,— Com-in' for to car-ry me home.

David Wiesner

I'VE BEEN WORKING
ON THE RAILROAD

Shortly after the Civil War ended, Americans labored
to link the country by rail.

John Henry

TRADITIONAL

Arranged by Elizabeth Poston

Fast, boldly

When John Hen - ry was a— lit - tle ba - by boy,— You could

hold him in the palm of your hand,——————— He——

gave a long— and a lone - some cry, "Gon - na

be a steel - dri - vin' man, Lawd, Lawd,

Gon - na be a steel - dri - vin' man."

2. Well, the captain said to John Henry,
   "Gonna bring that steam drill 'round,
    Gonna take that steam drill out on the job,
    Gonna whop that steel on down, Lawd, Lawd,
    Gonna whop that steel on down."

3. John Henry said to the captain,
   "Well, a man ain't nothin' but a man,
    And before I let a steam drill beat me down,
    Gonna die with the hammer in my hand,
        Lawd, Lawd,
    Gonna die with the hammer in my hand."

4. They took John Henry to the tunnel,
   Put him in the lead to drive,
   The rock so tall, John Henry so small,
   That he laid down his hammer and he cried,
        Lawd, Lawd,
   Laid down his hammer and he cried.

5. John Henry said to his shaker,
   "Now, Shaker, why don't you sing?
    I'm throwin' nine pounds from my hips on down,
    Just listen to the cold steel ring, Lawd, Lawd,
    Just listen to the cold steel ring."

6. Well, the man that invented the steam drill,
   He thought he was mighty fine,
   But John Henry drove his fifteen feet,
   And the steam drill only made nine, Lawd, Lawd,
   The steam drill only made nine.

7. John Henry looked up at the mountain,
   And his hammer was striking fire,
   He hammered so hard that he broke his heart
   And he laid down his hammer and he died,
        Lawd, Lawd,
   He laid down his hammer and he died.

8. They took John Henry to the tunnel,
   And they buried him in the sand,
   And ev'ry locomotive comes a-roarin' by
   Says, "There lies a steel-drivin' man, Lawd, Lawd,
   There lies a steel-drivin' man."

Building the Transcontinental Railroad

BY ADELE NATHAN

In 1866, there were no railroad tracks west of Omaha, Nebraska. In order to link the nation by rail, from the Atlantic to the Pacific, two companies, the Union Pacific and the Central Pacific, participated in a great competition sponsored by the federal government.

Twelve thousand men came to Omaha to work on the transcontinental railroad. They worked in the blacksmith shops, the roundhouses, and the terminal yards. They worked on the steamboats chugging up and down the river and they worked on the docks unloading supplies. And, of course, they worked laying rails.

Most of the laborers were Irish. Some were new immigrants, but a good many were ex-soldiers from both sides of the Civil War. They wore cast-off blue or gray uniforms with the scarves, broad-brimmed hats, high boots, and checked shirts that were the usual laborer's outfit.

The workers dug their way across the

prairie like terriers digging for bones. They called themselves "Tarriers."

The men either lived in tents out in the open plains or slept in hammocks slung in the boxcars that rested on the railroad sidings that had just been built. Train cars served as cookhouses, bakeries, butcher shops, general stores, and even saloons.

The most important person in a construction camp was the cook. Whether man or woman, black or white, a bad cook would be run out of camp at rifle point if the meals weren't satisfying.

Breakfast was best of all. There were platters of meat, potatoes, other vegetables, canned fruit, pie, and coffee. The men worked off all that heavy breakfast before noon and came back roaring for more.

The first railroad crews out were the graders and the bridge builders. Sometimes they worked a hundred miles ahead of the track, blasting out rock with black powder, piling up embankments with hand shovels and wheelbarrows, building stone culverts and wooden trestles.

Back in Omaha, railroad cars were loaded, each with a certain number of rails and the exact number of spikes needed to lay them. When the grading had been completed and the ties laid, two locomotives pushed the cars to the end of the

line. As fast as the trains from Omaha could bring up supplies, the trackmen laid the rails.

The rails were of iron, twenty-eight feet long, and each one weighed about three hundred fifty pounds. They were laid on wooden ties and held down by long iron spikes.

Once a newspaperman came out from the East to watch the Tarriers lay rails. This is how he described it:

"When the train arrived, the boarding cars were pushed as far as possible toward the end of track and a carload of rails unloaded behind them. The boarding cars were then drawn back and about forty rails with the proper number of chairs and spikes were loaded on a small car and dragged to the end of the track by horsepower. Here a man put a check under a wheel, bringing the load to a stop. On each side of the car were rollers.

"Before the car had well stopped, a rail was dropped on the rollers and twelve men, six on each side, took hold of it. At the command, 'Up! Forward!' they raised and carried it to the proper location. Then came the command, 'Ready! Down!' and it was lowered into place. Two parallel tracks were laid at the

same time by this method, and in thirty seconds the railroad was twenty-eight feet nearer the Pacific Ocean. Before the clang of the dropped rails had died away, willing hands pushed the car forward over the loose rails, and repeated the operation, as fast as a man could walk.

"Behind the car followed a man dropping spikes. Others came after, tamping the earth under the ties, and last came the bolters.

"The moment one railcar was empty, it was tipped off to one side, while a second was drawn up to the end of the track.

"A horseman riding at a gallop then pulled the first car at the end of an eighty-foot rope back to the rail dump. There it was quickly loaded to go up front again. Every few minutes the long, heavy train behind sent a puff up from its locomotive and, pushing the boarding cars and the cars of rails, caught up with the work."

And so the Tarriers crossed the plains, laying track as quickly as they could. From the west the men called Crocker's Pets labored just as hard. The two crews would meet at Promontory Point, Utah, and the nation for the first time would be linked by rail from sea to shining sea.

Drill, Ye Tarriers

WORDS AND MUSIC BY THOMAS CASEY

Arranged by Randa Kirshbaum

2. The new foreman was Jean McCann;
   By gosh, he was a blamed mean man!
   Last week a premature blast went off
   And a mile in the air went big Jim Goff.

   Chorus

3. When next payday it came around,
   Jim Goff a dollar short was found;
   When he asked what for, came this reply:
   "You were docked for the time you were up in the sky!"

   Chorus

Death of the Iron Horse

RETOLD BY PAUL GOBLE

There have been many trains wrecked by Indian people in the pages of fiction, but it really happened only once. On August 7, 1867, a Union Pacific freight train was derailed by Cheyennes. The train was traveling from Omaha to Fort McPherson (North Platte, Nebraska), which was then as far as the track had been laid to join the east and west coasts of the nation. The tribes opposed the construction through their land.

The Civil War had recently ended, and the might of the army was turned to driving the Indians onto reservations. The unequal struggle was almost over. The derailment was only a minor incident, but one that the Cheyenne people have remembered with pride and amusement. This account is loosely based on the incident. It tells a story of courage against the steam locomotive, a truly awesome and unknown invention of the white men. When Missouri riverboats had first been seen, they caused panic; tribes had fled at the mere rumor of the Fire Boat's approach.

Like everything else to do with war, the derailment had sad and unpleasant aspects. But from this distance in time, we can see that the Cheyennes were simply fighting for their lives, liberty, and their own pursuit of happiness.

Long ago, long before the white people ever came to this land, the Cheyenne Prophet, called Sweet Medicine, had a terrible dream: In his dream he saw strange, hairy people coming from the East. There were more of them than buffaloes — as many, even, as the grasshoppers. They killed his people, and those few who were left alive were made to live in little square houses. And Sweet Medicine saw them kill all the buffaloes, so there was nothing left to eat, and the people starved. He saw the hairy people tear open our Mother, the earth, exposing her bones, and they bound her with iron bands. Even the birds and animals were afraid, and no longer spoke with people. It was a terrible dream, and they say that Sweet Medicine died of awful sadness not long afterward.

And then, one day, white people did come from the East. First a few came, and then more and more; they wanted all the land for themselves. Soldiers attacked and burned the *tipi* villages. They killed women and children, and drove off the horses. The people fought back bravely to protect themselves and to keep the land they loved. But they lived in fear. People said that those things which Sweet Medicine had foretold were surely coming true.

One day scouts galloped into camp, and told of something they called the Iron Horse.

"It is huge! It breathes out smoke and has the voice of Thunder. It is coming this way. The white men are making an iron road for it to go on. *Nothing* can stop the Iron Horse!"

They tried to describe it. People had terrifying images in their minds.

Was it an enormous snake, or even an underwater monster that had crawled out of the river? Was this what Sweet Medicine had spoken about? Then there was even greater fear. In the minds of the children fear grew that the Iron Horse would suddenly come over the hill, right into camp.

Spotted Wolf, Porcupine, Red Wolf, Yellow Bull, Big Foot, Sleeping Rabbit, Wolf Tooth, and many others whose names are not now remembered wanted to protect the people from the Iron Horse. They were not much older than boys, and knew they would have to be brave, even ready to die, like the warriors who had died defending the helpless ones.

"The soldiers have defeated us and taken everything that we had, and made us poor. We have no more time to play games around camp. Let us go and try to turn back this Iron Horse."

They left camp without telling anyone. They rode all night and most of the next day, and came to a ridge overlooking the wide valley of the river. Thick black smoke was rising in the far distance.

"It is a grass fire," said one.

"No, the smoke has a strange shape. *Look!* The smoke is coming this way, *against the wind*!"

"Impossible," said another, "fire cannot go against the wind...."

But the smoke kept on coming, and underneath it something was growing larger.

"It is the Iron Horse; nothing else can make smoke go against the wind. See, it puffs and puffs like a white man's pipe."

When the Iron Horse had disappeared in the distance, the young men went on again.

"Let us see the trail it leaves," they said to each other. But nobody had ever seen anything like its tracks.

"These must surely be the iron bands binding our Mother, earth, which Sweet Medicine dreamed about. We must cut them apart and set her free."

With only tomahawks and knives it seemed an impossible task. But they dug down and chopped the ties in the middle, and hacked out spikes until the rails no longer joined together. The moon had long passed overhead when they finished.

Dawn was just showing when they saw a small light over the level plain.

"Morning Star is rising," someone said.

"No," said another, "it is the eye of the Iron Horse shining."

Those with the fastest horses galloped up the track to find out.

When they saw it was indeed the Iron Horse, they turned around, but their horses were not fast enough. The Iron Horse came up behind, huffing and panting, and belching out clouds of black smoke. It thundered alongside, sending forth screams and hissing and shooting sparks high into the air: *puff-a-puff-a-puff-a-puff-a-puff-a-puff-a-puff-a-puff-a-puff-a-puff-a-puff-a-puff-a-*

The young men shot their arrows; one tried to throw a rope over the engine, but the horses were terrified and ran from the monster. Suddenly the locomotive jumped right into the air, and all the boxcars slammed and zigzagged together with a dreadful crash.

Everything was twisted up in clouds of dust and smoke and steam.

The dust blew away. The hissing steam faded. There was silence. One white man was on the ground; another was in the cab. They were both dead.

"The Iron Horse does not breathe any longer," someone said. The sun rose as they stood looking in bewilderment at what they had done. Suddenly a door in the caboose opened: A man jumped down and started running back up the track. He died full of arrows.

"Come on; let us see what white people carry in these wagons."

They broke open the first car; inside was a jumble of broken boxes and barrels. The first box was filled with axes. Then everyone was hacking open cases, excited to see what was inside.

They had never seen so many different things; they did not know what most of them were. But there were pans and kettles; china plates and glass vases; cups, files, and knives, like those which cost many buffalo robes in trade with the white men. Everyone found something useful. There were mountains of boxes: shoes, shirts, pants, jackets, tall black hats, and hats with ribbons and feathers. They scattered them everywhere. Best of all, there were soldiers' uniforms and blankets, and glasses which the soldier chiefs used for looking into the distance. They even found flags, and someone uncovered a beautiful shiny bugle.

In the caboose there were things to eat, and bottles of sweet juice. There was also a heavy tin box, which would not open. They knocked off the lock; it was filled with bags of silver coins and bundles of little bits of green paper. The coins they took because the women knew to make holes in them and hang them on their dresses. But they threw the bits of green paper into the air and watched them blowing like leaves.

There were bolts of cloth in another boxcar; cloth of every color and pattern.

"Ha! Look at all this! Here is more than the stingy traders have! This is all ours! Look how much!"

"Well, this one is mine," someone said, and he ran off, holding onto an end while the cloth unrolled behind him. "I am taking this one," said another, and he jumped on his horse and galloped away with the cloth unfurling and floating after him like a long ribbon. And then everybody did it.

When one tied an end to his pony's tail, others tried to step on the cloth, hoping to jerk him out of the saddle. They had great fun. The horses joined in the excitement, galloping this way and that over the prairie with the lengths of cloth sailing behind them. When they became old men they loved to laugh about that day. . . .

It was only a smudge on the horizon, but first one, then another one stopped galloping to look.

"Another Iron Horse is coming. This time there will be soldiers with horses in the wagons."

They quickly gathered up all the precious things they could carry. And then someone said, "We will burn this and leave nothing for the soldiers." Taking red-hot coals out of the locomotive, they set the boxcars alight. They reached the high ridge and looked back. The valley was filled with smoke.

"Now our people need not fear the Iron Horse. We will make them glad when we give them all these things. Let's go."

This story has remembered the brave young men who defended their mothers and younger brothers and sisters from the Iron Horse. Whoever could have imagined that, almost within their lifetime, the Iron Horse would become the train on which we all ride?

The Iron Moonhunter

RETOLD BY KATHLEEN CHANG

This story takes place in the fall and winter of 1866 and the spring of 1867 as the Chinese immigrants known as Crocker's Pets struggled to build rail lines eastward from Sacramento, California, that would link with those being built westward from Omaha, Nebraska, by the Tarriers of the Union Pacific.

More than a hundred years ago, many Chinese people, *Tong Yun*, came to America to build a railroad. They came crowded in the holds of big ships. They suffered eight long weeks waiting to arrive in America, the land they called *Gum Sahn*, or Golden Mountain.

The men who had hired them in China said they would be welcome in *Gum Sahn* and paid high wages. But those who greeted them at the docks in San Francisco didn't want the *Tong Yun* in America. These *gweillo*, these white demons, cursed and threw bricks at the *Tong Yun*. They even shot at them.

The *Tong Yun* were angry and wanted to go home, but they had no money to pay the boat fare. So they stayed and went to work on the Central Pacific Railroad.

They worked high in the Sierra Nevada Mountains. From sunrise to sunset they chopped down the giant redwood trees and lifted tons of steel and rock. Often gangs of *gweillo* tried to make trouble. One day they set off an explosion that killed several of the *Tong Yun*.

A few weeks after this happened, the *Tong Yun* were blasting a ledge into a granite cliff. The Kwan cousins dangled over the edge of the cliff in baskets. They drilled holes in the rock, put gunpowder and a fuse in the holes, lit the fuses, and then pulled their baskets to safety as the rock beneath them exploded. Bit by bit a path wide enough for a railroad was carved into the granite face of the mountain.

The Kwans liked being high as hawks, able to see far across the Sierra Nevadas. They liked the rugged wilds of *Gum Sahn*. They said they would work hard and get rich and start their families here.

But one day the rope that held up Kwan Hop's basket broke. Kwan Hop fell to his death in the river gorge, two thousand feet below. Sadly, Kwan Ming and Kwan Cheong climbed down the cliff to bury their cousin by the side of the river.

Winter came and forty feet of snow fell. The *gweillo* wouldn't let the *Tong Yun* stop working, though even the tall trees were buried in snow. They dug caves in the snow for shelter and tunneled up to the surface through the packed snow, making air shafts so that they could breathe. To get to and from work they had to carve out a maze of snow tunnels, some of them two hundred feet long. Often huge hunks of the snow tunnels caved in and people were buried alive. One night it was Kwan Cheong who never came back from work.

Winter passed and the snow melted, but

the spring brought no pleasure to Kwan Ming. He missed Kwan Hop and Kwan Cheong. Sometimes he woke up in the night thinking that they were standing by his bed. When he washed his face, he sometimes saw their faces in the water. The rest were troubled, too, for many other men died in explosions, cave-ins, and landslides. All the living were haunted by the unhappy faces of their dead friends and brothers.

One night the cook, Ah Ding, dropped a big pot of hot soup, shouting, "Wang Sam! Why do you follow me? Are you hungry?"

"*Aiya!*" cried out Kwan Ming. "Wang Sam died in the landslides last winter. You're seeing a ghost spirit!"

Jeong Yum, the cook's helper, was so troubled by the spirits that he could not sleep. "When I sleep I dream of my brother," he said. "I dream that his ghost is looking for the arms he lost in the explosion."

Then Jeong Yum became angry. "It's because of the *gweillo* and their railroad that our friends and brothers have died! I hate the railroad! I want to blow it up!"

The other men began to shout and talk about blowing up the railroad, but Kwan Ming calmed them down. "Talk sense," he said. "The railroad is our work, and we should be proud of it. We're going to finish it because when we *Tong Yun* say we'll do something, we don't stop halfway."

The men were quiet for a few moments, then Ah Ding said, "The spirits of our friends and brothers are lost and alone in these barbarian mountains. We must take care of them somehow, or we'll know no peace ourselves."

"Let's build a railroad for the spirits," Kwan Ming said, "our own *Tong Yun* railroad. We'll build the finest train in the world, and we'll ride our train to find the spirits of our friends and brothers."

And that's what they did. While they built the Central Pacific Railroad, they saved some of the steel rails. When trains crashed and tumbled off the tracks, which happened all the time, they gathered up the parts. They built a train in the shape of a dragon and called it the *Iron Moonhunter.*

They mined the Sierras for gold and silver. They gave the *Moonhunter* silver whiskers and teeth that gleamed as he grinned in the night. They painted him bright colors and they inlaid designs and good-luck charms in gold. They gave the *Moonhunter* wings to help him balance on the high mountain ridges. They shaped his smokestacks into horns and flutes, so he played his song as he ran. His eyes were long searchlights, and he looked for *Tong Yun* who were lost far from home. And inside him was everything the *Tong Yun* needed.

The *Tong Yun* rode the *Moonhunter* back over the track they'd laid. Waiting in the tunnel where he had died was Kwan Cheong. Kwan Hop waited at the cliff's edge. The cousins wept with joy to see the beautiful train their friends had built to find them. Soon all the ghost spirits heard the *Moonhunter*'s song and one by one, out of the mountains' shadows, they stepped into the yellow light shining from the dragon's eyes. Now they were all together again.

The first railroaders grew old and died. But the ghosts of the *Tong Yun* still ride the *Moonhunter* through the Sierra Nevadas. They still look after the *Tong Yun* in *Gum Sahn,* and the *Iron Moonhunter* still plays his song.

A Gust of Fall Wind

TRADITIONAL

This lament, sung by the Chinese in America, uses the image of the coming winter as a metaphor for loneliness and sorrow.

Sadly

Arranged by Georgette LeNorth

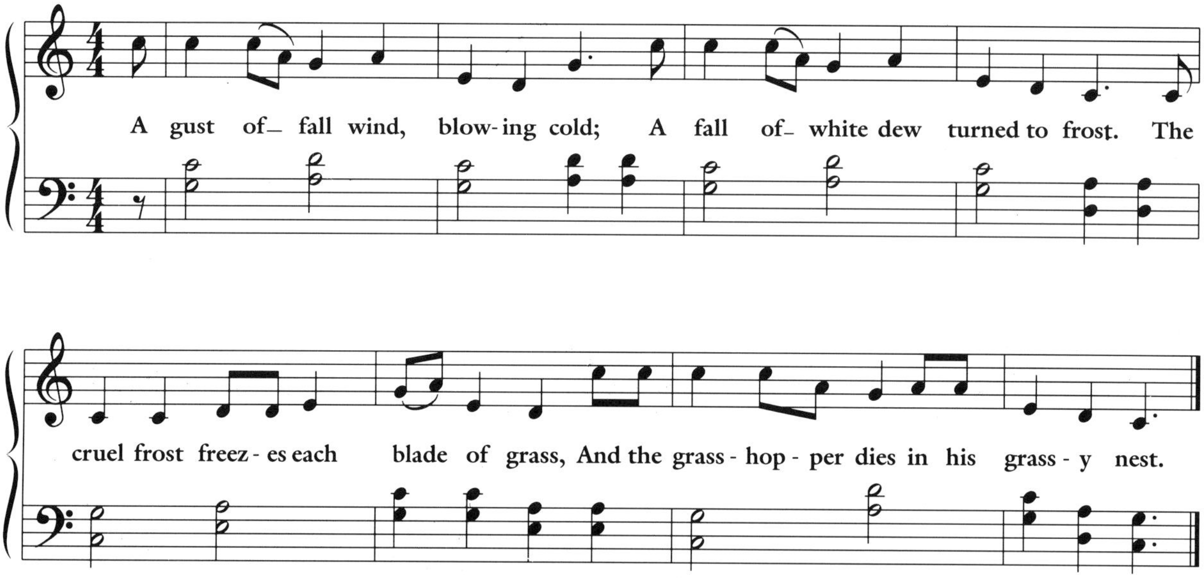

A gust of_ fall wind, blow-ing cold; A fall of_ white dew turned to frost. The cruel frost freez-es each blade of grass, And the grass-hop-per dies in his grass-y nest.

乍 起 秋 風 寒

CHA CHI CHIU FENG HAN

A gust of fall wind blowing cold;

酷 霜 凝 片 草

KU SHUANG NING PÍEN TS'AO

The cruel frost freezes each blade of grass,

白 露 化 成 霜

PAI LU HUA CHENG SHUANG

A fall of white dew turned to frost.

蚱 蜢 草 巢 殤

CHA MENG TS'AO CHÁO SHANG

And the grasshopper dies in his grassy nest.

169

Casey Jones, Railroad Man

RETOLD BY AMY L. COHN AND SUZY SCHMIDT

Casey Jones couldn't help but be a railroad man. He was born to the long, lonesome wail of a locomotive whistle. He grew up to the sound of an engine moan. He started out as a call boy, then moved to ticket agent, telegraph operator, brakeman, and fireman. At last he got to be an engineer — and not just any engineer at that. Casey drove the Illinois Central's crack train *Cannonball,* which ran between Memphis, Tennessee, and Canton, Mississippi.

Casey played a long, mournful call on the *Cannonball's* six-tone calliope whistle. It began softly, then rose, then died away almost to a whisper. The sound spread out over the countryside like the voice of a great whippoorwill calling: Kaaaaaaa-Seeeeeee Joooooooooooooooooones.

And up and down the line people would roll over in their beds and say, "Yup, there goes Casey Jones."

All engineers were daredevils in those days when orders were "Get her there and make the time, or come by the office and get your time." But no engineer pushed an engine to its limit quite like Casey. Casey loved highballing — flying down the track at breakneck speeds. Casey would lean out of the cab window to watch his drivers until he got his engine going so fast that the side rods looked solid. Then he'd tip back in his seat, look at his fireman, Sim, and grin all over, happy as a boy with his first pair of boots.

Late on April 29, 1900, when Casey had just finished his run, he offered to go out again for an engineer who was sick. When No. 382 pulled out of the Memphis' station, it was already ninety-five minutes late. Casey threw open the throttle: He'd highball his way back to being on time.

Two freight trains pulled onto the sidetrack near Vaughn, Mississippi, to let the *Cannonball* pass on its way south. The trains were four cars too long to clear the switches, but the engineers planned to "saw." They'd move south to clear the north switch, and after Casey had passed they'd move north to clear the south switch.

But as the two freights started to perform the "south saw," an air hose burst, leaving four cars blocking the main line at the north switch. The freight crews didn't count on Casey's final burst of speed — seventy miles an hour. And Casey couldn't hear, over the sound of his engine, the detonation of the warning torpedo the freight flagman had set on the track.

Within a hundred feet of the siding, Casey Jones and Sim saw the looming shape of several boxcars on the main line. There was no time to prevent a smash-up.

"Jump, Sim, and save yourself!" Casey cried. Casey threw his engine into reverse and applied the airbrakes. He pulled the whistle with all his might.

That final blast of warning was the last sound Casey ever heard. When they took his body from the wreckage, Casey's hands were clenched tight, one on the airbrake, the other on the whistle cord.

The Rock Island Line

TRADITIONAL

Arranged by Florence White

Freely

(Train whistle)

I got sheep,_____ goats,_____ cows,_____ hors - es,

I got all live stock. *(spoken)* That old Rock Island Line's getting on down the road. (Train whistle)

𝄋 *moving along steadily*

B♭

Oh, the Rock Is - land Line____ is a might-y good road,____ Oh, the

Rock Is-land Line— is the road to ride,— Oh, the Rock Is-land Line— is a

might-y good road,— If you want to ride you got-ta

Fine
B♭

take it like you find it, Buy your tick-et at the sta-tion on the Rock Is-land Line.—

more slowly

B♭/F   Gm   B♭   F7   B♭

D.S. al Fine

I may be right and I may be wrong, But you're gon-na miss me when I'm gone.

Barbara Cooney

O PIONEERS!

It was the Conestoga wagon, along with
the railroad, that brought thousands of immigrants
to the West, to build new communities,
to start farms, and to search for gold.

Handcart Song

TRADITIONAL

Between 1855 and 1860, thousands of Mormon pioneers pushed rough carts containing all their belongings over the plains for more than one thousand miles to join their brethren in a new city growing beside the Great Salt Lake in Utah.

Happily

Arranged by Darrell Peter

Ye Saints who dwell on Eu-rope's shore, Pre-pare your-selves for man-y more To
For you must cross the rag-ing main Be-fore the prom-ised land you gain, And

leave be-hind your na-tive land, For sure God's judg-ments are at hand.
with the faith-ful make a start To cross the plains with your hand-cart.

Chorus

For some must push and some must pull As we go march-ing up the hill; So

mer-ri - ly on the way we go Un - til we reach the val - ley-o!

da Capo

til we reach the val - ley - o!

2. And long before the valley's gained,
   We will be met upon the plains
   With music sweet and friends so dear
   And fresh supplies our heart to cheer.
   And then with music and with song,
   How cheerfully we'll march along
   And thank the day we made a start
   To cross the plains with our handcart.

Chorus

Febold Feboldson, First Citizen of Nebraska

RETOLD BY SUZY SCHMIDT

Ever wonder who invented the popcorn ball? Here's the answer: a strong, smart, and lucky fellow — Nebraska's first farmer, Febold Feboldson.

Way back in '48, when men were rushing to California to make their fortunes panning gold, the big Swede Febold Feboldson was running a wagon train of ox teams and prairie schooners on the long, hard trail from Kansas City to San Francisco. That winter there came a terrific snowstorm with a cold so deep the snow turned to stone. The Year of the Petrified Snow, they called it, for the snow stayed on the plains all the next summer, as hard and as cold as marble. For over a year Febold couldn't get a single gold rusher to poke his nose beyond the warmth of the fires in the Kansas City camp. In fact, it's on account of the Year of the Petrified Snow that the forty-eighters came to be called the forty-niners.

Having lost a whole season of business, Febold put his mind to work, and it wasn't long before the big Swede knew just what to do. He headed straight to Death Valley, California — the hottest desert he knew. With a wagon heaped full of desert sand, he headed back. Because the sand stayed blistering hot, it just about evened out the frigid air, and Febold had a mighty comfy ride. The frozen gold rushers, who were glad to pay the exorbitant price of fifty dollars a bushel, spread the sand on Febold's wagons and they all headed west. Sitting up on that hot sand, they no more felt the cold of the plains than if it hadn't existed. But before they reached the Rockies, the jolting of the wagons scattered the sand, spreading it far and wide and melting every bit of the petrified snow. And that's the reason the prairies get so all-fired hot in the summertime.

When Febold realized he was accountable for the sand now covering Nebraska, he cursed himself twenty times a day for twenty years. He vowed to settle there and undo the damage by making it a fit place for farming. Of course, the big Swede had his work cut out for him since Nebraska had the strangest weather in the country. If it wasn't one thing, it was another, and the Year of the Petrified Snow couldn't hold a candle to that strangest of all phenomena, the Year of the Striped Weather.

That summer was both hot and rainy. There was a mile-wide stripe of scorching sunshine, then a mile-wide stripe of gully washer. The sun shone so hot on Febold's cornfield that the corn began to pop, covering the ground like a July blizzard. The rain so soaked his sugarcane that syrup flowed from its stalks. Now, the corn was in the valley and the cane was on the hill, so the syrup ran down into the popped corn and rolled it into a giant ball, hundreds of feet high.

And that was the first time anyone had ever seen a popcorn ball, which proves that it is a truly American invention. The size of the popcorn ball was such that it would still be around today had not a great horde of grasshoppers devoured it one afternoon in July 1874. But that's another story.

Oh, Susannah

TRADITIONAL WORDS
MUSIC BY STEPHEN COLLINS FOSTER

When gold was found at Sutter's Mill near Sacramento, California, thousands came to try their luck in the goldfields. Here are the words the forty-niners made up and sang to the tune of Foster's popular song.

Lively

Arranged by Ruth and Norman Lloyd

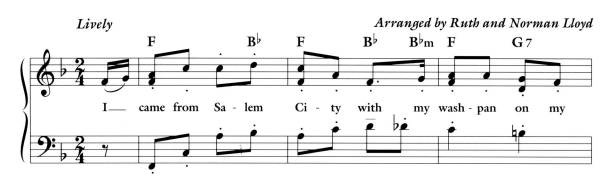

I— came from Sa - lem Ci - ty with my wash - pan on my

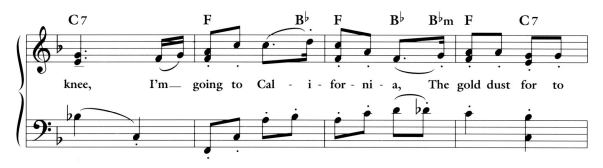

knee, I'm— going to Cal - i - for - ni - a, The gold dust for to

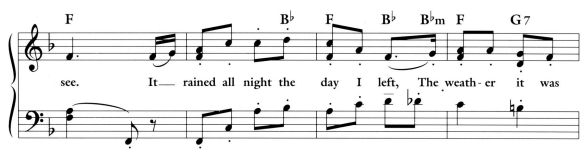

see. It— rained all night the day I left, The weath - er it was

dry, The— sun so hot I froze to death, Oh, bro - thers, don't you cry!

Chorus

Oh, Su - san - nah, Oh, don't you cry for me! I'm— going to Cal - i - for - ni - a, my wash - pan on my knee!

2. I soon shall be in Frisco
   And there I'll look around,
   And when I see the gold lumps there,
   I'll pick them off the ground.
   I'll scrape the mountains clean, my boys,
   I'll drain the rivers dry,
   A pocketful of rocks bring home,
   So, brothers, don't you cry!

   Chorus

The First Woman to Vote in the State of California

BY CAROLYN POLESE

All kinds of people came to California during the boom years, including champion stagecoach driver Charley Parkhurst.

Listen up and I'll tell you the story of the first woman to vote in the state of California. She cast her ballot almost fifty years before American women won the right to have their say at the polls.

First, though, I have to tell you about Charley.

Like thousands of other adventurous young folks, Charley Parkhurst came out West when gold was discovered up at Sutter's Mill. Instead of scrabbling in the dirt for those little flakes of shiny metal, Charley drove the stage.

Sitting up on the driver's box behind six spanking horses, Charley was admired by everyone. It wasn't just his stocky good looks and the beautiful fringed driving gloves he wore. Charley was admired for his skill and his daring.

Once, during the worst of the winter's rainstorms, Charley loaded up the Congress coach for his run out of Placerville.

"Can you get me into Stockton on time?" his one passenger asked. "I've got an important meeting and I can't be late."

Charley said nothing, but his blue-gray eyes shot that passenger a look that said, "My stage always gets in on time, Mister, come hell or high water."

The going was rough. It had rained hard for three days and in places the mud was nearly up to the hubs of the wagon wheels. Some spots were so bad that

Charley had to lay branches down for the wheels to roll over, but he kept on going.

Suddenly, a traveler appeared.

"Bridge up ahead is starting to shake," the dripping stranger called up to Charley. "Better not risk it."

But Charley Parkhurst just wiped the rain out of his face, tugged his broad-brimmed hat down further on his head, and urged the team on.

When they came in sight of the bridge, Charley could see the floodwaters leaping and pounding against the timbers that held up the bridge. The narrow span swayed and groaned.

The passenger knocked on the wall of the coach. "Let's go back," he shouted.

Charley didn't answer; he was judging the strength that remained in that bridge.

"Hy'yup, Jack. Hy'yup, Jessie," Charley called to his lead horses. Jack and Jessie pricked up their sodden ears and started off, with the swing horses and the wheel pair pulling hard behind them.

As they approached the bridge, Charley called out again. The trotting horses swung into a canter. Down onto the bridge the coach rattled. Beneath the flying hooves of the horses, the timbers creaked and swayed.

"Hy'yup. Hy'yup! HY'YUP!" Charley shouted, cracking his long whip in the air.

The coach wheels thundered over the last few yards of bridge. First the horses, then the coach, heaved up onto the solid road.

Seconds later, Charley and his passenger turned to watch as the bridge swayed one last time and collapsed like a pile of sticks into the roiling water of the Tuolumne River.

Floods weren't the only dangers in those days. A stagecoach driver never knew when masked men might appear in the road and demand the valuables stored in the express box under his seat.

Charley Parkhurst had sworn that no one — not even that notorious bandit Sugar Foot — would get the gold that he carried for the miners from the Mother Lode of the Sierra Nevada down to the banks in Stockton.

But one day, coming down the grade west of the Placerville mines, a man on horseback appeared out of the trees. Cantering up alongside the coach horses, he grabbed the left leader's headstall and tried to pull him to a stop. *SSSNAK!* Charley's whip shot out and caught the man around the wrist, but he still held on. Charley urged his horses into a run; maybe he could shake the man off.

Then Charley saw the man pull a pistol from his belt and wave it at the lead horse's head. Charley knew that if he didn't pull over, the horse would be shot, the stage wrecked, and the passengers probably killed.

"Whoa-aaa!" Charley reined his horses in.

Four more bandits on horseback appeared and leveled their guns at Charley. Their faces were hidden by masks made out of the leg sections of long johns, with holes cut out so they could see. Only the leader, who had stopped the coach, was barefaced.

"Throw down the strongbox," he demanded, keeping his gun pointed at the lead horse, Jack.

Charley reached under his seat and dragged out the box, heavy with gold. He heaved it over the side of the wagon, where it landed in the dust with a thud. Two of the bandits hauled it off behind the rocks, while the other two took the passengers' money, gold, and watches. Then the leader motioned Charley on with his gun.

As the coach started moving, Charley stood up in the driver's box. "You got me this time, Sugar Foot," he called in his tenor voice. "But next time I'll be ready. You'll never rob Charley Parkhurst's stage again."

A few weeks later, when Charley was carrying another big shipment of gold, Sugar Foot and his gang pulled Charley's coach to a halt again.

"Throw down that shotgun," Sugar Foot demanded, waving his pistol at the horses.

Charley had no choice but to heave his new shotgun onto the road.

"Now the strongbox, Charley-boy," Sugar Foot said.

Charley's mouth set in a line.

"Now!" Sugar Foot barked. He cocked his gun against the side of Jack's head and laughed.

Charley reached beneath his seat. His fingers groped for the leather handles of the strongbox, then closed over the silver pistol he had hidden there.

Charley's bullet hit Sugar Foot in the chest. The bandits' horses snorted and shied. In that instant of confusion, Charley shook the reins. The team took off with the miners' gold still safe on board.

A few days later, the sheriff found Sugar Foot's body in an abandoned mine shaft. The other bandits had fled. No one ever tried to rob Charley Parkhurst's stagecoach again.

There is another side of Charley that few folks saw. Although he would sometimes drink a bit or gamble with the other drivers, and he was known to swear a blue streak, Charley was a private kind of person. When Ulysses S. Grant ran against Horatio Seymour for president of the United States, Charley voted alongside the other fellows, but he never would say which side he was on. On hot days, the other drivers took off their clothes and jumped in the river. Charley always chose to bathe alone. When the other fellows went out with dance hall girls, good-looking Charley kept his own company. Although he was liked by women for his considerate ways, he was never what folks would call a ladies' man.

Once, though, there was a widow woman on one of Charley's runs. She fell on hard times and the sheriff had to put her farm up for sale to pay off her debts. Charley took his savings and bought that farm, then he deeded it right back to the woman.

At first, people thought that Charley had set his hat for the widow, or perhaps her beautiful daughter. But that wasn't the case. He'd simply helped them out of kindness. Charley was like that.

After the iron horse came to California, Charley gave up driving. He worked as a lumberjack for a while, and then as a farmer, until his rheumatism crippled him up and Charley retired to a little shack outside of Soquel.

Even then, folks had a lot of respect for Charley. He was known as a hard worker and a good friend. And though Charley wasn't one to boast, most of his neighbors knew about his exploits in the driver's box.

But it wasn't until after he died that folks learned the whole of Charley's story.

A few of his friends had gone up to Charley's little cabin to prepare the body for the funeral. When they did, they discovered one more amazing thing about Charley. That tough-minded, kindhearted, coolheaded hero of the gold rush days wasn't a man like everybody thought. Charley was a woman — the first woman to vote in the state of California.

Sweet Betsy from Pike

TRADITIONAL

Getting to California during the gold rush days was hard work — and so was living there! Some call this song the state's unofficial anthem.

Up-tempo waltz

Arranged by Randa Kirshbaum

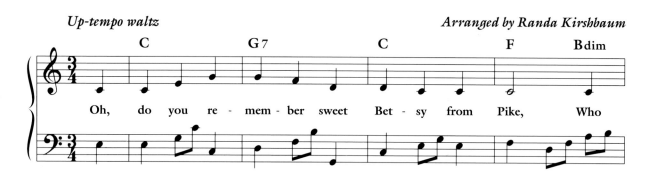

Oh, do you re-mem-ber sweet Bet-sy from Pike, Who

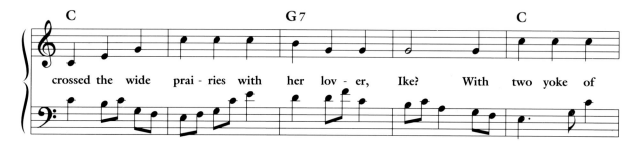

crossed the wide prai-ries with her lov-er, Ike? With two yoke of

ox-en, a big yal-ler dog, A— tall Shang-hai roos-ter, and

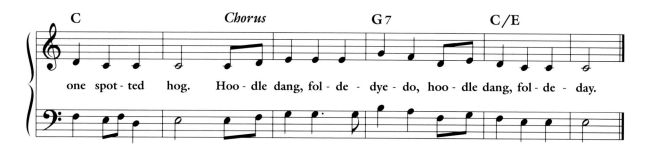

one spot-ted hog. Hoo-dle dang, fol-de-dye-do, hoo-dle dang, fol-de-day.

2. The rooster ran off and the oxen all died;
   The last piece of bacon that morning was fried.
   Poor Ike got discouraged and Betsy got mad;
   The dog wagged his tail and looked wonderfully sad.

   Chorus

3. The alkali desert was burning and hot,
   And Ike, he decided to leave on the spot:
   "My dear old Pike County, I'll go back to you."
   Said Betsy, "You'll go by yourself if you do."

   Chorus

4. They swam the wide rivers, they crossed the tall peaks,
   They camped out on prairies for weeks and for weeks,
   Fought off starvation and big storms of dust,
   Determined to reach California or bust.

   Chorus

5. They passed the Sierras through mountains of snow,
   'Til old California was sighted below.
   Sweet Betsy, she hollered, and Ike gave a cheer,
   Said, "Betsy, my darlin', I'm a made millioneer."

   Chorus

The Darning Needle

BY ERIC A. KIMMEL

*Jews, though not numerous, took part in the great migration west. Here's
a story about one who made all the difference to a tiny town in Oregon.*

Between 1841 and 1866, three hundred and fifty thousand men, women, and children loaded their belongings on covered wagons and headed west along the Oregon Trail. The Oregon Trail, also known as the California Road, was actually several trails with different destinations. The trail began in the area of what is now Kansas City, Missouri, and led, by various routes, to Oregon's Willamette Valley, Utah's Great Salt Lake, and northern California.

Among these early pioneers were two brothers from Bavaria, Julius and Emanuel Meier, who owned a general store in Downeyville, California. In 1855, their younger brother, Aaron, came from Germany to join them in the business. Aaron had a taste for adventure. He convinced his brothers to stake him to a pack mule and a load of trade goods, then headed north to the Oregon Territory.

Aaron Meier roamed the mountains and valleys of northern California and southern Oregon for the next two years, braving all kinds of dangers to bring manufactured goods to mining camps and farming communities.

His travels took him to a remote Oregon settlement called Pass Creek Canyon, a canyon so isolated from any source of manufactured goods that the settlers there were down to their last darning needle. The families in the area took turns using it. The women in the lower canyon borrowed the needle for a day or two to catch up on their mending. Then they sent it along to the upper canyon.

Months earlier, young Jimmy Chitwood was assigned the chore of carrying the needle along the canyon trail to Grand-

mother Drain's cabin. In case he dropped it, Mrs. Chitwood threaded a long piece of red wool through the needle's eye, knotted it into a loop, then stuck the needle in a potato. But she didn't anticipate Jimmy's running into a mother bear and two cubs along the way.

Jimmy ducked behind a serviceberry bush and waited until the bears were out of sight. Then he continued on. Suddenly he realized his hand was empty. He had left the potato with its precious darning needle under the serviceberry bush. Jimmy turned back, hoping to retrieve it. But hundreds of bushes grew in the thickets along the trail. How would he find the right one?

Jimmy searched for hours until he realized he had no choice but to go home and confess. Mrs. Chitwood did not scold. She knew how easy it was for an eight-year-old boy to be distracted by a bear and its cubs. But all the same, the needle had to be found.

The next day every settler in Pass Creek Canyon combed every inch of the hillside, peering under every serviceberry bush for a glimpse of bright-red wool. Suddenly Jimmy plunged into a thicket of bracken. He came out holding a potato with a long loop of red wool hanging from it. The darning needle was found!

But nothing lasts forever. Several months later, when Grandmother Drain was doing her mending, the darning needle broke in two. All mending and sewing in Pass Creek Canyon ceased. There would be no more until another needle could be obtained. But who knew when that might be?

Then Aaron Meier came over the pass, leading his mule down through the canyon.

Children ran to tell their parents a peddler had arrived. The news spread quickly through Pass Creek Canyon.

Everyone came to look at the peddler's wares and hear the news from the outside world. They examined lengths of calico, ribbons, candy, crockery, tools, and notions. "Do you have any needles?" Mrs.

Chitwood asked the peddler. "What we need most is a darning needle. At least one." She told him the story of Pass Creek Canyon's last darning needle; how it had been lost, then found, then lost forever.

Meanwhile Jimmy Chitwood stroked the mule's neck, pretending not to hear. But the peddler listened carefully. Then he said, "Christmas is coming soon, and I suppose that you good people will be having a holiday with presents." He glanced at Jimmy. "Are you going to be giving any presents, sonny?"

"Yes, sir. I guess," Jimmy answered quickly, although he had no idea what he had to give that anyone would want or need.

"Well, suppose you and I give the ladies of Pass Creek Canyon a Christmas present right now?" The peddler reached into his pocket for a thin package. He opened it. "Here are some darning needles. They are all I have, but I believe there will be enough for every family in the canyon to have one. Merry Christmas!"

That was the first of Aaron Meier's many visits to Pass Creek Canyon.

In 1857, Aaron Meier gave up the peddler's life to open a dry goods and clothing store in Portland. That little store at 137 Front Avenue grew into Meier and Frank, which has been one of the Pacific Northwest's greatest department stores for over a century.

Acres of Clams

TRADITIONAL

*When folks got good and fed up with panning for gold, they headed north
to the beautiful shores of Puget Sound.*

With lusty spirit

Arranged by Denes Agay

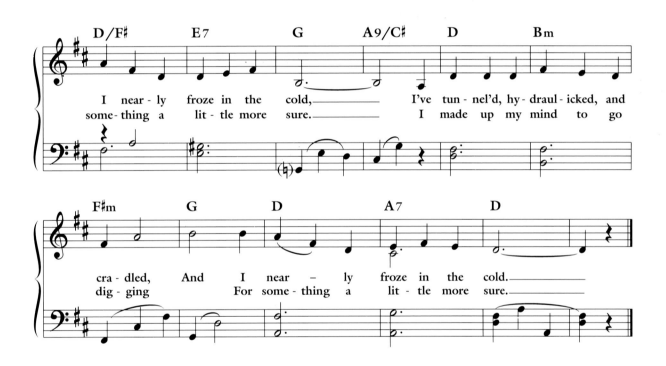

I near-ly froze in the cold,_____ I've tun-nel'd, hy-draul-icked, and
some-thing a lit-tle more sure._____ I made up my mind to go

cra-dled, And I near — ly froze in the cold._____
dig-ging For some-thing a lit-tle more sure._____

3. I rolled up my grub in my blanket,
I left all my tools on the ground,
I started one morning to shank it
For the country they call Puget Sound.
For the country they call Puget Sound,
For the country they call Puget Sound,
I started one morning to shank it
For the country they call Puget Sound.

4. No longer the slave of ambition,
I laugh at the world and its shams,
And think of my happy condition
Surrounded by acres of clams.
Surrounded by acres of clams,
Surrounded by acres of clams,
And think of my happy condition
Surrounded by acres of clams.

Dakota Dugout

BY ANN TURNER

Homesteading demanded incredible mental and physical strength, yet many young couples committed themselves to the life wholeheartedly in order to ensure a better future for their families.

T ell you about the prairie years? I'll tell you, child, how it was.

When Matt wrote, "Come!" I packed up all I had, cups and pots and dresses and rope, even Grandma's silver boot hook, and rode the clickety train to a cave in the earth, Matt's cave. Built from sod, you know, with a special iron plow that sliced the long earth strips. Matt cut them into bricks, laid them up, dug into a hill that was our first home.

I cried when I saw it. No sky came into that room, only a paper window that made the sun look greasy. Dirt fell on our bed, snakes sometimes, too, and the buffalo hide door could not keep out the wind or the empty cries in the long grass.

The birds visited me, there was no one else, with Matt all day in the fields. A hawk came, snake in its claws, a heron flapped by with wings like sails, and a sparrow jabbered the day long on a gray fence post. I jabbered back.

Winter came sudden. Slam-bang! the ground was iron, cattle breath turned to ice, froze their noses to the ground. We

lost twelve in a storm and the wind scoured the dugout, *whish*-hush, *whish*-hush.

Spring, child, was teasing slow then quick, water booming in the lake, geese like yarn in the sky, green spreading faster than fire, and the wind blowing *shoosh*-hush, *shoosh*-hush.

First summer we watched the corn grow, strode around the field clapping hands. We saw dresses, buggies, gold in that grain until one day a hot wind baked it dry as an oven, *ssst-ssst, ssst-ssst.*

Matt sat and looked two whole days, silent and long.

Come fall we snuggled like beavers in our burrow, new grass on the floor, wil-lows on our roof under the earth. I pasted newspaper on the walls, set the bread to bake on the coals, and the wind was quiet.

Corn grew finally, we got our dresses, buggies, some gold, built a clapboard house with windows like suns, floors I slipped on, and the empty sound of too many rooms. Didn't think I'd miss the taste of earth in the air. Now the broom went *whisp*-hush, and the clock tocked like a busy heart.

Talking brings it near again, the sweet taste of new bread in a Dakota dugout, how the grass whispered like an old friend, how the earth kept us warm.

Sometimes the things we start with are best.

By'm Bye

TRADITIONAL

Singing this gentle song to welcome the evening surely helped many pioneers feel safe and secure in their new homes.

Part 3

~

ONLY IN AMERICA

All the different people who came to America brought with them stories and songs of their own. But living here changed those tales and tunes into something unique — into something American.

~

Trina Schart Hyman

TRICKSTERS, ON TWO FEET, FOUR—OR MORE

Tricksters use their wits instead of their fists to outsmart more powerful opponents. Stories about these wily characters are told all over the nation.

Tía Miseria

RETOLD BY OLGA LOYA

Once there was an old woman named Tía Miseria, Aunt Misery. She lived outside a little town. Tía Miseria was poor but happy. She had her *jardín con verduras,* her garden with vegetables. She had her *pollos grandes,* her big chickens. And she had her *árbol de peras,* her pear tree.

Oh, how she loved her pears. She would pick a pear and feel the pear's smooth shape and when she bit into that sweet pear flesh, she would sigh and say, "*¡Ay, que deliciosa, que maravillosa!* Oh, how delicious, how marvelous!"

Tía Miseria was a very proud woman who would walk through the village with her back straight and her hair pulled back in a *moño,* in a bun. Although Tía Miseria was very old, her face was quite smooth except for a few wrinkles around her eyes.

But Tía had a *problema,* a problem. It was the boys in the neighborhood, the ones who had named her Tía Miseria. They would run right through her garden, step on all of her vegetables, and yell tauntingly, "Tía, Tía, Tía Miseria." They would climb her pear tree and take bites out of the pears. The juice would run down the sides of their mouths as they teased the old woman, "Tía, Tía, Tía Miseria."

Poor Tía, she would get so upset! She would go under the tree and yell, "*Bajen de mi árbol ahora mismo.* Come down from my tree right now."

But the boys would just look down at her, and tease, "Tía, Tía, Tía Miseria."

When they were good and ready, they would climb down and run through her garden screaming, "Tía, Tía, Tía Miseria!"

Poor Tía. After the boys had run away, she would have to replant her garden and then she would have to get her *pollos,* her chickens, out of the bushes because they would get so scared by the *muchachos,* the boys. But what was worst of all was that those boys were eating all of her sweet, delicious pears.

One night as she was cooking supper, she heard a knock at the door. When she went to see who it was, there was a man there who said, "*¡Ay, por favor, me puedo quedar la noche? ¡Hace tanto frío!* Oh, can I please stay the night? It is so cold!"

"*Pues, como no,* well, why not," said Tía. "*Entre, entre.* Come in, come in." Tía gave him *frijoles,* beans; *arroz,* rice; *tortillas,* pancakes; and more. Oh, they had a fine dinner.

In the morning the man said, "Tía, I am a magician. Because you have been so kind and generous, I will give you one wish."

"*¡Un deseo!* One wish!" exclaimed Tía. "Let me see, maybe I will wish for *plata,* for silver; no, maybe I will wish for *oro,* for gold." Then she stopped and smiled a very big smile and said, "I know what I want. Once someone is in my pear tree, they cannot come down until I say some magic words."

"Fine," said the magician. He said good-bye and went walking down the road.

That day the *muchachos* came to the house. They came running through the garden yelling, "Tía, Tía, Tía Miseria." They climbed the tree and picked pears and took one bite of the pears and then threw the pears at the chickens and the cats. The boys threw the pears all over the garden.

But Tía did not act like she usually did. Instead of going under the tree and yelling, she went into the kitchen and brought out a cup of coffee. She stood on the porch, sipping her coffee with a smile on her face. The boys knew there was something very very wrong. She never acted that way! So they did the one thing they knew always made her angry. "Tía, Tía, Tía Miseria," they taunted.

But Tía just smiled and sipped her coffee. She said, "*Muchachos,* come down from the tree."

The boys said, "*¡No, no estámos listos!* No, we are not ready!"

When the boys tried to come down from the pear tree, they couldn't — the magic spell was on.

The *muchachos* cried out to her, "*Por favor déjanos bajar.* Please let us down."

Tía smiled, sipped her coffee, looked at the boys, and said, "No!"

The boys called out to her again. "*¡Por favor!* Please! Let us down, it is getting late!"

Tía was enjoying this very much. She looked, took a sip of her coffee, smiled, and said, "NO!"

Oh, the boys cried, begged, and pleaded. Finally Tía went under the tree and said, "If I let you out of that tree,

will you promise me never to come back?"

The boys responded immediately. "*¡Sí! Yes!*"

So she said her magic words, "*Bajen, bajen, bajen de mi árbol.* Come down, come down, come down from my tree."

The boys climbed down that pear tree as fast as they could. When they were down, they ran through the garden, and they did not return.

Now Tía was very happy. She had her garden, her chickens were safe, and, now, she had her precious *árbol de peras,* her pear tree.

One night as she was cooking supper and thinking about everything that had happened, she heard a knock at the door.

She thought, *Ah, mi amigo volvió.* Oh, my friend has returned. She went to the door, and there was a man there. But he was not her friend. He was a tall, thin man and when she looked into his eyes, it was like falling into a deep, dark hole. She felt a shiver come over her body, and she stepped back.

The man stepped toward her, looked deep into her eyes, and said in a deep, raspy voice, "*Yo soy la muerte y he venido por usted.* I am death and I have come for you."

Tía Miseria said, "*Pues, yo sabía que iba a venir.* Well, I knew you were going to come. But before we go, let us take a few pears with us."

Death said, "No, no. I have a big list of people to pick up tonight. I have no time!"

But Tía wouldn't stop talking about her pears, how wonderful and delicious they were to eat. Finally he could see he wasn't ever going to get out of there. So he said, "Go and get some pears. I want to leave!"

But Tía replied, "*¿Yo? Yo soy una viejita.* Me? I am a little old lady. Look at you. You are tall and lanky and besides you look like you could use a pear or two!"

Death was so exasperated that he said, "Oh, all right, I'll go and get some pears."

So he climbed the tree and picked some pears. He picked a few here and a few there, and soon he was ready to climb down. But — he could not get down. Oh, Death called Tía the most terrible things you have ever heard and probably some things you have never heard! But she didn't mind. She just said to him, "Throw me a pear, why don't you?"

She left him up there for a day, a week, a month, a year.

Finally the village priest came by and said, "Please let Death down. No one is coming to church because they know they are not going to die."

Tía just looked at the priest and shrugged her shoulders.

Then the undertaker came by and said, "*Por favor,* please. Let Death down. I have no work, and my children are hungry."

Tía looked at the undertaker and said, "Change your trade."

But finally her very oldest friend came by and said in a slow, halting voice, "*Por favor . . . déjalo bajar. Estoy muy cansada y me quiero ir. . . . Todo me duele. Por favor . . . me quiero morir.* Please . . . let him down. I am very tired and I want to go. . . . Everything hurts me. Please . . . I want to die."

Tía could not refuse the request of her oldest friend. She went under the tree and looked up at Death and said, "Death, if I let you down will you promise me that you will never come back for me?"

Death said, "*Sí.*" He was tired of being up in that pear tree.

Tía said her magic words, "*Baje, baje, baje de mi árbol.*"

Death came down from the pear tree and scooped up Tía's old friend and went running down the road.

Death did keep his promise. So Tía Miseria lives on and on. And that's why some say that as long as Death keeps his promise, there will be misery in this world.

205

The Devil's Questions

TRADITIONAL

Freely

Arranged by Rachel Miller

If you don't an-swer my ques-tions well, Sing nine-ty-nine and nine-ty! I'll take you off, with me to dwell, And you the weav-er-ing bon-ty!

2. Oh, what is whiter far than milk?
    Sing ninety-nine and ninety!
And what is softer far than silk?
    And you the weavering bonty!

3. Oh, snow is whiter far than milk,
    Sing ninety-nine and ninety!
And down is softer far than silk,
    And me the weavering bonty!

4. Oh, what is louder than a horn?
    Sing ninety-nine and ninety!
And what is sharper than a thorn?
    And you the weavering bonty!

5. Oh, thunder's louder than a horn,
    Sing ninety-nine and ninety!
And death is sharper than a thorn,
    And me the weavering bonty!

6. Oh, what is higher than a tree?
    Sing ninety-nine and ninety!
And what is deeper than the sea?
    And you the weavering bonty!

7. Oh, Heaven's higher than a tree,
    Sing ninety-nine and ninety!
And Hell is deeper than the sea,
    And me the weavering bonty!

8. Oh, what red fruit September grows?
    Sing ninety-nine and ninety!
And what thing round the whole world goes?
    And you the weavering bonty!

9. The apple in September grows,
    Sing ninety-nine and ninety!
And air around the whole world goes,
    And me the weavering bonty!

10. Oh, you have answered my questions well,
    Sing ninety-nine and ninety!
I cannot take you with me to dwell,
    And you the weavering bonty!

Iktome and the Ducks

RETOLD BY LAME DEER

One day Iktome, the wicked spider man, was taking a walk to see what he could see. Tiptoeing through the woods, he saw water sparkling through the leaves. "I am coming to a lake," Iktome said to himself. "There might be some fat ducks there. I shall creep up to this lake very carefully so that I cannot be seen. Maybe I shall catch something."

Iktome crept up to the water's edge on all fours, hiding himself behind some bushes. Sure enough, the lake was full of nice, plump ducks. At the sight of them Iktome's mouth began to water. But how was he to catch the birds? He had neither a net nor his bow and arrows. But he had a stick. He suddenly popped up from behind the bushes, capering and dancing.

"Ho, Cousins, come here and learn to dance. I have eight legs and I am the best dancer in the world."

All the ducks swam to the shore and lined up in a row, spellbound by Iktome's fancy dancing. After a while Iktome stopped. "Cousins, come closer still," he cried. "I am the gentle, generous spider man, the friend of all fowl, and I shall teach you the duck song. Now, when I start singing, you must all close your eyes in order to concentrate better. Do not peek while I sing, or you will be turned into ugly mud hens with red eyes. You don't want this to happen, do you? You have, no doubt, noticed my stick. It is a drumstick, which I will use to beat out the rhythm. Are you ready? Then close your eyes."

Iktome started to sing, and the foolish ducks crowded around him, going as he had told them, flapping their wings delightedly and swaying to and fro. And with his stick Iktome began to club them dead, one after another.

Among the ducks was a smart young one. "I better check on what is going on," this duck said to himself. "I don't quite trust that fellow with his eight legs. I'll risk one eye. One red eye isn't so bad." He opened his left eye and in a flash saw what Iktome was up to. "Take off, take off," he cried to the other ducks, "or we all wind up in the cooking pot!" The ducks opened their eyes and flew away, quacking loudly.

Still, Iktome had a fine breakfast of roast duck. The spider man's power turned the smart young duck into a mud hen.

This is why, to this day, mud hens swim alone, away from other ducks, always on the lookout, diving beneath the water as soon as they see or hear anyone approaching, thinking it might be the wicked spider man with a new bag of tricks. Better a live, ugly mud hen, than a pretty, dead duck.

Glooskap and Wasis

RETOLD BY ALAN GARNER

G looskap and his brother, Malsum the Wolf, made the world. Their mother died at their birth, and from her they took the things of their choice. Glooskap shaped the sun and the moon, animals, fish, and men, and Malsum gave mountains, ravines, snakes, and all that he hoped would be a plague. He was so wrong that Glooskap killed him, and then went on with the work.

Glooskap subdued the sorcerer Win-pe, and Pamola of the Night, and the Kewawkque giants, and the Medecolin wizards, and the tribes of the witches and the goblins and the living dead. He leveled the hills, controlled the floods, and gave life to the maize.

"Ho," said Glooskap, "there is nothing I cannot command. The heavens turn for me."

But a woman of the Mohican laughed, and said, "There is in my wigwam, O Glooskap, one you have not conquered, nor shall you, for no power can overcome him."

"What is this god or wizard?" said Glooskap.

"His name is Wasis," she said. "And I advise you not to try him."

"Show me this Wasis," said Glooskap. "Is he greater than the Mede-colin? I had strength of mind in plenty for them. Is he more terrible than the Kewawkque? They woke no fear in me. Is he more dangerous than Pamola of the Night? I carry no scars from that battle. Is he Huron or Tuscarora? Is he Cayuga or Mohawk? Oneida? Onondaga? Is he Susquehannock? Is he Cherokee? Let him be all, and I shall conquer him!"

"He is none of these," said the woman, "and he sits on the floor of my wigwam."

Wasis sucked a piece of maple sugar and crooned a little to himself. Glooskap stood in front of him, filling the wigwam with power.

"My visit is peace," said Glooskap. "Come you to me."

Wasis smiled at him and did not move.

"I am not wrathful," said Glooskap. "Come to me." And he sang the song of the blackbird. Wasis sucked the maple sugar.

"The world obeys me!" shouted Glooskap. "Come!"

Wasis frowned.

"I fear no threat! Come to me on your knees!" roared Glooskap.

But Wasis did not.

Then Glooskap unleashed his rage, and the winds answered his cry about the wigwam, but Wasis opened his mouth and gave a scream that pierced the wind as an arrow through a bird in flight.

Glooskap brought all magic to his mind, and chanted spells, and summoned ghosts, and made the knots that raise the dead.

But Wasis closed his eyes and slept.

Glooskap rushed from the wigwam and flung himself into the river, and the heat of his fury boiled the river dry.

"Goo," said Wasis.

And even now babies say this word, each remembering the day he conquered Glooskap, there on the wigwam floor, with maple sugar in his mouth.

Brer Rabbit
in Mr. Man's Garden

RETOLD BY JULIUS LESTER

If there was one thing in the world Brer Rabbit liked, it was lettuce. He would do anything for lettuce. One day he was going down a road and passed by a field of lettuce, more lettuce than he had seen in all his life! As far as he could see there were rows and rows and rows and rows and rows of lettuce. But between Brer Rabbit and all that lettuce was a wire fence.

Just as he started putting his mind to how he was going to get it, a little girl walked across the road, opened the gate, went in, picked a head of lettuce, and left.

Next morning, bright and early, Brer Rabbit was back. When the little girl came down the road, Brer Rabbit went to meet her.

"Good morning, young lady," he said.

"How you this morning, Brer Rabbit?"

"Just fine. Just fine. Say, you not Mr. Man's little girl, are you?"

"I am," she said proudly.

"Sho' nuf'!" he exclaimed, looking at her admiringly. "He told me about you, but I didn't expect to meet such a pretty young lady."

She blushed. "Why, thank you very much."

"He said he had a daughter who would let me in that field of lettuce over yonder, but I sho' didn't expect nobody as pretty as you."

The little girl just grinned and blushed and giggled. "Well, come on and I'll open the gate for you."

"Obliged," said Brer Rabbit.

He went to a far corner of the field and started eating. And he ate, and he ate, and he ate. The next morning he was back. The little girl let him in again and Brer Rabbit took up where he'd left off. This went on for about a week before Mr. Man noticed he was missing a whole lot of lettuce. He was right angry about it, too, and accused the folks what worked on his place of stealing it. He was about to fire all of them when the little girl said, "Daddy, you must've forgot. You told Brer Rabbit he could have all the lettuce he wanted."

Mr. Man wanted to know what she was talking about, and the little girl told him. Mr. Man nodded. "I see. Well, if Brer Rabbit comes tomorrow, you let him in the field, then come and tell me. There's something I want to talk to him about."

Next morning after the little girl let Brer Rabbit in the field, she went and told her daddy. Mr. Man rushed down to the field with a fishing line and slipped in the gate. Brer Rabbit was eyeball deep in the lettuce, going at it like the statute of limitations on eating was about to expire. Suddenly Mr. Man grabbed him around the neck and Brer Rabbit found himself dangling in the air, staring Mr. Man in the face.

Mr. Man tied Brer Rabbit up tight. "You know what I'm going to do to you?"

"No, but I got a feeling it ain't gon' be to my liking. In fact, I know it ain't."

"It's gon' be to mine. First I'm going to give you a whupping. And for that I got a red cowhide whip. Then I'm going to skin you. Then I'm going to nail your hide to the barn door, and then I just might start all over again from the beginning." Mr. Man told his little girl to watch Brer Rabbit while he went up to the house to get his whip.

No sooner had Mr. Man left than Brer Rabbit began to sing, and he could sing. Women had been known to faint when Brer Rabbit sang. So he started, and this is what he sang:

> *The Jaybird hunts the sparrow's nest,*
> *The bee martin sails all around;*
> *The squirrel hollers from the top of the tree,*
> *Mr. Mole, he stay in the ground;*
> *He hide and he stay 'til the dark*
>   *drops down —*
> *Mr. Mole, he hide in the ground.*

The little girl thought that was the prettiest song she'd ever heard and she laughed and clapped her hands and asked him to sing another one. Brer Rabbit said he couldn't. His throat was hurting from where Mr. Man had been holding him. But the little girl begged and pleaded. Brer Rabbit said, "If you think I can sing, you ought to see me dance!"

"Would you dance for me? Please, Brer Rabbit? Please?"

"How can I dance all tied up like this?"

"I'll untie you," said the little girl.

"You do and I'll show you some dancing."

The little girl untied him, and he danced all right. Danced all the way home. Made up some new steps getting there, too!

Now, Mr. Man's garden was too delicious-looking for Brer Rabbit to leave alone. And anyway, it wasn't right for Mr. Man to have all them pretty vegetables to himself. Obviously, he didn't believe in sharing. Being worried about Mr. Man's soul, Brer Rabbit decided he'd *make* Mr. Man share.

A few mornings later Mr. Man went to town. As he was leaving he hollered to his daughter, "Janey! Don't you let Brer Rabbit get in my green peas. You hear me?"

"Yes, Daddy," she said.

Brer Rabbit was hiding in the bushes, listening. Soon as Mr. Man left, Brer Rabbit walked up to the little girl as bold as day.

"Ain't you Janey?" he asked.

"My daddy call me Janey. What your daddy call you?"

"Well, my daddy dead, but when he was living he called me Billy Malone." He smiled. "I passed your daddy in the road, and he said for me to come tell you to give me some sparrow grass."

Janey had been warned against Brer Rabbit, but not Billy Malone, so she opened the gate and let Brer Rabbit into the garden. Brer Rabbit got as much sparrow grass as he could carry and left.

Mr. Man came back and saw that somebody had been in his garden. He asked Janey about it. She told him that Billy Malone said it was all right for him to go in and get some sparrow grass. Mr. Man knew something was up but didn't say anything.

Next morning when he got ready to go, he told Janey to keep an eye out for Brer Rabbit and not let *anybody* get any sparrow grass.

When Mr. Man was out of sight, Brer Rabbit come walking down the road and greeted the little girl, bowing low like a real gentleman. "I saw your daddy just now. He said I couldn't have no sparrow grass today, but it would be all right if I helped myself to the English peas."

The little girl opened the gate and Brer Rabbit made off with enough English peas to feed all of England.

When Mr. Man came back, his pea vines looked like a storm had hit 'em, and he was hot! "Who been in my peas?" he asked his daughter.

"Mr. Billy Malone," she said.

"What this Billy Malone look like?"

"He got a split lip, pop eyes, big ears, and a bobtail, Daddy."

Mr. Man didn't have a bit of trouble recognizing that description. He fixed a box trap and set it in the garden among the peanuts. The next morning he told Janey, "Now, whatever you do today, don't let nobody have any sparrow grass, and don't let 'em get any more English peas, the few I got left."

Soon as Mr. Man was out of sight, here come Brer Rabbit. He bowed low and said, "Good morning, Miz Janey. I met your daddy down the road there and he said I can't have no more sparrow grass or English peas, but to help myself to the peanuts."

Janey let him in the garden. Brer Rabbit headed straight for the peanut patch, where he tripped the string and the box fell right on top of him.

He was caught, and he knew it.

Wasn't long before Mr. Man came back. He went to the peanut patch and saw the overturned box. He stooped down, peered through the slats, and saw Brer Rabbit inside, quivering.

Mr. Man whooped. "Yes, sir! I got you this time, you devil! I got you! And when I get through with you, ain' gon' be nothing left. I'm gon' carry your foot in my pocket, put your meat in the pot, and wear your fur on my head."

Words like that always put a chill up and down Brer Rabbit's spine. "Mr. Man, I know I done wrong. And if you let me go, I promise I'll stay away from your garden."

Mr. Man chuckled. "You gon' stay away from my garden if I don't let you go, too. I got to go to the house to get my butcher knife."

Mr. Man went to the house, but he forgot to close the garden gate behind him. Brer Fox came down the road, and seeing the open gate, took it as an invitation and walked on in. He heard something hollering and making a lot of racket. He wandered around until he found the noise coming from underneath a box. "What the dickens is that?" he asked.

Brer Rabbit would've known that voice anywhere. "Run, Brer Fox! Run! Get out of here right now if you care about your life!"

"What's wrong, Brer Rabbit?"

"Mr. Man trapped me in here and is making me eat lamb. I'm about to bust wide open I done ate so much lamb. Run, Brer Fox, before he catch you."

Brer Fox wasn't thinking about running. "How's the lamb?"

"It tastes good at first, but enough is enough and too much is plenty. You better get out of here before he catches you."

Brer Fox wasn't running anywhere. "I like lamb, Brer Rabbit." He took the box off Brer Rabbit. "Put the box over me." Brer Rabbit did so gladly and decided not to wait around for the next chapter.

The story don't say what happened to Brer Fox. Brer Rabbit took care of himself. Now it's up to Brer Fox to take care of himself. That's the name of that tune.

Oh, John the Rabbit

TRADITIONAL

The Connecticut Peddler

RETOLD BY MARIA LEACH

One night a Connecticut peddler traveling through southern Virginia stopped at a tavern and asked to spend the night. There was great prejudice against Yankee peddlers in that section, and for a time the innkeeper refused. At last he consented. "But," he said, "only if you play us a Yankee trick before you go." The peddler said he would be glad to do this and, being tired, went to bed.

In the morning he carefully folded up the coverlet on the bed and put it in his case. He went downstairs to breakfast and, while eating, he opened the case and urged the landlady to buy some of his wares. She was greatly taken with the coverlet. It exactly matched one of hers, she said, and the low price the peddler put on it soon turned the deal.

The peddler counted his money, got into his buggy, and drove off. But before he was out of earshot the innkeeper called after him. "I didn't see any Yankee trick!"

"You will," said the peddler, and drove on.

Sharing the Crops

RETOLD BY HAROLD COURLANDER

The way it was, there was a big plantation down the river a ways, and a man went to the owner and say he want to rent a piece of it on shares. Plantation owner, he say, sure, he willin' to rent twenty acres on shares. He go out and show the man the land he got to rent. Everything all set then, but the man gets to talkin' to other croppers in the neighborhood.

"Boy," they say, "you made a sad bargain. That captain you rent your land from goin' to starve you to death."

Naturally, the man got to worryin' about this. All the time he's plowin' up the ground he's studyin' about it. So before he plants anything he goes callin' on the owner, sayin', "Captain, 'scuse me, just one small thing I forgot to ask you. What part of the crop is yours and what part is mine?"

"You got that ground all plowed?" the owner says.

"Yes, sir," farmer say, "got it all plowed."

"You got it all harrowed down fine?" the owner ask him.

"Yes, sir, Captain, got it all harrowed," the man say.

"Well, I tell you what," the owner say. "The top half of the crop is mine, and the bottom half is yours."

"Thank you, Captain, thank you, that'll be mighty fine with me," the cropper say, and he go on home.

Now that owner, he was a cotton man. Didn't think nothin' but cotton. He figured to get all the value out of the crop and leave the cropper with nothin' at all.

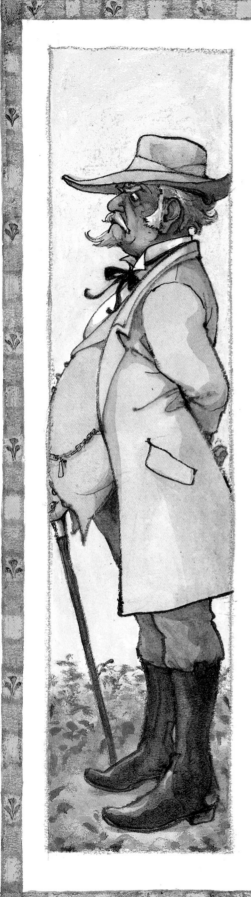

But when the cropper got back to the land, he didn't plant cotton. He planted 'tatoes instead. Couple of months pass by, and the owner come to see how his new cropper doin'. Met him on the road and say, "Man, you ain't forget our agreement, 'bout me takin' the top half and you the bottom?"

"No, sir, didn't forget it," the man say.

Just then they come to the field. When the owner see all those 'tatoes and not one boll of cotton, he had a fit.

"When you want me to bring all them 'tato tops over, Captain?" the cropper ask him.

"Keep 'em, keep 'em," the owner say, "you can have my half this year. Next year we goin' to make a different agreement."

Next year, 'bout plowin' time, the cropper go to see the owner again and say, "Captain, you say you like to make a better arrangement this year. What part of the crop you want?"

"I likes to rotate the arrangement," the owner say, "so this year I'll take the bottom half and you take the top half."

"Yes, sir, Captain, that's agreeable to me," the cropper say. He went right home to do his plantin', but he didn't plant no more 'tatoes. He planted oats.

Couple of months went by and the owner come down to see how his crop was doin'.

"Man, you just in time," the cropper say, "come out and look the way everything is growin'."

"Don't forget," the owner say, "this year I get the bottom share and you get the top."

"No, sir, I don't forget it at all," the cropper say.

Right then they come to the field, and the owner sees it's all in oats.

"Where you want the straw delivered?" the cropper ask him. Well, when the owner see he been outsmarted twice, he was plenty mad. "If I let you farm my ground *at all* next year, there's got to be a new arrangement," he say.

"Yes, sir, Captain, you just say the word," the cropper tell him.

"Next year," the owner say, "I'll take the bottom and I'll take the top, too."

Cropper scratched his head. "What part that leave for me?" he say.

"The middle part," the owner say, "you can have the middle part."

Next year the cropper plant his field again. 'Round July the owner come down to look things over. Met the cropper on the road again, and they went up to the field together.

"I expect you recollect the nature of our arrangement this year?" he say.

"Oh, yes, Captain. Top and bottom for you, the middle for me."

And when they got there, you know what the owner find? That whole field been planted in *corn*.

"You got a mighty fine crop of stalks below and tassels above," the cropper say. "But me and my family prefers the ears in the middle. What kind of arrangement you want to make for next year?"

That plantation owner just shake his head.

"Next year won't be no top, bottom, or middle arrangement," he say. "I'll take same as you take, half and half."

And that's the way it was after that. But the first three years gave that cropper a mighty good start in life, and he been doin' fine ever since.

Donald Crews

NO-SENSE NONSENSE

Humor appears in countless American stories and songs,
including these favorites.

The Talking Mule

COLLECTED BY ZORA NEALE HURSTON

Old feller one time had a mule. His name was Bill. Every morning when that old feller went to catch him he'd say, "Come 'round, Bill!"

But one morning he slept late so he decided while he was drinking some coffee that he'd send his son to catch old Bill.

Told his son, "Go down there, boy, and bring that mule up here."

That boy was such a fast aleck he grabbed the bridle and went on down to the lot. When he got there, he said, "Come 'round, Bill!"

The mule looked 'round at the boy. The boy told the mule, " 'Tain't no use rollin' your eyes at me. Pa wants you this morning. Come on 'round and stick your head in this bridle."

The mule kept on looking at him and said, "Every mornin' it's 'Come 'round, Bill! Come 'round, Bill!' I can't hardly rest at night before it's 'Come 'round, Bill!' "

The boy threw down the bridle, flew back to the house, and told his pa, "That mule's talkin'!"

"Oh, come on, boy, tellin' your lies! Go on and catch that mule."

"No, sir, Pa, that mule's started to talk. You'll have to catch that mule all by yourself. I'm not goin' ta do it."

The old feller looked at his wife and said, "Do you see what a lie this boy is tellin'?"

He got up and went on down after the mule himself. When he got down to the lot he hollered, "Come 'round, Bill!"

The old mule looked 'round and said, "Every mornin' it's 'Come 'round, Bill!'"

Now, the old feller had a little dog that followed him everywhere. So when he ran for home the little dog was right behind him. The old feller told his wife, "The boy didn't tell much of a lie! That mule *is* talkin'. I've never heard a mule talk before."

L'il dog said, "Me neither."

The old feller got scared again. Right through the woods he ran with the little dog behind him. He nearly ran himself to death. Finally, he stopped, all out of breath, and said, "I'm so tired I don't know what to do."

The l'il dog caught up, sat right in front of him, panting, and said, "Me neither."

That man is running yet.

Keemo Kyemo

TRADITIONAL

Cheerfully

Arranged by Allan Miller

There was an old frog and he lived in a spring,

Sing - song kit - ty catch - ee kye - mee - oh. He was so hoarse he

could - n't sing, Sing - song kit - ty catch - ee kye - mee - oh.

Chorus

Kee - mo kye - mo dell - way Hi - ho

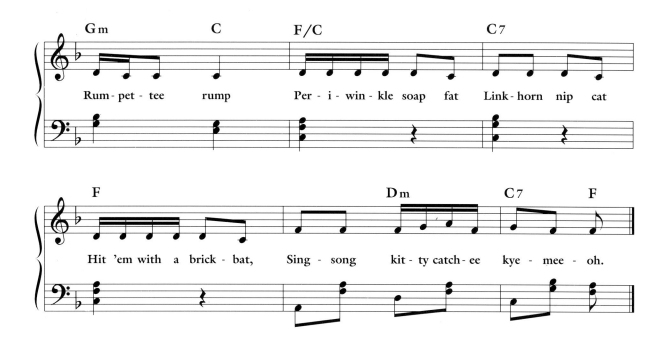

Rum-pet-tee rump Per-i-win-kle soap fat Link-horn nip cat

Hit 'em with a brick-bat, Sing-song kit-ty catch-ee kye-mee-oh.

2. Cheese in the springhouse nine days old,
   Singsong kitty catch-ee kye-mee-oh.
   Rats and skippers awful bold,
   Singsong kitty catch-ee kye-mee-oh.

   Chorus

3. There was a man and he was rich,
   Singsong kitty catch-ee kye-mee-oh.
   He got a rash and began to itch,
   Singsong kitty catch-ee kye-mee-oh.

   Chorus

4. Roses are red, violets are blue,
   Singsong kitty catch-ee kye-mee-oh.
   Sugar is sweet and so are you,
   Singsong kitty catch-ee kye-mee-oh.

   Chorus

5. I see England, I see France,
   Singsong kitty catch-ee kye-mee-oh.
   I see Mary's polka-dot pants,
   Singsong kitty catch-ee kye-mee-oh.

   Chorus

THREE TALL TIDBITS

'Twas Midnight

TRADITIONAL

'Twas midnight on the ocean,
Not a streetcar was in sight;
The sun was shining brightly,
For it rained all day that night.
'Twas a summer day in winter
And snow was raining fast,
As a barefoot boy with shoes on
Stood sitting in the grass.

The Split Dog

RETOLD BY RICHARD CHASE

Had me a little dog once, the best rabbit dog you ever saw. Well, he was runnin' a rabbit one day, and some fool had left a scythe lyin' in the grass with the blade straight up. That poor little dog ran smack into it, and it split him open from the tip of his nose right straight on down to his tail.

Well, I saw him fall apart and I ran and slapped him back together. I jerked off my shirt, wrapped him up in that right quick, and ran to the house. Set him in a box and poured turpentine all over the shirt. I kept him near the stove. Set him out in

the sun part of the time. Oh, I could see him still breathin' a little, and I hoped I wouldn't lose him. And after about three weeks, I could see him tryin' to wiggle now and then. I let him stay bandaged another three weeks — and then one morning I heard him bark. So I started unwrappin' him and in a few minutes out he jumped, spry as ever.

But — don't you know! — in my excitement, blame if I hadn't put him together wrong-way-to. He had two legs up and two legs down.

Anyhow, it turned out he was twice as good a rabbit dog after that. He'd run on two legs till he got tired, and then flip over and just keep right on.

Ah, me! That little dog could run goin' and comin', and bark at both ends.

The Sad Tale of Tom the Catfish

RETOLD BY M. A. JAGENDORF

There lived a little fellow in Grant County in Indiana who loved fishing more 'n anything. One day he caught a catfish young as himself and, so, too little to eat.

It was a mighty pretty catfish glistening in the sun, with fine, long whiskers, so little Obediah put him in a horse trough and fed him every day the same way he fed his dog and his cat and his bird. Soon that little catfish knew Obediah the same as his dog and cat and canary knew him. Fact is, the fish came to know the boy's voice even far away. When he'd be way off, that fish'd come to the edge, stick out his head, and wait for his master and the hand that fed 'm. After a time, the fish got

kind o' used to breathing the air in the outside world even as he did under the water. Soon he got so used to the air, he'd keep his head out o' the water for hours, waiting for his master.

Next thing you know, that fish jumped out of the trough an' began following the boy. Followed him everywhere just like his dog. Followed him even in the house,

and slept under the bed just the same as the dog, and ate out o' the same plate, too.

That kept on for a long time till fall came, when the boy had to go to school.

Jedediah honeysuckle! If the dog and Tom — that's what the boy called his catfish — didn't follow the boy right t' the schoolhouse, the dog barking, the fish flopping. When they came to the school, dog and fish, they lay down in the grass while their master blabbed his lesson with the others in the classroom.

Tom the catfish followed Obediah every day t' school for months and months, every blessed day. He flopped pretty near as fast as the dog could run.

Many was the time fish and dog, and maybe the cat, too, 'd play together like a bunch o' rollicking puppies. Reckon that catfish liked it better 'n rollin' around in cold water and getting all wet. By this time he had no use for water at all except for drinking.

One day, it was right around Thanksgiving, and the air was tangy and crisp like a Baldwin apple, Obediah, Rover the dog, and Tom were romping and jumping through the yellow leaves on the road. It was a sight t' see that catfish going flippidy flop — up and down and all around. Soon Rover and Obediah, they got ahead while Tom was flopping after 'em the best he could. So they came to a creek that had a round log for crossing. Obediah skipped and jumped across it, singing "Yankee Doodle," the dog followed, barking joyfully, and Tom came flopping behind. He had got near over the log when, *kerplap!*, he flopped sideways and fell into the water.

The water was cold and running fast, and Tom was carried away. Dog and master ran so fast and so far they never noticed it, and Tom, the poor catfish, could not even cry out for help. Y' see, he was so unused to being a fish that the water filled his mouth and eyes. He gurgled and

he gasped and came up three times trying to catch a breath of air . . . but it was no use. Tom the poor catfish . . . he drowned!

'Twasn't long afore Obediah and Rover missed Tom and looked for him everywhere. They didn't find him so they figured he'd gone back to his home to the river. 'Deed he had, but not the way they figured.

The Boy Who Ate Too Much

RETOLD BY EDWARD L. KEITHAHN

A small boy once lived in an igloo with an old, old woman. This boy was always hungry and always begging for food. But one day the last of the food was eaten, so the old woman sent him down to the beach to search for food.

The first thing he found was a little tomcod. He picked it up and after pulling off its head, swallowed it at one gulp. Continuing his search he presently came upon a seal. As before, he pulled off its head and ate the whole seal. On he went, still hungry, until he came upon a large bearded seal, or *oogrook,* sunning itself on the sand. Before it could scramble back into the water he caught it, pulled off its head, and ate it. Not satisfied yet, he continued down the beach until he caught sight of a white whale stranded high and dry on the sand. In the same manner as he had done with the tomcod, the seal, and the *oogrook,* he pulled off its head and ate the whale, skin, bones, blubber, and all.

After the boy had finished the whale he felt better and presently began to sing. He rubbed his belly and sang to his stomach. For the first time in his life he had had enough to eat. But soon he became very, very thirsty so he went to a nearby pond and began to drink. He drank and drank and drank until the pond was quite dry. Then he started off for the igloo in which he lived with the old woman.

Reaching the igloo he tried to get in at the door but could not get through. He had eaten too much. "How am I to get in?" he called to the old woman. "Come in through the window," she answered. The window was much smaller than the door but he tried it anyway and found he could just get his head through. "I can't get through the window," he called to the old woman. "Come in through the ventilator!" cried the old woman in answer. This seemed ridiculous to the boy since the ventilator was very much smaller than the window but he tried it anyway. This time he got his head and shoulders through but could go no further. Again he called to the old woman for advice. "Come in through the eye of my needle," she shouted, holding up the needle, and through it the boy came tumbling onto the floor.

When the old woman saw how swelled he was from eating so much she shouted, "Look out! Keep away from the seal oil lamp!" But in spite of himself the boy stumbled toward the lamp. At the same instant the lamp sprang toward him. The old woman barely had time to rush out through the door. Boom! There was a sound like a mighty clap of thunder. When all was again still, the old woman crawled up to the window and peered in. The boy had disappeared. The lamp was gone, too. But down in the room where they had been was a deep, dark pool and in it were swimming a tomcod, a seal, an *oogrook,* and a big white whale.

Mrs. Murphy's Chowder

TRADITIONAL

Rowdy

Arranged by Allan Miller

Won't you bring back, won't you bring back Mis - sus Mur - phy's chow - der? It was tune - ful. Ev - 'ry spoon - ful made you yo - del loud - er. Af - ter din - ner, Un - cle Ben used to fill his foun - tain pen From a plate of Mis - sus Mur - phy's chow - der.

It had ice cream, cold cream, ben-zine, gas-o-line, Soup beans, string beans, float-ing all a-round;
Sponge cake, beef steak, mis-take, stom-ach ache, Cream puffs, ear-muffs, man-y to be found;

Silk hats, door-mats, bed slats, Dem-o-crats; Cow-bells, door-bells beck-on you to dine;

Meat-balls, fish balls, moth-balls, can-non-balls. Come on in; the 'chow-der's fine!

2. Won't you bring back, won't you bring back
   Missus Murphy's chowder?
From each helping you'll be yelping for a
   headache powder,
And if they had it where you are, you might
   find a trolley car
In a plate of Missus Murphy's chowder.

Chorus

3. Won't you bring back, won't you bring back
   Missus Murphy's chowder?
You can pack it, you can stack it all around the
   larder.
The plumber died the other day; they
   embalmed him right away
In a bowl of Missus Murphy's chowder.

Chorus

Juan Bobo and the Buñuelos

RETOLD BY LUCÍA M. GONZÁLEZ

H ere is a story about a poor farmer who was not very bright. He was so foolish and so easily cheated that everyone around town called him Juan Bobo, which means Juan the Fool in Spanish. He was always doing things that got him into trouble.

One evening, as Juan was coming home after a long day of hard work in the fields, he saw three strange-looking bags hidden between the bushes to the side of the road. He looked inside and saw that they were filled with gold. He took the three bags home and showed them to his wife.

She said, "*¡Ay, Dios mío, Juan!* That gold must belong to some wicked men! Don't tell anyone that you found that gold. It must be a secret."

But immediately she thought, *Ay, no, my husband cannot keep any secrets.* So she came up with a plan.

"Juan, I need you to bring me a sack of cornmeal, three gallons of milk, three dozen eggs, and ten pounds of butter."

Poor Juan had to go to town and bring everything his wife had asked for. He was so tired when he got back that he went right to sleep.

As soon as he fell asleep his wife began to make *buñuelos*, fritters made of cornmeal, milk, eggs, and butter and deep-fried like doughnuts. She spent that whole night kneading and cutting and cooking. She made so many *buñuelos* that they piled all the way to the ceiling. Then she took

them outside and threw them all over the ground.

The following morning Juan woke up and looked outside. He saw all of the ground covered with *buñuelos*. He couldn't believe his eyes. And Juan's wife said, "*¡Ay, Dios mío!* It must have rained *buñuelos* last night!" While poor Juan stood there looking at the ground and looking at the sky, puzzled over what had happened, his wife rushed to the stable where their donkey was eating from a pile of hay. The woman turned the donkey so that its tail faced the hay. Just then, Juan entered the stable and heard his wife saying, "This is a great miracle! Our donkey has been eating with its tail!"

Poor Juan. He went to work with a terrible headache, amazed at the strange happenings of the day.

About a week later three mean-looking men with long beards and matted hair showed up at the house. They said to the woman, "Where is the gold your husband's telling everyone he's found? He'd better give it back — or else!"

Just then Juan walked into the house, and the men rushed to him, asking, "Where is the gold?"

With a pleased smile, Juan said, "*¡Mujer!* Bring out the gold you hid the other day."

Looking very innocent, the wife answered, "I don't remember anything about any gold."

Juan replied, "Sure you do. It was the gold I brought the day before it rained *buñuelos,* and our donkey ate with its tail."

The three men looked at one another and said, "This poor soul must be crazy!" And they left, feeling sorry for the woman who had to put up with such a fool.

From that day on, Juan Bobo and his wife lived a very pleasant and very comfortable life.

The Twist-Mouth Family

TRADITIONAL

There was once a father and a mother and several children, and all but one of them had their mouths twisted out of shape. The one whose mouth was not twisted was a son named John.

When John got to be a young man he was sent to college, and on the day he came home for his first vacation the family sat up late in the evening to hear him tell of all he had learned. But finally they prepared to go to bed, and the mother said, "Father, will you blow out the light?"

"Yes, I will," was his reply.

"Well, I wish you would," said she.

"Well, I will," he said.

So he blew, but his mouth was twisted, and he blew upward — this way — and he couldn't blow out the light.

Then he said, "Mother, will you blow out the light?"

"Yes, I will," was her reply.

"Well, I wish you would," said he.

"Well, I will," she said.

So she blew, but her mouth was twisted, and she blew downward — this way — and she couldn't blow out the light.

Then she spoke to her daughter and said, "Mary, will you blow out the light?"

"Yes, I will," was Mary's reply.

"Well, I wish you would," said her mother.

"Well, I will," Mary said.

So Mary blew, but her mouth was twisted, and she blew out of the right corner of the mouth — this way — and she couldn't blow out the light.

Then Mary spoke to one of her brothers and said, "Dick, will you blow out the light?"

"Yes, I will," was Dick's reply.

"Well, I wish you would," said Mary.

"Well, I will," Dick said.

So Dick blew, but his mouth was twisted, and he blew out of the left corner of the mouth — this way — and he couldn't blow out the light.

Then Dick said, "John, will you blow out the light?"

"Yes, I will," was John's reply.

"Well, I wish you would," said Dick.

"Well, I will," John said.

So John blew, and his mouth was straight, and he blew straight — this way — and he blew out the light.

The light was out and they were all glad that John had succeeded, and the father said, "What a blessed thing it is to have larnin'!"

Michael Finnegan

TRADITIONAL

Capriciously

Arranged by Allan Miller

2. There was an old man named Michael Finnegan,
   He kicked up an awful dinnegan,
   Because they said he must not sing again,
   Poor old Michael Finnegan.
   Begin again.

3. There was an old man named Michael Finnegan,
   He went fishing with a pinnegan,
   Caught a fish and dropped it in again,
   Poor old Michael Finnegan.
   Begin again.

4. There was an old man named Michael Finnegan,
   He grew fat and then grew thin again,
   Then he died and had to begin again,
   Poor old Michael Finnegan.
   Begin again.

John Schoenherr

FEATHERS AND FUR, SCALES AND TAILS

No matter where you find yourself in the United States, there's sure to be a tale to tell about the animals that live there.

Wake, Snake

TRADITIONAL

Playfully   *Arranged by Rachel Miller*

Wake, snake, day is a-break-in', peas in the pot and the

hoe-cakes a-bak-in'; Green corn, *(clap)*

Green corn, *(clap)* Green corn. *(clap)*

Brer Possum's Dilemma

RETOLD BY JACKIE TORRENCE

Back in the days when the animals could talk, there lived ol' Brer Possum. He was a fine feller. Why, he never liked to see no critters in trouble. He was always helpin' out, a-doin' somethin' for others.

Ever' night, ol' Brer Possum climbed into a persimmon tree, hung by his tail, and slept all night long. And each mornin', he climbed outa the tree and walked down the road to sun 'imself.

One mornin' as he walked, he come to a big hole in the middle of the road. Now, ol' Brer Possum was kind and gentle, but he was also nosy, so he went over to the hole and looked in. All at once, he stepped back, 'cause layin' in the bottom of that hole was ol' Brer Snake with a brick on his back.

Brer Possum said to 'imself, "I best git outa here, 'cause ol' Brer Snake is mean and evil and low-down, and if I git to stayin' around 'im, he jist might git to bitin' me."

So Brer Possum went on down the road.

But Brer Snake had seen Brer Possum, and he commenced to callin' for 'im.

"Help me, Brer Possum."

Brer Possum stopped and turned around. He said to 'imself, "That's ol' Brer Snake a-callin' me. What do you reckon he wants?"

Well, ol' Brer Possum was kindhearted, so he went back down the road to the hole, stood at the edge, and looked down at Brer Snake.

"Was that you a-callin' me? What do you want?"

Brer Snake looked up and said, "I've been down here in this hole for a mighty long time with this brick on my back. Won't you help git it offa me?"

Brer Possum thought, then said, "Now listen here, Brer Snake. I knows you. You's mean and evil and low-down, and if'n I was to git down in that hole and git to liftin' that brick offa your back, you wouldn't do nothin' but bite me."

Ol' Brer Snake just hissed.

"Maybe not. Maybe not. Maaaaaaybe not."

Brer Possum said, "I ain't sure 'bout you at all. I jist don't know. You're a-goin' to have to let me think about it."

So ol' Brer Possum thought — he thought high, and he thought low — and jist as he was thinkin', he looked up into a tree and saw a dead limb a-hangin' down. He climbed into the tree, broke off the limb, and with that ol' stick, pushed that brick offa Brer Snake's back. Then he took off down the road.

Brer Possum thought he was away from ol' Brer Snake when all at once he heard somethin'.

"Help me, Brer Possum."

Brer Possum said, "Oh, no, that's 'im agin."

But bein' so kindhearted, Brer Possum turned around, went back to the hole, and stood at the edge.

"Brer Snake, was that you a-callin' me? What do you want now?"

Ol' Brer Snake looked up outa the hole and hissed.

"I've been down here for a mighty long time, and I've gotten a little weak, and the sides of this ol' hole are too slick for me to climb. Do you think you can lift me outa here?"

Brer Possum thought.

"Now, you jist wait a minute. If'n I was to git down into that hole and lift you outa there, you wouldn't do nothin' but bite me."

Brer Snake hissed.

"Maybe not. Maybe not. Maaaaaaaybe not."

Brer Possum said, "I jist don't know. You're a-goin' to have to give me time to think about this."

So ol' Brer Possum thought.

And as he thought, he jist happened to look down there in that hole and see that ol' dead limb. So he pushed the limb underneath ol' Brer Snake and he lifted 'im outa the hole, way up into the air, and threwed 'im into the high grass.

Brer Possum took off a-runnin' down the road.

Well, he thought he was away from ol' Brer Snake when all at once he heard somethin'.

"Help me, Brer Possum."

Brer Possum thought, That's 'im agin.

But bein' so kindhearted, he turned around, went back to the hole, and stood there a-lookin' for Brer Snake. Brer Snake crawled outa the high grass just as slow as he could, stretched 'imself out across the road, rared up, and looked at ol' Brer Possum.

Then he hissed. "I've been down there in that ol' hole for a mighty long time, and I've gotten a little cold 'cause the sun didn't shine. Do you think you could put me in your pocket and git me warm?"

Brer Possum said, "Now you listen

here, Brer Snake. I knows you. You's mean and evil and low-down, and if'n I put you in my pocket, you wouldn't do nothin' but bite me."

Brer Snake hissed.

"Maybe not. Maybe not. Maaaaaaaybe not."

"No, sireee, Brer Snake. I knows you. I jist ain't a-goin' to do it."

But jist as Brer Possum was talkin' to Brer Snake, he happened to git a real good look at 'im. He was a-layin' there lookin' so pitiful, and Brer Possum's great big heart began to feel sorry for ol' Brer Snake.

"All right," said Brer Possum. "You must be cold. So jist this once I'm a-goin' to put you in my pocket."

So ol' Brer Snake coiled up jist as little as he could, and Brer Possum picked 'im up and put 'im in his pocket.

Brer Snake laid quiet and still — so quiet and still that Brer Possum even forgot that he was a-carryin' 'im around. But all of a sudden, Brer Snake commenced to crawlin' out, and he turned and faced Brer Possum and hissed.

"I'm a-goin' to bite you."

But Brer Possum said, "Now wait a minute. Why are you a-goin' to bite me? I done took that brick offa your back, I got you outa that hole, and I put you in my pocket to get you warm. Why are you a-goin' to bite me?"

Brer Snake hissed.

"You knowed I was a snake before you put me in your pocket."

And when you're mindin' your own business and you spot trouble, don't never trouble trouble 'til trouble troubles you.

Turtle Makes War on Man

RETOLD BY JOSEPH BRUCHAC

One day Turtle decided he would go on the warpath against the Human Beings. He painted his cheeks red and climbed into his canoe, singing a war song. He had not paddled far down the river before he saw a figure standing on the bank. It was Bear.

"Greetings! Thanks be given that you are strong, Little Brother," said Bear. "Where are you going?"

"I am going to make war on the Human Beings," said Turtle. "Too long have they made war on animals. Now is the time for us to strike back."

"Hah!" Bear said. "Perhaps you are right. I would like to go with you."

Turtle looked at the huge form of Bear and at his own small canoe. "What can you do as a warrior?" Turtle quickly asked. "Why should I take you on my war party?"

"I am very big and strong," said Bear. "I can crush an enemy in my arms."

Turtle shook his head and paddled away. "No," he said. "You would be too slow to go on the warpath with me."

After Turtle had gone a few more miles down the stream, he saw another figure waving to him from the banks of the river. He paddled his canoe closer and saw it was Wolf.

"Turtle," shouted Wolf, "I hear you are going to make war on the Human Beings. You must take me with you!"

Turtle looked at Wolf and at Wolf's long, sharp teeth. Wolf was not as big as Bear, but he was still big enough to make Turtle worry if his small canoe would hold so much weight.

"What can you do?" asked Turtle.

"I can run very fast to attack the enemy. With my long teeth I can bite them."

But Turtle was already paddling away down the river. "No," he called back over his shoulder. "You would not do to go with me on my war party. You are too fast and you would run away and leave me behind."

When Turtle had rounded the bend in the river, he saw a strange animal standing on the banks. The animal was no larger than Turtle himself and was wearing a beautiful black and white robe. Turtle pulled his canoe in to the shore.

"You," Turtle said. "Do you want to go with me to make war on the Human Beings?"

"That is a good idea," said the strange animal. "I know that with my secret weapon I can be of help."

"What is your secret weapon?" asked Turtle.

"I cannot tell you," said the animal, turning his back toward Turtle. "But I can show you."

The animal, whose name was Skunk, was certainly right. His secret weapon was very powerful and after Turtle had washed himself off in the river, it was agreed that Skunk would accompany Turtle. The two of them set off down the river, only stopping when another strange animal called to them from the forest.

"Take me with you," called the animal. "I wish to make war on the Human Beings also."

"Who are you?" asked Turtle.

"I am Rattlesnake," said the long, thin animal. "I have great magic in my long fangs and can kill any animal by touching them. Shall I show you?"

Turtle shook his head quickly, remembering his experience with Skunk. "No," he said, "I believe you. Come into the boat and we will go together and make war. With a war party as powerful as our own, we will soon destroy all of the Human Beings in the world!"

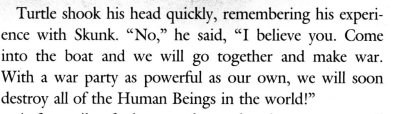

A few miles farther on down the river was a small village of Iroquois. It was there that Turtle decided to make his first raid. The three warriors talked over the strategy and it was decided that surprise attack would be most effective. Skunk hid himself in the bushes near the small spring where the women came each morning to fill their water pots, Snake coiled up in a pile of firewood beside one of the lodges, and Turtle pulled his head and feet into his shell after placing himself next to the overturned cooking pots.

Bright and early the next morning, a woman went to the spring to get water. As soon as she bent over to fill her pot, Skunk shot her with his weapon. This woman was very brave, however, and even though she was coughing and choking, she beat Skunk with her fists until he was almost dead and then staggered back to the village. When Skunk recovered, he crawled away into the bushes, resolving never to attack Human Beings again. Turtle's war party was now down to only two.

Rattlesnake's turn was not far off. A man asked his wife to bring in some wood to start the cooking fire. This woman had very sharp eyes and she saw the telltale coils of Rattlesnake hidden among the logs. Grabbing a handful of stones, she began to hurl them at Rattlesnake and it was all he could do to manage to escape with his

life. So many of the stones struck him that his head was flattened out and to this day all Rattlesnakes have a flattened head as a result of Turtle's war party.

Now Turtle was the only warrior left. He bided his time, waiting for a chance to strike. The chance finally came when a man walked over to the cooking pots, intending to pick one up to use for the morning meal. Instead of picking up a pot, he grabbed Turtle who shot his head out of his shell and bit the man firmly on his leg.

"Ow! Ohhh!" shouted the man. "Let go of me." But Turtle would not let go. The man grabbed a big stick and began beating Turtle with it so hard that it cracked Turtle's shell in many places, but still Turtle would not let go.

"I am going to place you in the fire and burn you," panted the man, and this frightened Turtle very much.

I have not used my wits, thought Turtle and then cried out in a loud, boasting voice, "Put me in the fire. It is my home and will make me grow stronger. Only do not put me in the water."

"Ah-hah!" cried the man. "So you are afraid of the water!" He gritted his teeth from the pain and hobbled down to the river where he thrust in his leg with Turtle still holding on firmly. Turtle waited until he was deep enough and then, letting go of the man's leg, he swam away underwater as fast as he could.

Ever since that day, even though Turtle still wears the red paint of war on his cheeks, he has avoided Human Beings, his cracked shell a reminder to him of what happened when he decided to make war on People.

255

The Travels of a Fox

TRADITIONAL

A fox digging behind a stump found a bumblebee. The fox put the bumblebee in his bag, and traveled.

The first house he came to he went in, and said to the mistress of the house, "Can I leave my bag here while I go to Squintum's?"

"Yes," said the woman.

"Then be careful not to open the bag," said the fox.

But as soon as the fox was out of sight the woman just took a little peep into the bag, and out flew the bumblebee, and the rooster caught him and ate him all up.

After a while the fox came back. He took up his bag, and he saw that his bumblebee was gone, so he said to the woman, "Where is my bumblebee?"

And the woman said, "I just untied the string, and the bumblebee flew out, and the rooster ate him up."

"Very well," said the fox. "I must have the rooster, then."

So he caught the rooster and put him in his bag, and traveled.

And the next house he came to he went in, and said to the mistress of the house, "Can I leave my bag here while I go to Squintum's?"

"Yes," said the woman.

"Then be careful not to open the bag," said the fox.

But as soon as the fox was out of sight the woman just took a little peep into the bag, and the rooster flew out, and the pig caught him and ate him all up.

After a while the fox came back. He took up his bag, and he saw that his rooster was gone, so he said to the woman, "Where is my rooster?"

And the woman said, "I just untied the string, and the rooster flew out, and the pig ate him up."

"Very well," said the fox. "I must have the pig, then."

So he caught the pig and put him in his bag, and traveled.

And the next house he came to he went in, and said to the mistress of the house, "Can I leave my bag here while I go to Squintum's?"

"Yes," said the woman.

"Then be careful not to open the bag," said the fox.

But as soon as the fox was out of sight the woman just took a little peep into the bag, and the pig jumped out, and the ox gored him.

After a while the fox came back. He took up his bag, and he saw that his pig was gone, so he said to the woman, "Where is my pig?"

And the woman said, "I just untied the string, and the pig jumped out, and the ox gored him."

"Very well," said the fox. "I must have the ox, then."

So he caught the ox and put him in his bag, and traveled.

And the next house he came to he went in, and said to the mistress of the house, "Can I leave my bag here while I go to Squintum's?"

"Yes," said the woman.

"Then be careful not to open the bag," said the fox.

But as soon as the fox was out of sight the woman just took a little peep, and the ox got out, and the woman's little boy broke off his horns and killed him.

After a while the fox came back. He took up his bag, and he saw that his ox was gone, so he said to the woman, "Where is my ox?"

And the woman said, "I just untied the string, and the ox got out, and my little boy broke off his horns and killed him."

"Very well," said the fox. "I must have the little boy, then."

So he caught the little boy and put him in his bag, and traveled.

And the next house he came to he went in, and said to the mistress of the house, "Can I leave my bag here while I go to Squintum's?"

"Yes," said the woman.

"Then be careful not to open the bag," said the fox.

The woman was making cake, and her children were around her teasing for it.

"Oh, Ma, give me a piece!" said one, and "Oh, Ma, give me a piece!" said the others.

And the smell of the cake came to the little boy weeping and crying in the bag, and he heard the children beg for the cake, and he said, "Oh, Mammy, give me a piece!"

Then the woman opened the bag and took the little boy out, and she put the house dog in the bag in the little boy's place. And the little boy stopped crying and joined the other children.

After a while the fox came back. He took up his bag, and he saw that it was tied fast, and he put it on his back, and traveled deep into the woods. Then he sat down and untied the bag, and if the little boy had been in the bag, things would have gone badly with him.

But the little boy was safe at the woman's house, and when the fox untied the bag the house dog jumped out and caught the fox and killed him.

The Fox, the Goose, and the Corn

TRADITIONAL

A man started to town with a fox, a goose, and a sack of corn. He came to a stream that he had to cross in a boat. He could take only one across at a time, and he could not leave the fox alone with the goose or the goose alone with the corn. How did he get them all safely over?

He took the goose over first and came back. Then he took the fox across and brought the goose back. Next he took the corn over. He came back alone and took the goose over.

The Cat's Purr

RETOLD BY ASHLEY BRYAN

Once upon a time, Cat and Rat were the best of friends. Uh-huh, uh-huh, they really were! They lived in huts right next to each other. And since Rat liked to copy Cat, their huts matched.

Cat planted a coconut palm tree by his hut. Rat planted one, too.

Cat wove a straw mat for the corner of his hut. Rat wove one, too. When Rat visited Cat, he'd sit on Cat's mat; and on visits to Rat, Cat sat on Rat's mat.

Cat made a bamboo flute and played sweet tunes.

"Let me play a tune, too," said Rat.

Cat let Rat play a tune, too: *too-de-loo, too-de-loo.*

Cat and Rat worked in their vegetable patch together, and after work they headed home, each with his hoe.

"When the vegetables are ready, let's have a big feast," said Cat one day.

"A grand party with dancing and singing," said Rat, "uh-huh, uh-huh!"

They laughed and talked of the feast as they walked along singing, "Ho, for a feast and hi, for a song."

One night, Cat's old uncle visited and brought Cat a present. It was a small drum, the smallest drum Cat had ever seen.

"It's a cat drum," the uncle said, "passed down in the family. Now it's just for you."

"It's so small. Can I play it?" asked Cat.

"Oh, yes!" said Cat's uncle. "But there's a special way to play it. Don't rap it or beat it or poke it, or you won't get a good sound. Stroke it gently and listen."

Cat stroked the drum gently. The drum went: *purrum, purrum.*

"Oh, *meow!*" said Cat. "How soothing, how beautiful!"

"Take good care of the drum," Cat's old uncle said as he was leaving. "Remember now, don't rap it or beat it or tap it or poke it. Just stroke it gently. And don't let anyone else play it."

The next morning Rat called on Cat, as he always did, on the way to work in the fields. He tapped on Cat's hut door: *rap-a-tap tap, rap-a-tap tap.*

Purrum, purrum, purrum came the sound from inside Cat's hut. Rat had never heard such music before. He opened Cat's door and went in. There sat Cat on his bed, playing a small drum.

"*Pit-tap-a-la-pat,*" cried Rat. "What a big, sweet sound and from such a small drum! It's so small you could swallow it whole! *Squee-eek,* play it, Cat, uh-huh!"

Purrum, purrum, purrum, played Cat. *Purrum, purrum, purrum.*

Rat twirled about. He hummed and kicked up his feet to the *purrum, purrum* beat until Cat stopped drumming.

"Me now!" Rat cried.

"Oh, no!" said Cat. "*Mee-ow!* This is a Cat family drum from my uncle."

"*Pit-tap-a-la-pat,*" said Rat. "So what? I made my hut like yours, *squeak, squee-eek.* I played in the shade of your coconut tree; I sat on your mat, drank coconut milk, too. I played your flute, *too-de-loo, too-de-loo.*"

"That was different, Rat," Cat said. "My uncle said no one else plays this Cat drum. Anyway, this is not a time for drumming. Let's get to work."

Cat set the drum down on the bed.

I must think of a good plan so that I can play Cat's drum, Rat thought. Let me think.

"I'm hungry," Rat said. "*Squee-eek!* If I'm to work in the fields, I've got to eat food first. I'll faint if I go without breakfast."

Cat cooked cornmeal mush and served Rat. Rat ate, but he couldn't keep his eyes off the drum. It still sang in his ears, *purrum, purrum.* His fingers itched to play it.

Rat ate slowly, bowl after bowl of cornmeal mush. Still not one good drum-playing plan popped into his head. He dawdled so long over the breakfast that it was teatime when he finished. His stomach was as tight as a drum.

"It's teatime," Rat said. "*Squee-eek,* and I'm still hungry. We'll work better after tea, Cat. Don't you agree?"

"*Meow,* I'm not hungry now," said Cat. "How can you still be hungry after swallowing so much mush?"

"It just wasn't enough mush, I guess," said Rat.

"Oh, *meow,*" said Cat, and he served Rat the tea. "Now don't get sick. Remember, we have lots of work to do for our feast."

Sick! Rat thought. That's it!

Cat had given Rat the idea he needed. Now he knew just what to do.

"*Pit-tap-a-la-pat,*" Rat cried as he pushed aside his cup and plate. "I'm full now and ready for work. *Squee-eek.*"

"*Pit-tap-a-la-po,*" Cat cried. "Here's your hoe. *Meow,* let's go!"

Rat was almost to the door when he moaned and fell to the ground. He turned and tossed at Cat's feet.

"*Ooo-ooo,*" Rat groaned. "My belly's hurting me too bad. *Squeak, squee-eek.*"

"I knew you'd be sick," Cat said.

Cat helped Rat to his feet.

"Ah, poor Rat. Don't lie on the floor. Come, lie on my bed."

"*Ooo-ooo.* Thank you. *Squee-eek, ooo-ooo.*" Cat put Rat to bed and spread a coverlet over him.

"Rest," said Cat. "When your belly is cool, come and help me till the fields."

"I will come, *oh-ooo,* when I'm well. We two do work so well together. *Oh-ooo, oh-ooo!*"

Though Rat wailed well, he was not ill at all, uh-uh! He stretched out on Cat's bed till his toes touched the drum. His plan was working, and he felt happy.

Cat left Rat to rest and set out for their vegetable patch. Rat waited until he was sure that Cat had reached the field. Then Rat threw off the coverlet, sat up, and began to sing:

> "*Pit-tap-a-la-pat*
> *Pit-tap-a-la-ping*
> *Eat off Cat's food*
> *And don't pay a thing.*"

Rat reached for Cat's drum and hugged it.

"I'd rather hug a drum than do hum-drum hoeing." Rat laughed. "Now it's my turn to play Cat's drum."

Rat had danced while Cat drummed, so he had not learned Cat's secret of how best to beat it.

Rat tapped the drum, no *purrum.* Rat beat the drum, no *purrum.* He poked it, no-no, no *purrum!* Instead of hugging Cat's drum now, Rat was so mad he could have pounded it. But by chance he stroked it. And there it was: *purrum, purrum, purrum.*

"*Pit-tap-a-la-pat!*" cried Rat. "What a thing, this drum. Rap it, tap it, beat it, poke it — no loud, sweet *purrum.* But when you stroke it — *purrum, purrum, purrum.*"

Far off in the field, Cat heard the sound. It was his drum — *purrum, purrum, purrum.* He dropped his hoe and ran toward his hut.

Rat saw Cat coming across the field. Quickly he replaced the drum at the foot of the bed. He stretched out and drew the coverlet up to his chin. He closed his eyes and pretended to be asleep. Cat ran into the room, shook Rat awake, and shouted:

> "*Pit-tap-a-la-pat*
> *Pit-tap-a-la-pum*
> *Who's that knocking*
> *On my drum?*"

"I fell asleep," said Rat. "I didn't hear a thing. *Squee-eek, oh-ooo!* My belly's hurting me too bad."

"You mean your belly's not cool yet, Rat?" Cat asked. "Well, lie down, but keep your eyes open."

"I will do as well as I can, Cat, even though I'm ill."

Cat set out alone to till the fields.

And Rat could hardly wait to play the drum again. When Cat was well out of sight, he sat up in bed and sang:

> "*Pit-tap-a-la-pat*
> *Pit-tap-a-la-ping*
> *Eat off Cat's food*
> *And don't pay a thing.*"

Rat shook with excitement when he took up the drum. First he hugged it, then he stroked it more lightly than before. An even louder *purrum, purrum, purrum* came from the drum.

As Cat hoed a row of vegetables, he heard *purrum, purrum, purrum.* At once he dropped his hoe and headed for home.

Rat was again in bed and under the coverlet when Cat ran in. Cat shook Rat and cried:

> "*Pit-tap-a-la-pat*
> *Pit-tap-a-la-pum*

Who's that knocking
On my drum?"

"You make my belly ache more when you shake me up so," said Rat. "*Oh-ooo*, my belly's hurting me too bad. I didn't hear a thing."

"But, Rat, I tell you someone is knocking on my drum. I hear it in the field — *purrum, purrum, purrum*. Come now, help me, Rat."

"How can I?" said Rat. "I'm lying down, and my belly is hurting me."

"Stay in my bed till your belly's cool. But keep your eyes open. Find out who's knocking on my drum and tell me."

Cat left and closed the door. This time, though, Cat didn't go far along the path to the field. He doubled back, ducked down, and crept to the side of the hut. There he climbed in through the kitchen window and hid under the table.

When Rat thought that Cat was far out of sight, he sat right up in bed.

"What's this?" Cat asked himself. "Maybe Rat's belly is cool now."

He watched Rat from the hiding place under the table. He saw Rat take up the drum. Cat did not move. Rat began to sing:

"I fooled Cat once."

Cat kept quiet.

"I fooled Cat twice."

Cat blinked his eyes.

"I play Cat's drum."

Cat's ears twitched.

"Purrum, purrum, purrum."

"Drop that drum, Rat," cried Cat. "I've caught you at it. *Mee-ow*."

"You haven't caught me yet," cried Rat.

Rat dodged and scampered down as Cat leapt onto the bed.

So Cat jumped off the bed and trapped Rat in the corner.

All Rat saw was Cat's wide-open mouth and Cat's very sharp teeth. And that gave Rat a new idea.

As Cat flung himself at Rat, Rat plunged the drum into Cat's open mouth and fled.

Cat fell against the bed. He gulped and swallowed. Down went the drum. To his surprise, Cat realized that instead of swallowing Rat, he had swallowed his drum.

Cat stroked his stomach to settle the drum. A muffled sound came from within: *purrum, purrum, purrum.*

Rat ran out of Cat's hut and past his own. He didn't stop to pack a thing, uh-uh! He kept on going, and he didn't look back. By the time Cat finally ran out of doors, Rat was long gone.

"That's that for our vegetable feast," Cat cried. "If I ever catch that Rat, I'll feast on him. *Meow!"*

Since that day, Cat carries his drum safely within. You can't fool Cat anymore with belly cool this and belly cool that. Uh-uh! Cat always knows now who's playing his drum because Cat alone chooses whom he'll let play.

If you're kind to Cat, he'll let you play his drum. Remember, though, don't tap it or beat it, don't rap it or poke it. Just stroke Cat gently, very, very gently. Uh-huh, uh-huh!

Listen now. Can you hear Cat purring — *purrum, purrum, purrum*?

That's Cat's drum!

Purrum, purrum, purrum.

Bought Me a Cat

TRADITIONAL

With ease

Arranged by Rachel Miller

C   Dm sus 4   C Maj7 / Em   Dm sus 4

Bought me a
1. cat,   cat
2. hen,   hen
3. duck,   duck
4. goose,   goose
5. sheep, the sheep pleased me, I
6. hog,   hog
7. cow,   cow
8. horse,   horse
9. dog,   dog

1st verse only:
al 𝄋

C   F   G 9   C

fed my
cat
hen
duck
goose
sheep   un - der yon - der tree.
hog
cow
horse
dog

Verses 3 - 9, include preceding verses in reverse order

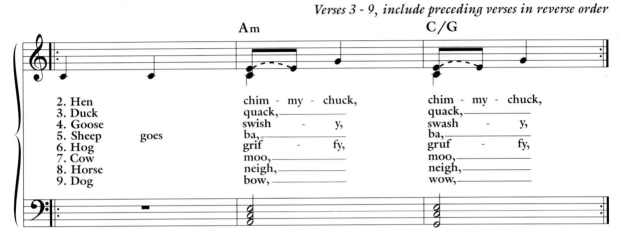

Am   C/G

2. Hen   chim - my - chuck,   chim - my - chuck,
3. Duck   quack,   quack,
4. Goose   goes   swish - y,   swash - y,
5. Sheep   goes   ba,   ba,
6. Hog   grif - fy,   gruf - fy,
7. Cow   moo,   moo,
8. Horse   neigh,   neigh,
9. Dog   bow,   wow,

F   G 7   C   G 7

Cat   goes   fid - dle - i - fee,   fid - dle - i -

1. - 8.   *da Capo*   9.

C   Dm7   C Maj 7/Em   Dm7   C

fee.   fee.

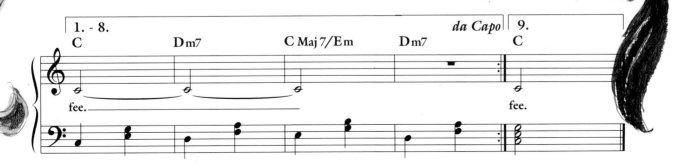

Owl

COLLECTED BY DIANE WOLKSTEIN

Owl thought he was very ugly. But one evening he met a girl and talked with her and she liked him. If it had been day, Owl thought, and she had seen my face, she never would have liked me. But still she had liked him.

So Owl went to her house the next night. And the next. And the night after that. Every evening he would arrive at the girl's house at seven, and they would sit outside on the porch steps, talking together politely.

Then one evening after Owl had left, the girl's mother said to her, "Why doesn't your fiancé visit you during the day?"

"But, Mama, he's explained that to me. He works during the day, and he cannot get here before seven."

"Still, I would like to see his face before the marriage," the mother said. "Let's invite him to our house for a dance this Sunday afternoon. Surely he doesn't work on Sunday."

Owl was very pleased with the invitation: a dance in his honor. But he was also very frightened. He told his cousin, Rooster, about the girl and asked that he accompany him to the dance. But that Sunday afternoon, as Owl and Rooster were riding on their horses to the party, Owl glanced over to Rooster. Rooster held himself with such assurance, he was so elegantly and fashionably dressed, that Owl imagined the girl seeing the two of them and was filled with shame.

"I can't go on," he choked. "You go and tell them I've had an accident and will be there later."

Rooster rode to the dance. "Tsk, tsk, poor Owl," he explained. "He has had an accident, and he has asked me to let you know that he will be here later."

When it was quite dark, Owl tied his horse a good distance from the dance and stumbled up to the porch steps.

"Pssst," he whispered to a young man sitting on the steps. "Is Rooster here?"

"Well, now, I don't know."

"Go and look. Tell him a friend is waiting for him by the *mapou* tree."

Rooster came out. "Owl!"

"Shhhhhhh — "

"Owl!"

"Shhhh — "

"Owl, what are you wearing over your head — I mean your face?"

"It's a hat. Haven't you ever seen a hat before? Look, tell them anything. Tell them I scratched my eyes on a branch as I was riding here and the light — even the light from a lamp — hurts them. And you must be certain to watch for the day for me, and to crow as soon as you see the light, so we can leave."

"Yes, yes," Rooster said. "Come in and I shall introduce you to the girl's relatives."

Rooster introduced Owl to everyone, explaining Owl's predicament. Owl went around shaking hands, his hat hung down almost completely covering his face. Owl then tried to retreat into a corner, but the girl came over.

"Come into the yard and let's dance," she said.

Dong ga da, Dong ga da, Dong ga da, Dong. Dong ga da, Dong. Eh-ee-oh.

Owl danced. And Owl could dance well. The girl was proud of Owl. Even if he wore his hat strangely and had sensitive eyes, he *could* dance.

Dong ga da, Dong ga da, Dong ga da, Dong. Dong ga da, Dong. Eh-ee-oh.

Rooster was dancing, too. When Owl noticed that Rooster was dancing, instead of watching for the day, Owl was afraid that Rooster would forget to warn him, and he excused himself to the girl. He ran out of the yard, past the houses, to a clearing where he could see the horizon. No, it was still night. Owl came back.

Dong ga da, Dong ga da, Dong ga da, Dong. Dong ga da, Dong. Eh-ee-oh.

Owl motioned to Rooster, but Rooster was lost in the dance. Owl excused himself again to the girl, ran to the clearing; no, it was still night. Owl returned.

Dong ga da, Dong ga da, Dong ga da, Dong. Dong ga da, Dong. Eh-ee-oh.

Owl tried to excuse himself again, but the girl held on to him. "Yes, stay with me," she said. And so they danced and danced and danced.

Dong ga da, Dong ga da, Dong ga da, Dong. Dong ga da, Dong. Eh-ee-oh.

The sun moved up in the sky, higher and higher, until it filled the house and the yard with light.

"Now — let us see your fiancé's face!" the mother said.

"*Kokioko!*" Rooster crowed.

And before Owl could hide, she reached out and pulled the hat from his face.

"My eyes!" Owl cried, and covering his face with his hands, he ran for his horse.

"Wait, Owl!" the girl called.

"*Kokioko!*" Rooster crowed.

"Wait, Owl, wait."

And as Owl put his hands down to untie his horse, the girl saw his face. It was striking and fierce — the most handsome face she had ever seen.

"Owl — "

But Owl was already on his horse, riding away, farther and farther away.

Owl never came back.

The girl waited. Then she married Rooster. She was happy, except sometimes in the morning when Rooster would crow, "*Kokioko-o-o.*" Then she would think about Owl and wonder where he was.

All the Pretty Little Horses

TRADITIONAL

*Arranged by John A. Lomax
and Alan Lomax*

Tenderly

Dm   Gm/B♭   Am

Hush - a - bye, don't you cry, Go to sleep - y, lit - tle

B♭   Dm/A   Dm   Gm

ba - by; When you wake, you shall have cake, And

Am ... **G7/B** **Gm7/B♭** **F/C**

all the pret-ty lit-tle hors es. Black and bay,

B♭ **G7/B** **Am** **Dm**

dap-ple and gray, Coach and six— white— hors - es,

Am **B♭** **Dm**

All the pret-ty lit-tle hors - es.

Chris Van Allsburg

AMERICAN GIANTS ON THE JOB

Building America was a colossal undertaking, and it took some larger-than-life characters to do the job.

When I First Came to This Land

WORDS AND MUSIC BY OSCAR BRAND

Brightly

Arranged by David Fiorenza

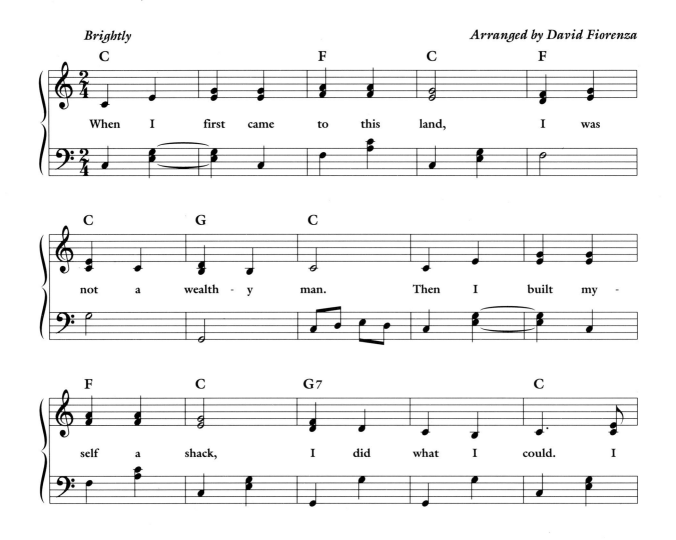

When I first came to this land, I was not a wealthy man. Then I built my-self a shack, I did what I could. I

2. When I first came to this land,
   I was not a wealthy man.
   Then I bought myself a cow,
   I did what I could.
   I called my cow, *No-milk-now,*
   I called my shack, *Break-my-back.*
   But the land was sweet and good;
   I did what I could.

3. When I first came to this land,
   I was not a wealthy man.
   Then I bought myself a duck,
   I did what I could.
   I called my duck, *Out-of-luck,*
   I called my cow, *No-milk-now,*
   I called my shack, *Break-my-back.*
   But the land was sweet and good;
   I did what I could.

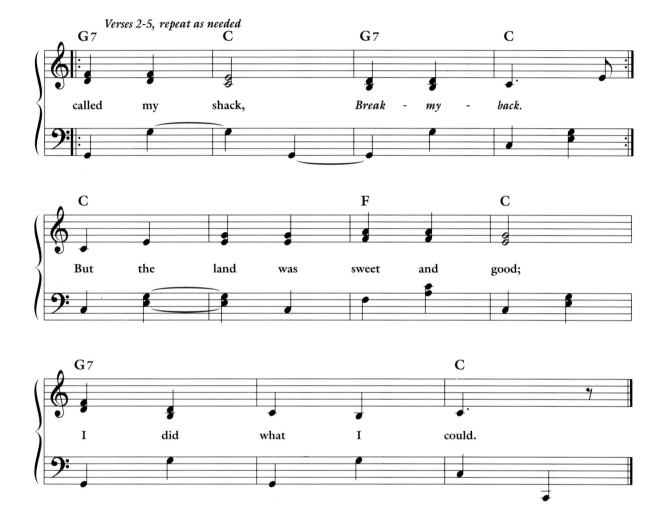

Verses 2-5, repeat as needed

called my shack, Break - my - back.

But the land was sweet and good;

I did what I could.

4. When I first came to this land,
   I was not a wealthy man.
   Then I got myself a wife,
   I did what I could.
   I called my wife, *Run-for-your-life,*
   I called my duck, *Out-of-luck,*
   I called my cow, *No-milk-now,*
   I called my shack, *Break-my-back.*
   But the land was sweet and good;
   I did what I could.

5. When I first came to this land,
   I was not a wealthy man.
   Then I got myself a son,
   I did what I could.
   I called my son, *My-work's-done,*
   I called my wife, *Run-for-your-life,*
   I called my duck, *Out-of-luck,*
   I called my cow, *No-milk-now,*
   I called my shack, *Break-my-back.*
   But the land was sweet and good;
   I did what I could.

Johnny Appleseed! Johnny Appleseed!

RETOLD BY MARION VALLAT EMRICH
AND GEORGE KORSON

O f all the tales that Pennsylvanians tell, they may like best the story of a strange fellow who rode into Pittsburgh on the lazyboard of a Conestoga wagon back in 1794. He said his name was Jonathan Chapman, and he built himself a log cabin on Grant's Hill.

There are some people who say he told it around Pittsburgh that he had been born in Boston in the year of the Battle of Bunker Hill and that the first thing his baby eyes ever saw was a branch of apple blossoms outside the window of his home. If that is true, the sight must have influenced the rest of his life, for as soon as he had his house built in Pittsburgh he planted a big apple orchard. There, on the hill now known as Pittsburgh's Hump, the bees in Jonathan Chapman's hives made honey from the apple blossoms, and Jonathan gave it away to his neighbors because, he said, the bees didn't charge him anything for it.

In the twelve years he lived in Pittsburgh an idea kept growing in Jonathan Chapman's brain until it got a powerful hold on him. He would take a load of apple seeds westward to the pioneers on the frontier so that they might have flowering, fruitful orchards like his own.

So, in 1806, Jonathan loaded two canoes with apple seeds and started down the Ohio River. When he got to the Muskingum he followed that to White Woman Creek, and he finally ended up along Licking Creek where his load of seeds ran out. Behind him farmers were rejoicing in their seedlings — soon to be waving orchards — and they talked about the man who had brought them. They called him Johnny Appleseed.

Johnny went back to the Pennsylvania cider mills to get more seeds. They're still talking about him around Shadeland and Blooming Valley and Cool Spring — the odd, blue-eyed man with long hair hanging to his shoulders, barefooted, wearing ragged clothes. When he had disposed of a second load and come back to Pennsylvania for seeds again, his appearance had changed still more. On his head as a cap he wore a tin kettle in which, when he needed it, he cooked his food. His only garment now, winter or summer, was a coffee sack with holes cut in it for his arms and legs.

Strange stories came out of the western frontier.

A trapper had come upon Johnny Appleseed playing with three bear cubs

while their mother looked on placidly.

Johnny Appleseed entertained frontier families by showing them how he could stick pins and needles through his flesh without hurting himself.

Johnny Appleseed knew direction by instinct and never carried a compass in the trackless woods.

He did not feel the cold and could walk barefoot in below-zero weather without freezing his toes.

Wherever Barefoot Johnny walked, he brought apple seeds.

Soon, hundreds of Ohio acres were abloom with pink blossoms, and Pennsylvania seeds had reached the banks of the Wabash. Everywhere Johnny Appleseed was welcomed by the grateful farmers. When he sat down at table with them he would not eat until he was sure that there was plenty of food for the children. After he had eaten he would stretch himself out on the floor, take out the Bible he carried inside the coffee sack, and read aloud what he called "news fresh from heaven" — the Sermon on the Mount. His voice, one good housewife said, was "loud as the roar of wind and waves, then soft and soothing as the balmy airs that quivered the morning-glory leaves about his gray beard."

One day he trudged along for twenty miles to reach the home of a friend near Fort Wayne, Indiana. He sat down on the doorstep to eat his evening meal of bread and milk. He read aloud from the Bible for a while. Then he went to sleep stretched out on the floor, and he did not wake up.

When the news reached Washington, old Sam Houston, Texas Sam Houston, made a speech about Johnny Appleseed in the American Congress. He said: "This old man was one of the most useful citizens of the world in his humble way. Farewell, dear old eccentric heart. Your labor has been a labor of love, and generations yet unborn will rise up and call you blessed."

Farmers who own apple orchards along Johnny Appleseed's path, which stretched over a territory of a hundred thousand square miles, have been blessing him ever since. And all the folks in western Pennsylvania do, too, for they know that when spring comes to the land known now as the Midwest, hundreds of thousands of Ohio and Indiana acres will be pink and white with Pennsylvania apple blossoms.

Strong as Annie Christmas

RETOLD BY AMY L. COHN AND SUZY SCHMIDT

The New Orleans waterfront sure has changed. Where tourists eat ice cream and shop for souvenirs, keelboat captains and roustabouts once worked like dogs and drank like fish. And no one did either better than one particular lady.

Annie Christmas stood six feet, eight inches in her stockinged feet and weighed more than two hundred and fifty pounds. She had a fine growth of a mustache and a voice as loud and as deep as a foghorn. Black folks said she was black, and white folks said she was white. Seems like everybody wanted to claim her as their own.

Even tough keelboatmen like Mike Fink stood in awe of Annie Christmas, and there wasn't a stevedore who didn't jump when Annie snapped her fingers. She could lick a dozen of them with one arm tied behind her back, and they knew it. Annie was fearless. The red turkey feather she wore stuck in her hatband warned all who saw it not to trifle with her. She fought however you liked, with fists, fire, or knife, and she wore a long necklace made from the ears, eyes, and noses that had been gnawed, torn, or ripped off during the battles with those she'd whipped. That necklace was twenty feet long when she died. Yes it was.

Most of the time Annie dressed like a man and worked even harder. She pulled sweeps and hauled cordelles. She could carry a barrel of flour under each arm and another balanced on her head. One time she wanted to get a loaded flatboat from New Orleans up the river to Natchez in a hurry, so she just grabbed the towline and set out on a dead run. The bottom of that flatboat scarcely touched the water for the entire trip. "As strong as Annie Christmas" became the saying in all the river towns she raced through.

Every once in a while, Annie would start to feeling feminine and get gussied up to take a ride on the *River*

Queen. One time she bought herself fifteen yards of the finest red satin and sewed herself the prettiest frock you ever saw. You can bet Annie was a sight to see when she stepped aboard the riverboat, wearing her red dress and dangly necklace.

That was the night Annie met Charlie, a riverboat gambler. Annie fell head over heels in love with that fancy Dan. And Charlie fell right along with her.

Charlie and Annie often took the riverboats so Charlie could gamble. One night Charlie played roulette with Annie at his side. He played twenty-five dollars on red, and he leaned forward on his elbows and watched the ball roll and rest. Red won!

Charlie let it ride, and red won again. Five times in a row Charlie let it ride and five times he won. Annie begged him to stop. But Charlie never moved a muscle and he never said a word. Ten times he won. Even Charlie's friends begged him to stop now. His luck couldn't hold out and he'd lose everything in one spin. Sixteen times the ball rolled red.

When the captain saw Charlie had won ten thousand dollars of the house's money, he told Charlie he couldn't play anymore. Annie grabbed Charlie by the arm as she got up to leave, and when she did he fell straight to the floor.

Charlie was dead. He'd been dead for a long time. The riverboat had been playing against a dead man, and the dead man had won.

Annie's grief was more than she could bear. After she gave Charlie a big, fancy funeral with his winnings, she went home, put on her prize necklace and her long red dress, and shot herself. Yes she did.

They laid out Annie in a black coffin on a black barge. They cut the ropes, and the barge drifted down the Mississippi in the dark of the new moon. And as the barge slowly made its way to the sea, all the boats on the river let loose one long, mournful whistle to pay their last respects to Annie Christmas.

279

Paul Bunyan, the Mightiest Logger of Them All

RETOLD BY MARY POPE OSBORNE

It seems an amazing baby was born in the state of Maine. When he was only two weeks old, he weighed more than a hundred pounds, and for breakfast every morning he ate five dozen eggs, ten sacks of potatoes, and a half-barrel of mush made from a whole sack of cornmeal. But the baby's strangest feature was his big, curly black beard. It was so big and bushy that every morning his poor mother had to comb it with a pine tree.

Except for that black beard, the big baby wasn't much trouble to anybody until he was about nine months old. That was when he first started to crawl, and since he weighed over five hundred pounds, he caused an earthquake that shook the whole town.

The baby's parents tried putting him in a giant floating cradle off the coast of Maine but every time he rolled over, huge waves drowned all the villages along the coast.

So his parents hauled the giant toddler to a cave in the Maine woods far away from civilization and said goodbye. His father gave him a fishing pole, a knife, some flint rocks, and an axe. "We'll think of you often, honey," his mother said, weeping. "But you can't come back home — you're just too big."

That's the story of how Paul Bunyan came to take care of himself in the Maine woods. And even though he lived alone for the next twenty years, he got along quite well.

In those times, huge sections of America were filled with dark green forests. It would be nice if those trees could have stayed tall and thick forever. But the pioneers needed them to build houses, churches, ships, wagons, bridges, and barns. So one day Paul Bunyan took a good look at all those trees and decided to invent logging.

"Tim-ber!" he yelled, and he swung the bright steel axe his father had given him in a wide circle. There was a terrible crash, and when Paul looked around, he saw he'd felled ten white pines with a single swing.

After that Paul traveled plenty fast through the untamed North Woods. He cut pine, spruce, and red willow in Minnesota, Michigan, and Wisconsin. He cleared cottonwoods out of Kansas so farmers could plant wheat and oaks out of Iowa so farmers could plant corn.

When next heard of, Paul was headed to Arizona. He dragged his pickaxe behind him on that trip, not realizing he was leaving a big ditch in his tracks. Today that ditch is called the Grand Canyon.

When Paul got back from the West, he decided to start a logging camp. Word spread fast. Since all the woodsmen had heard of Paul Bunyan, thousands of them hurried to Paul's headquarters at Big Onion on the Big Onion River in Minnesota to be part of his crew.

"There's only two requirements," Paul announced to the men who'd gathered to apply for the job. "All my loggers have to be over ten feet tall and able to pop six buttons off their shirts with one breath."

Well, about a thousand of the lumberjacks met those requirements, and Paul hired them all. Then he built a gigantic logging camp with bunkhouses a mile long and bunks ten beds high. The camp's chow table was so long that it took a week to pass the salt and pepper from one end to the other. Paul dug a few ponds to provide drinking water for everyone. Today we call those ponds the Great Lakes.

Things went pretty well at the Big Onion Lumber Company until the Year of the Hard Winter. One day Shot Gunderson, the crew boss, complained to Paul, "Boss, it's so cold that the flames for all the lanterns are freezing. And, Boss, when I give orders to the woods crew, all my words freeze in the air and hang there stiff as icicles."

"Well, haul away your frozen words and store them somewhere next to the lantern flames," Paul advised. "They'll both thaw out in the spring."

Sure enough, they did. The only problem was that, come spring, the melting lantern flames started some mean little brush fires. And when Shot's frozen words thawed, old cries of "Timber!" and "Chow time!" started to echo throughout the woods, causing all sorts of confusion. But other than that, things ran pretty smoothly.

Well, there's stories and stories about Paul Bunyan. For many years, old loggers sat around potbellied stoves and told about the good old times with Paul. Those loggers are all gone now, but many of their stories still hang frozen in the cold forest air of the North Woods, waiting to be told. Come spring, when they start to thaw, some of them might just start telling themselves. It's been known to happen.

The Frozen Logger

WORDS AND MUSIC BY JAMES L. STEPHENS

2. I see you are a logger
   And not a common bum,
   For no one but a logger
   Stirs coffee with his thumb.

3. My lover was a logger,
   There's none like him today;
   He held me in a fond embrace
   That broke three vertebrae.

4. He never shaved the whiskers
   From off his horny hide,
   But he drove them in with a
      hammer
   And bit 'em off inside.

5. He kissed me when we parted
   So hard he broke my jaw;
   I could not speak to tell him
   He'd forgot his mackinaw.

6. I saw my logger lover
   Sauntering through the snow,
   A-going gaily homeward
   At forty-eight below.

7. The weather tried to freeze him,
   It tried its level best;
   At one hundred degrees below
      zero
   He buttoned up his vest.

8. It froze clean through to China,
   It froze to the stars above;
   At one thousand degrees below
      zero
   It froze my logger love.

9. They tried in vain to thaw him,
   And if you'll believe me, sir,
   They made him into axe blades
   To chop the Douglas fir.

10. And so I lost my lover,
    And to this café I come,
    And here I wait till someone
    Stirs his coffee with his thumb.

Ride 'em, Round 'em, Rope 'em:
The Story of Pecos Bill

RETOLD BY BRIAN GLEESON

There aren't that many cowboys these days, not real ones like Pecos Bill. Bill was a piece of work, all right. He was the dog-gonedest, gol-dingest, dad-blamest son of the prairie sod who ever rode across these here United States.

Before he came on the scene, cowboys didn't know a thing about cows. But we're putting our socks on over our boots here, sliding down the hill before we know where the cactus is, getting a little bit ahead of ourselves, you know? Because to understand what Bill was about, you've got to know he was half-coyote.

Bill started out his life just like you and me. He was the youngest of fourteen brothers and sisters and his folks lived right smack in the middle of Texas. They

were your regular family of prairie settlers, except Bill's father had a powerful fear of getting hemmed in by neighbors. When Bill was only a couple of weeks old, the family decided to move. Some other family had moved in right next door, only two hundred miles away.

"If it's one thing I can't stand," said Bill's father, "it's being cramped by squatters."

So Bill's family piled into their Conestoga wagon and headed west. They traveled in that wagon for two weeks, when quite by accident, little Bill squirted out the back. Bill's parents didn't realize he was gone until they took a head count three weeks later. By that time, they decided to chalk up the loss of their youngest son to experience, and didn't bother backtracking to find the little devil.

So there was poor Bill, all alone on the range. His parents and his brothers and sisters were gone forever. Pecos Bill's prospects looked mighty slim. He was lower than a snake's belly in a wagon rut.

Luckily, the first critter to happen upon Bill was a coyote. Like all coyotes, this one had a soft spot for young'uns, so she took him to her den. There Bill grew up just like a coyote — a darn good coyote, too.

One day, Bill was scouting down by the Pecos River looking for his coyote buddies, when he came across the strangest creature. Mind you, Bill had never seen a cowboy. So Bill sidled up to the cowboy, coyote-style, and investigated the situation. Bill had never seen anything like this sorry dude before.

The cowboy couldn't believe his eyes either. Because as you can imagine, Bill was quite a sight for the stranger to behold. He looked down at Bill from his horse and said, "You're naked as a jaybird, pardner! Why in tarnation are you running around without your clothes? Did you lose them in a poker game or something?"

"What do you mean, naked?" Bill howled. "I'm a coyote, and coyotes don't wear no clothes."

"You're no coyote," said the cowboy. "Shucks, you don't even have a tail. You're a human being."

Bill turned his head to look down along his backside and, by jiminy and whoo-de-do, he *didn't* have a tail. But Bill was not completely convinced.

"But I've got fleas and I howl at the moon at night," Bill replied.

"Aw, g'wan," said the cowboy with a laugh. "Everybody knows that all Texicans got fleas and howl at the moon."

Bill didn't want to believe he was no longer a coyote, but this stranger had made several valid points. The cowboy was a neighborly sort, so he gave Bill the extra set of duds he kept in his saddlebag. And as soon as Bill put on these clothes, it was like he was a natural-born cowboy.

Bill didn't waste any time and set right out across the range to find out what it was like being a cowboy. Before he got too far, he was surprised by a forty-two-foot rattlesnake sunning himself on a rock. That rattler saw Bill and figured it was lunchtime. But old Bill had another idea.

"I needed a rope, and now I've got one!" Bill cried with delight. "And it's got a rattle attached to it, too!"

Once he found his rope, Bill decided he needed a critter to ride. Up in the hills, he bumped into a cougar that was two tons bigger than any horse and he knew he was in business.

Bill jumped on that cat's back, heeled him in the ribs, and gave him a loud, "Giddap!" That cougar didn't take too kindly to his coyote-cowboy passenger; but then again, the cat didn't have too much to say about it.

Day and night, Bill rode his snarling cougar and twirled his rattlesnake rope and generally whooped it up. On the twelfth day, he came across a cowboy camp.

Never one for fancy introductions, Bill stood there looking at the cowboys and inquired, "What do you fellers do, anyway?"

"Not much," said Sourdough, the ugliest and meanest of all them cowpokes. "We eat beans. We ride around a bit. And other than that, it's pretty slow 'round these parts."

"Then what do you do with all these cows?" said Bill.

"We got so many of 'em, we don't know what to do with 'em all," Sourdough replied.

"Well," said Bill, who was always thinking. "Let's take these cows up to Kansas. Folks up there could use them as pets. Leastways, it'll give us something to do."

And just like that, easy as pie, Bill had invented the cattle drive. Bill and his men commenced marching those cows right up to Kansas — or bust!

For five months the cattle drive pushed on until finally Bill and his cowboys were less than a day's ride from the Kansas border. It was time to celebrate.

Bill gave the fellers the rest of the day off, and they held a hootenanny with singing and dancing. They were having a foot-stompin' good time, when right in the middle of a do-si-do, the biggest cyclone ever seen in the West darkened the horizon.

The twister, swirling around at five hundred miles an hour sucking up everything in its path, was heading right toward the cattle. Bill threw his lariat and lassoed the cyclone by the neck. Bill tried with all his might to pull it down, but this was no ordinary tornado. No-sir-ee.

The cyclone snapped its head forward. Bill hung on to the rope and dug his heels into the plains to get the twister under control. But there was nothing doing. The cyclone stopped short and the backlash yanked Bill smack onto his back.

"All right, you big bag of wind," hollered Bill. "Show me what you can do! Yeeeeee-ha!"

The cyclone spun faster and faster to try to get Bill to loosen his grip. Fat chance, *amigo*! All that cyclone ended up doing was fanning the lakes dry. Now that made Bill mad. Bill pulled so tight with his rope that he made the cyclone cry. That twister bawled so hard its tears welled up and made the Great Salt Lake.

Out over the Gulf of Mexico that twister went, tail-dancing across the water like a king salmon, spitting prawns all over Louisiana. Bill gave a crank and the twister rolled on its back, crazier than a bronco on locoweed, moving and scraping the land flat.

But Bill hung on. And the two of them went back and forth like that for ten full days until Bill finally managed to steer the twister up toward heaven. Up and up they went riding through the clouds, up and up . . . and . . .

And that was the last anybody ever heard of Pecos Bill.

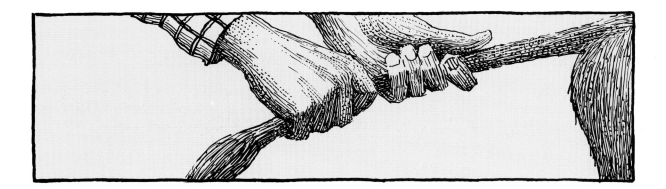

Git Along, Little Dogies

TRADITIONAL

With steady motion

Arranged by Tom Glazer

As I was out walk-ing one morn-ing for pleas-ure,——— I spied a cow-punch-er a-rid-ing a-long;——— His hat was throwed back and his

spurs was a-jing-ling;——— As he ap-proached he was sing-ing this

Chorus

song:_____ Whoop - ee - ti - yi - yo,— git a - long, lit - tle dog - ies._____

_____ It's your mis - for - tune and none of my own; Whoop - ee - ti - yi -

yo, git a - long, lit - tle dog - ies, you know that Wy - o - ming will be your new home._____

2. Your mother was raised way down in Texas,
   Where the jimson weed and the sandburs grow.
   We'll fill you up on prickly pear and cholla,
   Then throw you on the trail to Idaho.

   Chorus

3. Early in the spring we round up the dogies,
   We mark 'em and brand 'em and bob off their tails,
   Round up the horses, load up the chuck wagon,
   Then throw the dogies out on the long trail.

   Chorus

I Hear America Singing

BY WALT WHITMAN

I hear America singing, the varied carols I hear,
Those of mechanics, each one singing his as it should be
    blithe and strong,
The carpenter singing his as he measures his plank or beam,
The mason singing his as he makes ready for work, or
    leaves off work,
The boatman singing what belongs to him in his boat,
    the deckhand singing on the steamboat deck,
The shoemaker singing as he sits on his bench, the hatter
    singing as he stands,
The woodcutter's song, the ploughboy's on his way in
    the morning, or at noon intermission or at sundown,
The delicious singing of the mother, or of the young
    wife at work, or of the girl sewing or washing,
Each singing what belongs to him or her and to none else,
The day what belongs to the day — at night the party of
    young fellows, robust, friendly,
Singing with open mouths their strong melodious songs.

Marc Simont

TAKE ME OUT
TO THE BALL GAME

*The cry of "play ball" has echoed in our land for more
than one hundred years. Baseball is our national pastime,
and it has inspired a folklore all its own.*

Take Me Out to the Ball Game

WORDS BY JACK NORWORTH
MUSIC BY ALBERT VON TILZER

With enthusiasm   *Arranged by Randa Kirshbaum*

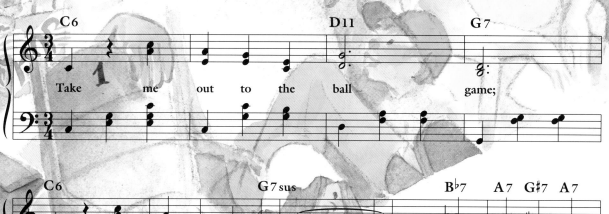

Take me out to the ball game;

Take me out to the crowd. _____ Buy me some

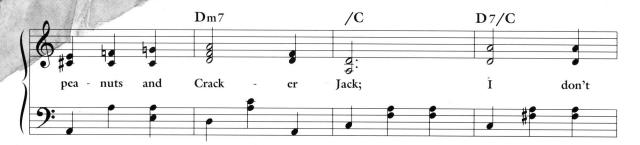

pea- nuts and Crack - er Jack; I don't

care if I nev - er get back, Let me root, root,

root for the home team; If they don't win it's a

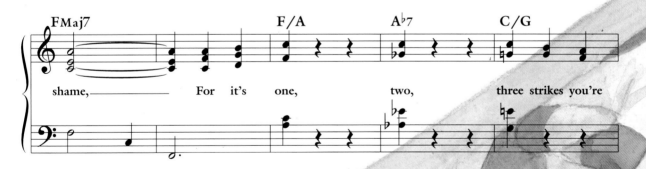

shame, ———— For it's one, two, three strikes you're

out at the old ball game.

Alexander J. Cartwright

How It All Began

BY LAWRENCE S. RITTER

Baseball has been providing us with fun and excitement for more than a hundred years. The first game resembling baseball as we know it today was played in Hoboken, New Jersey, on June 19, 1846. The New York Nine beat the New York Knickerbockers that day, 23–1.

The game was played according to rules drawn up by Alexander J. Cartwright, a surveyor and amateur athlete. Although many people believe otherwise, it is a myth that Abner Doubleday invented baseball. It was Alexander Cartwright, not Abner Doubleday, who first laid out the present dimensions of the playing field and established the basic rules of the game.

The first *professional* baseball team was

the Cincinnati Red Stockings, who toured the country in 1869 and didn't lose a game all year. Soon, baseball began to attract so many fans that in 1876 the National League was organized — the same National League that still exists today.

Although the game as it was played in 1876 was recognizable as baseball — nobody would confuse it with football or basketball — it was quite a bit different from baseball as we know it now. For example, pitchers had to throw underhand, the way they still do in softball; the batter could request the pitcher to throw a "high" or "low" pitch; it took nine balls, rather than four, for a batter to get a base on balls; and the pitching distance was only forty-five feet to home plate.

The rules were gradually changed over the following twenty years, until by about 1900 the game was more or less the same as it is today. In 1884, pitchers were permitted to throw overhand; in 1887, the batter was no longer allowed to request a "high" or "low" pitch; by 1889, it took only four balls for a batter to get a base on balls; and, in 1893, the pitching distance was lengthened to the present sixty feet, six inches.

Players didn't start to wear gloves on the field until the 1880s. At first, they wore only a thin piece of leather over the palm of the hand, with five holes cut out for the fingers to go through. By the 1890s, however, the gloves began to look like today's baseball gloves, although they were not nearly as large.

Gloves remained more or less the same from around 1900 to the mid-1950s. The ball was caught in the "pocket" of the glove, covering the palm of the hand, and it was held with the fingers. The fingers of the glove were short and fairly flexible. The only purpose of the glove was to protect the palm and fingers from injury, although until the 1930s many players insisted on cutting a rather large hole in the palm of the glove in order to grip the ball better.

Nowadays, the glove is much larger than it used to be, and the ball is not caught in the palm of the hand but trapped in the glove's webbing, between the thumb and forefinger. Since the mid-1950s, the glove has become more of a net with which to snare the ball rather than just a protective covering for the hand.

The baseball fields were nowhere near as well taken care of as they are now, so that it was not at all unusual in the old days for the ball to take bad bounces because of pebbles in the infield or uneven ground in the outfield.

Sometimes the ball took a crazy bounce because it was a little lopsided. Since only two or three baseballs would be used for a whole game, by the seventh or eighth inning the ball was often in pretty bad shape. Indeed, this was true until the 1920s. If a ball, like a foul ball or a home run, went into the stands, the ushers would try to get it back, sometimes offering whoever had it a free pass to another game. If the ushers succeeded in getting it back, it would be returned to the field, and the game would resume with the same ball. Now, of course, fifty to sixty baseballs are used in an average big-league game.

Until the early 1900s, one umpire took care of the entire field. Typically, he would call balls and strikes from behind the catcher until a man got on base, and then move out and call balls and strikes from behind the pitcher so he could be closer to the bases in case of an attempted steal.

With only one umpire, there was plenty of opportunity for mischief. A favorite trick was pulled by a man who was on second base, with the umpire working from behind the pitcher. If the batter got a hit to right field, the umpire would have to watch the ball and possibly the batter

rounding first base and trying for second. Meanwhile, the man who had been on second base would veer off toward home before he got as far as third, never coming anywhere close to third base.

Tim Hurst, a famous umpire in the 1890s who knew all the tricks of the trade, once called a player out who slid across home plate in a cloud of dust even though no one was even trying to tag him. Tim had been looking toward right field and second base all the while, but then he whirled around and yelled, "You're out!"

"What do you mean I'm out?" the

player screamed. "They didn't even make a play on me."

"You never touched third base," Tim shouted back.

"Of course, I did," the player responded. "And anyway, how do *you* know? You weren't even watching."

"That's just it," the umpire said. "For when I wasn't watching, you got home *too* fast!"

Needless to say, Tim Hurst won the argument, as have almost all umpires before and since.

In 1901, a second major league, the American League, was established along-side the twenty-five-year-old National League. Many of the stars of the National League jumped over to the new American League because they were offered higher salaries. Ball players didn't make the kind of money in those days that they make now, of course, but even then dollars and cents played an important role in professional baseball.

After some initial hard feelings, the pennant winners of the two major leagues met each other in 1903 in the first modern World Series. The stage was set for a great and long-lasting rivalry, one that continues to this very day.

Jackie Robinson Breaks the Color Barrier

They traveled in dilapidated buses, stayed in fourth-rate hotels — when they could find one that would accept them — took their meals on the run, and played as many as four games in a day and night in farm towns and in major-league stadiums.

Their teams were the Kansas City Monarchs, St. Louis Stars, Nashville Elite Giants, Homestead Grays, Pittsburgh

Crawfords, Baltimore Black Sox, New York Black Yankees, Atlanta Black Crackers, Birmingham Black Barons, Chattanooga Black Lookouts, New York Cubans, and the Cuban Giants.

They played in such leagues as the Negro National League, Southern League, Eastern Colored League, and the Negro American League.

Their names were Cool Papa Bell, Buck Leonard, Josh Gibson, Smokey Joe Williams, John Henry Lloyd, Oscar Charleston, Rube Roster, Ray "Hooks" Dandridge, Martin Dihigo, and Judy Johnson.

These men never made it into the so-called "major leagues." They were denied entry into the major leagues because of the color of their skin. So they played in the Negro Leagues both before and after 1947, the year Jackie Robinson and the Brooklyn Dodgers shattered the color line.

Branch Rickey, the general manager of the Brooklyn Dodgers, knew integrating the major leagues was inevitable and wanted to start the process on the Dodgers with a man he believed would have both the talent and courage to persevere. The man he chose was Jackie Robinson, a four-sport college star at UCLA and the star of the Kansas City Monarchs. "I'm looking for a ball player with guts enough *not* to fight back," Rickey told Robinson. To his credit, Robinson, one of the game's fiercest competitors, kept his pledge to Rickey and turned the other cheek. His courage forced open the doors of the sport to people of color from all over the Western Hemisphere. But it wasn't easy, especially that first year.

Abuse poured down on him regularly from the stands, where fans cupped their hands around their mouths and shouted racial insults, and from the dugouts, where opposing players did the same thing. One afternoon at Cincinnati's Crosley Field, as the Dodgers faced the Reds, it was particularly intense. Jackie Robinson, the first black man to make it to the major leagues, stood with his hands on his hips and tried not to show his emotions.

After a few moments Robinson felt an arm around his shoulders. There beside him stood Pee Wee Reese, a native of nearby Kentucky and captain of the Brooklyn Dodgers during that summer of 1947. Reese's gesture was symbolic, a gesture of support from one teammate to another, a gesture of support from a teammate for a man facing the greatest pressure and test of character imaginable. Those who were there say the crowd watched, and was silenced. A few months later, at the end of the season, Robinson was named Rookie of the Year.

Jackie Robinson was so much more than a symbol. In ten seasons with the Brooklyn Dodgers, he achieved a .311 batting average and hit over .300 six times. He played on six pennant winners. He was the National League batting champion and most valuable player in 1949 when he batted .342. His base path daring — he taunted pitchers with fake starts — and his clutch hitting made him the unquestioned leader of the Dodgers. He was elected to the Hall of Fame in 1962, his first year of eligibility, an honor granted only a handful of major leaguers, an honor granted only to the best.

A Baseball Lexicon

BY ALEXANDRA DAY

"The meal ticket threw smoke but the batter put his foot in the bucket and lifted a Texas Leaguer over the second baseman." Baseball has a language all its own. For a translation, keep reading!

Around the Horn A ball thrown from third base to second and then to first, usually leading to a double play.

Boner A bad play by a fielder that is the result of a failure to think properly.

Break One Off To throw a curveball.

Can of Corn A fly ball that can be easily caught.

Chin Music A ball pitched close to the batter's chin. A brushback pitch.

Cup of Coffee A minor-league player's very brief opportunity to play in the major leagues.

Dinger A home run.

Dish Home plate.

Ducks on the Pond Runners on the bases waiting to be driven home.

Fly Hawk A skilled outfielder who moves toward the ball like a hawk to its prey.

Foot in the Bucket A hitter who moves his front foot sideways, and away from home plate as he swings at the ball, hits with his foot in the bucket.

Heat (Smoke) A ball pitched at a fast speed, also called gas, heater, hummer, mustard, pill.

Hot Dog A player who goes out of his way to draw the fans' attention during the game.

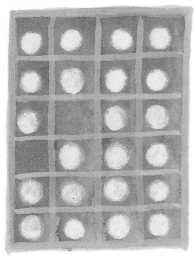

Juice   To hit the ball a long way.

Lumber   A bat. A team with many powerful hitters is said to have a lot of lumber.

The Meal Ticket   A team's best pitcher, the one they can count on for a good performance.

Payoff Pitch   The pitch delivered when there is a count of three balls and two strikes on the batter.

Phenom   A young player who is expected to be a star. It is taken from the word *phenomenon*.

Rabbit Ears   A player, or umpire, who is easily offended by others' remarks is said to have rabbit ears.

Rhubarb   A noisy, active argument between players on opposing teams.

Scroogie   A short form of screwball, a pitch that breaks in the opposite direction from a curveball.

Sent to the Showers   What happens to a pitcher who is pitching badly and has to be removed from the game.

Shoestring Catch   A catch made by an outfielder just before the ball touches the ground.

The Show   What ball players call the major leagues.

Texas Leaguer   A hit ball that falls just beyond the reach of the infielders and doesn't go far enough to be caught by the outfielders.

Tweener   A ball hit between two outfielders.

Wheels   A player's legs. If they are injured, a player is said to have bad wheels.

Whitewash   A pitcher whitewashes a team when he pitches a shutout.

Woodpile   The rack where a team keeps its bats.

Say It Ain't So, Joe

BY JOHN THORN

Joe Jackson earned the sobriquet "Shoeless Joe" because that's the way he played ball back home in the "hollers" of South Carolina. When the hillbilly came to the majors, he was still illiterate, but he had accustomed himself to wearing spikes on the field.

After a five-game trial with Connie Mack's A's in 1908 and another in 1909, Jackson was traded to Cleveland. The Naps, as they were then called, sent him to the minors for more polishing.

In 1911, Jackson finally got the chance to play every day. And what a rookie year he had! He fielded brilliantly and hit .408. In the nine years that followed, Shoeless Joe never hit below .300, and three times topped .370. His lifetime mark of .356 was bettered only by Ty Cobb and Rogers Hornsby.

Yet Shoeless Joe's name cannot be found on any plaque in the Hall of Fame. Though his playing credentials are certainly worthy of Cooperstown, Jackson was one of eight Chicago White Sox players who conspired with gamblers to throw the 1919 World Series.

On September 28, 1920, Jackson left the Cook County Courthouse after confessing to his role in the plot. As he walked down the steps, surrounded by photographers and newsmen, Jackson was accosted by a ragged little boy who pleaded, "Say it ain't so, Joe!"

But it was so, and Jackson went back to South Carolina in disgrace. He and the seven other "Black Sox" were banished from baseball for life.

The Babe Calls His Shot

BY JOHN THORN

When Babe Ruth hit sixty homers in 1927, he surpassed the old mark of fifty-nine set by — Babe Ruth in 1921. And the mark of fifty-nine topped the previous record of fifty-four, collected by the Bambino in 1920. And the fifty-four shattered the previous pinnacle of twenty-nine, attained by the budding Sultan of Swat in the days when he still pitched enough for the Red Sox to garner eight wins.

But of all the homers he hit during his career, perhaps this was the most miraculous.

No one but the Babe would have been brash enough to try it. No one but the Babe would have gotten away with it. Set against the magnificent backdrop of the 1932 World Series, it provided one of the most dramatic climaxes ever recorded in baseball.

The Chicago fans had been riding the Babe unmercifully on that October 1, 1932. On the field the Cubs themselves, stung by two defeats, were also taking it out on the Babe. The catcalls rose to a crescendo when the hulking spindle-legged Babe stepped to the plate in the top half of the fifth. The score stood at 4–4. There was one out, and the bases were empty.

Charlie Root split the plate with a sizzling beauty — a perfect strike. The Babe beat the ump to the gesture when he raised his right index finger in token of *Strike One!* The rabid crowd howled its glee.

Root wound up again and zipped another pitch down the groove. The Babe didn't wait for the umpire to call this one either. With a grin he raised two index fingers in the air, calling *Strike Two!* on himself. From the stands came an unholy roar of delight.

Ruth stepped out of the batter's box waiting for the hubbub to die down. The clatter only rose to new heights. In anticipation, the fans were tasting the joy of seeing the Mighty Babe, the fabulous Sultan of Swat, strike out. Root proceeded to waste the next two pitches, trying to get the Babe to bite on a bad one.

It was then that Ruth made his immortal gesture of defiance. He lifted his hand and pointed toward the flagpole in deep center field. "That," said the gesture, "is where the next pitch is going to go."

And that is exactly where the ball went. On Root's next pitch the Babe swung from his ankles and sent the ball soaring far into the center-field bleachers. It landed but a few feet to the side of the flagpole.

Stunned, the Chicago fans sat speechless as the grinning Babe cruised triumphantly around the bases.

Willie Mays's Miraculous Catch

When Cleveland first baseman Vic Wertz blasted a long drive to center field during the eighth inning of the World Series opener between the Indians and the New York Giants at the Polo Grounds in New York City on September 29, 1954, all the fans were sure it would mean extra bases and two runs batted in. But Willie Mays, the Giants center fielder, with his back to the plate, hauled the ball in, whirled, and threw to the infield, holding the runners at their bases. Willie's catch is one of the most famous in the history of baseball.

The Bad News

RETOLD BY ALVIN SCHWARTZ

Leon and Todd loved baseball. When they were young, they had played on the town's baseball team. Leon had been the pitcher, and Todd had played second base. Now that they were a lot older, they spent their free time watching baseball games on TV and talking about baseball.

"Do you think they play baseball in heaven?" Leon asked Todd one day.

"That's a good question," said Todd. "The one who gets there first should let the other one know somehow."

As it turned out, Todd got to heaven first, and Leon waited patiently to hear from him. One day Leon found Todd sitting in the living room waiting for him.

Leon was very excited to see him. "What is it like up there?" he asked. "And what about baseball?"

"When it comes to baseball," said Todd, "I have some good news, and I have some bad news. The good news is that we do play baseball in heaven. We have some fine teams. I play second base on my team, just like I used to in the old days. That's the good news."

"What's the bad news?" asked Leon.

"The bad news," said Todd, "is that you are scheduled to pitch tomorrow."

Who's on First?

BY BUD ABBOTT AND LOU COSTELLO

Confused? Bewildered? Just ask "Who's on first?" and maybe someone will straighten you out. This classic comedy routine by Bud Abbott and Lou Costello has inspired a phrase that is now part of our folklore.

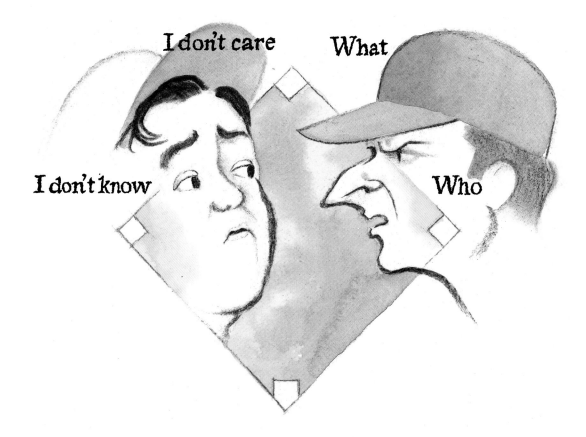

Costello When we get to St. Louis, will you tell me the guys' names on the team so when I go to see them in that St. Louis park I'll be able to know those fellows?

Abbott All right.

Costello I wanta — I wanta find out the fellows' names.

Abbott Strange as it may seem, they give ball players nowadays very peculiar names.

Costello Funny names?

Abbott Nicknames. Nicknames.

Costello Nicknames?

Abbott Oh, yes, yes, yes!

Costello Funny nicknames?

Abbott Oh, absolutely. Yes. Now, on the St. Louis team we have Who's on first, What's on second, I Don't Know is on third —

Costello That's what I want to find out. I want you to tell me the names of the fellows on the St. Louis team.

Abbott I'm telling you. Who's on first,

What's on second, I Don't Know is on third.

Costello You know the fellows' names?

Abbott Yes.

Costello Well, then, who's playing first?

Abbott Yes.

Costello I mean the fellow's name on first.

Abbott Who.

Costello The fellow playin' first base for St. Louis.

Abbott Who.

Costello The guy on first base.

Abbott Who is on first.

Costello Well, what are you askin' *me* for?

Abbott I'm not asking you — I'm telling you. Who is on first.

Costello I'm asking you. Who is on first?

Abbott That's the man's name!

Costello That's whose name?

Abbott Yes.

Costello Well, go ahead and tell me!

Abbott Who.

Costello The guy on first.

Abbott Who.

Costello The first baseman.

Abbott Who is on first.

Costello Have you got a baseman on first?

Abbott Certainly.

Costello Then who's playing first?

Abbott Absolutely.

Costello When you pay off the first baseman every month, who gets the money?

Abbott Every dollar of it. And why not? The man's entitled to it.

Costello Who is?

Abbott Yes.

Costello So who gets it?

Abbott Why shouldn't he? Sometimes his wife comes down and collects it.

Costello Whose wife?

Abbott Yes. After all, the man earns it.

Costello Who does?

Abbott Absolutely.

Costello Well, all I'm trying to find out is what's the guy's name on first base.

Abbott Oh, no, no. What is on second base.

Costello I'm not asking you who's on second.

Abbott Who's on first.

Costello That's what I'm trying to find out.

Abbott Well, don't change the players around.

Costello I'm not changing nobody.

Abbott Now, take it easy.

Costello What's the guy's name on first base?

Abbott What's the guy's name on second base.

Costello I'm not askin' ya who's on second.

Abbott Who's on first.

Costello I don't know.

Abbott He's on third. We're not talking about him.

Costello How could I get on third base?

Abbott You mentioned his name.

Costello If I mentioned the third baseman's name, who did I say is playing third?

Abbott No, Who's playing first.

Costello Stay offa first, will ya?

Abbott Well, what do you want me to do?

Costello Now what's the guy's name on first base?

Abbott What's on second.

Costello I'm not askin' ya who's on second.

Abbott Who's on first.

Costello I don't know.

Abbott He's on third.

Costello There I go back on third again.

Abbott Why?

Costello I don't know. And I don't care.

Abbott What was that?

Costello I said, I don't care.

Abbott Oh, that's our shortstop.

Casey at the Bat: A Ballad of the Republic, Sung in the Year 1888

BY ERNEST LAWRENCE THAYER

The outlook wasn't brilliant for the Mudville nine that day;
The score stood four to two with but one inning more to play.
And then when Cooney died at first, and Barrows did the same,
A sickly silence fell upon the patrons of the game.

A straggling few got up to go in deep despair. The rest
Clung to that hope which springs eternal in the human breast;
They thought if only Casey could get a whack at that —
We'd put up even money now with Casey at the bat.

But Flynn preceded Casey, as did also Jimmy Blake,
And the former was a lulu and the latter was a cake;
So upon that stricken multitude grim melancholy sat,
For there seemed but little chance of Casey's getting to the bat.

But Flynn let drive a single, to the wonderment of all,
And Blake, the much despis-ed, tore the cover off the ball;
And when the dust had lifted, and the men saw what had occurred,
There was Jimmy safe at second and Flynn a-hugging third.

Then from five thousand throats and more there rose a lusty yell;
It rumbled through the valley, it rattled in the dell;
It knocked upon the mountain and recoiled upon the flat,
For Casey, mighty Casey, was advancing to the bat.

There was ease in Casey's manner as he stepped into his place;
There was pride in Casey's bearing and a smile on Casey's face.
And when, responding to the cheers, he lightly doffed his hat,
No stranger in the crowd could doubt 'twas Casey at the bat.

Ten thousand eyes were on him as he rubbed his hands with dirt;
Five thousand tongues applauded when he wiped them on his shirt.
Then while the writhing pitcher ground the ball into his hip,
Defiance gleamed in Casey's eye, a sneer curled Casey's lip.

And now the leather-covered sphere came hurtling through the air,
And Casey stood a-watching it in haughty grandeur there.
Close by the sturdy batsman the ball unheeded sped —
"That ain't my style," said Casey. "Strike one," the umpire said.

From the benches, black with people, there went up a muffled roar,
Like the beating of the storm waves on a stern and distant shore.
"Kill him! Kill the umpire!" shouted someone on the sand;
And it's likely they'd have killed him had not Casey raised his hand.

With a smile of Christian charity great Casey's visage shone;
He stilled the rising tumult; he bade the game go on;
He signaled to the pitcher, and once more the spheroid flew;
But Casey still ignored it, and the umpire said, "Strike two."

"Fraud!" cried the maddened thousands, and echo answered fraud;
But one scornful look from Casey and the audience was awed.
They saw his face grow stern and cold, they saw his muscles strain,
And they knew that Casey wouldn't let that ball go by again.

The sneer is gone from Casey's lip, his teeth are clenched in hate;
He pounds with cruel violence his bat upon the plate.
And now the pitcher holds the ball, and now he let's it go,
And now the air is shattered by the force of Casey's blow.

Oh, somewhere in this favored land the sun is shining bright;
The band is playing somewhere, and somewhere hearts are light,
And somewhere men are laughing, and somewhere children shout;
But there is no joy in Mudville — mighty Casey has struck out.

Ed Young

SCARY, CREEPY, SPOOKY GHOST STORIES

These tales of terror come from every corner
of the United States.

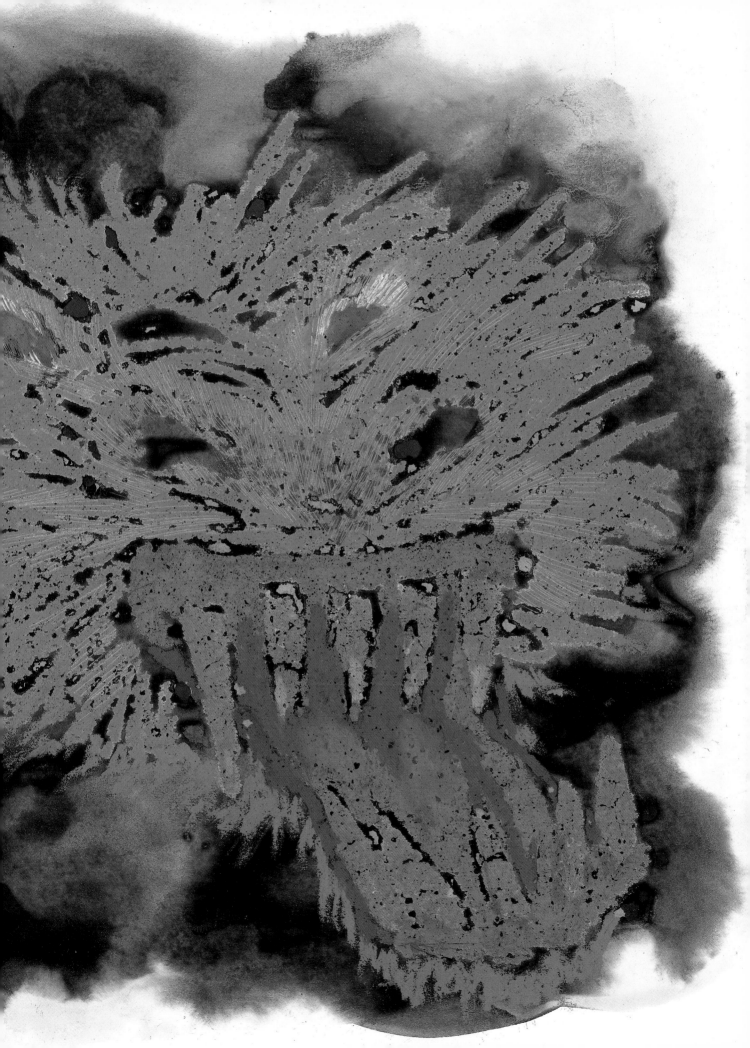

The Ghost of Jean Lafitte

RETOLD BY SUZY SCHMIDT

Deep in the twisted bayous of Barataria Bay a colony of privateers lived surrounded by swamps and creeks filled with snakes and alligators. This was Grande Terre Island, and these were the Baratarians. Their boss was Jean Lafitte. He and his men controlled the waters of the Gulf of Mexico from their hideout in New Orleans. And although he called himself a privateer, Lafitte was no better than a pirate.

Lafitte captured more treasure than any man could use or sell. So he buried it. He stuffed coins into cannons, sealed the barrels, and dumped them overboard. He sank gold in the swamps of Barataria Bay. He hid handfuls of jewels in Galveston. He buried trunks of treasure along the coasts of Louisiana and Texas. Then, he vanished.

People have been searching for his loot ever since.

Some say a ghost guards Lafitte's treasure. Once a soldier riding along the Gulf Shore near LaPorte got caught in a storm and found shelter in a broken-down house. Inside, grand furniture stood covered with cobwebs and sand. The soldier was able to build up a good fire and soon fell asleep despite the wild shrieks of the wind.

In the middle of the night he awoke with a start. Standing over him was a tall man wearing a long, dark cape and a beautiful old-fashioned suit with a brocaded vest and lace cuffs. He motioned to the soldier to follow, and led the way through room after room until the two came to a small cellar hidden away at the back of the house. The man lifted a trapdoor by its heavy iron ring. The soldier gasped, for there, beneath the floor, lay an open chest filled with magnificent jewels and old Spanish doubloons.

"I am the spirit of Jean Lafitte." The trembling soldier shrank from the hollow-voiced apparition. "All this treasure is yours, but only if you do not speak to anyone about it." The trapdoor fell with a bang, and the ghost disappeared.

The stunned soldier groped for the handle of the trapdoor. But he couldn't lift it. In the morning he rode to camp and asked his friends for help.

When they returned to the house, the soldier swiftly led the way to the back room. But there was no trapdoor, and no sign of treasure. There was only the low, wailing moan of the betrayed ghost of Jean Lafitte.

Another time, a woman heard of a place on Grande Terre Island where Lafitte's treasure was supposed to be buried. She didn't want to share the riches with anyone, so she started her search just after midnight on a moonless night. When she had dug about six feet deep, she heard a crowing noise. Out of the hole appeared a rooster surrounded by a puff of smoke. It disappeared instantly.

Next from the hole came a screeching ghost-cat that vanished into thin air. Then a horse trotted right out of the ground. Smoke spewed from its nostrils, and fire leapt out of its eyes and ears.

The woman fled for her life, and Lafitte's treasure stayed where it was. And it's still there for anyone to find — anyone who's not afraid of ghosts.

The Dancing Skeleton

RETOLD BY CYNTHIA C. DeFELICE

Aaron Kelly was dead.
There wasn't anything anybody could do about it.
And, to tell you the truth, nobody much cared.
Aaron had been so downright mean and ornery
in his life that folks were glad to see him go.
Even his widow never shed a tear. She just
bought a coffin, put Aaron in it, and buried him.
Good-bye, Aaron Kelly, and good riddance!
But that very night, Aaron got up out of his grave,
walked through the graveyard, and came home.
His widow was sitting in the parlor, thinking
how peaceful and quiet it was without Aaron
around, when he walked right in the door.
"What's all this?" he shouted. "You're all dressed in
black. You look like somebody died. Who's dead?"
The widow pointed a shaking finger at Aaron.
"You are!" she said.
"Oh, no, I ain't!" hollered Aaron. "I don't feel
dead. I feel fine!"
"Well, you don't look fine," said the widow.
"You look dead! Now you just get yourself
back in that coffin where you belong."
"Oh, no," said Aaron. "I ain't goin' back
to that coffin till I feel dead."
Just plain ornery, he was.
Well, since Aaron wouldn't go back to
the grave, his widow couldn't collect
the life insurance. Without that money,
she couldn't pay for the coffin.
If she didn't pay for the coffin,
the undertaker might take it back.

And if he did that, she'd *never* be rid
of Aaron! Aaron didn't care. He just
sat in his favorite rocking chair,
rocking back and forth, back
and forth, day after day,
night after night. But
after a while, Aaron
began to dry up.
Pretty soon he was
nothing but a skeleton.
Every time he rocked,
his old bones clicked and clacked.
His widow did her best to ignore him, but
it wasn't easy with all the racket he made.
Then one night, the best fiddler in town came to call
on Aaron's widow. He'd heard Aaron was dead, and
he thought he might marry that woman himself.
The fiddler and the widow sat down together,
cozylike, on the bench . . . and ole Aaron
sat right across from them, just a-creakin'
and a-crackin' and a-grinnin'. Fiddler
said, "Woman, how long am I going to
have to put up with that old bag o' bones
sitting there? I can't court you proper
with him staring at me like that!" Widow
answered, "I know! But what can we do?"
The fiddler shrugged. The widow sighed.
The clocked ticked. And Aaron rocked. Finally,
Aaron said, "Well, *this* ain't any fun at all.
Fiddler, take out your fiddle. I feel like dancin'!"
So the fiddler took out his fiddle and he began
to play. My, my! He could make that fiddle sing!
Aaron Kelly heard that sweet music and he couldn't
sit still. He stood up. Oooh, his dry bones felt stiff!
He stretched himself. He shook himself. He cracked
his knucklebones — aaah! And he began to dance.

With his toe bones a-tappin' and his feet bones
a-flappin', round and round he danced like a fool!
With his finger bones a-snappin' and his arm bones
a-clappin', how that dead man did dance!
The music grew wilder, and so did Aaron
until, suddenly, a bone broke loose from
that dancing skeleton, flew through the air,
and landed on the floor with a CLATTER!

"Oh, my!" cried the fiddler. "Look at that!
He's dancing so hard, he's *falling apart!*"
"Well, then," said the widow, *"play faster!"*
The fiddler played faster.
Bones began flying every which way, and still
that skeleton danced!
"Play louder!" cried the widow.
The fiddler hung on to that fiddle. He fiddled
a tune that made the popcorn pop. He fiddled
a tune that made the bedbugs hop. He fiddled
a tune that made the rocks get up and dance!
Crickety-crack, down and back!
Old Aaron went a-hoppin', his dry bones a-poppin'.
Flippin' and floppin', they just kept droppin'!
Soon there was nothing left of Aaron but a pile
of bones lying still on the floor . . . all except for
his old bald head bone, and *that* looked up at the fiddler,
snapped its yellow teeth, and said,
"O O O O O W E E E ! AIN'T WE HAVING FUN!"
It was all too much for the fiddler. He dropped his fiddle,
said, "Woman, I'm getting out of here!" and ran out
the door. The widow gathered up Aaron's bones and
carried them back to the graveyard. She put them
in the coffin and mixed them all around in there,
so Aaron could never put himself back together.
After that, Aaron Kelly stayed in his grave
where he belonged.
But folks say that if you walk by the graveyard
on a still summer night when the crickets are fiddling
their tunes, you'll hear a faint clicking and clacking
down under the ground.
And you'll know . . .
it's Aaron's bones, still trying to dance.
And what about the fiddler and the widow?
Well, they never did get together again.
Aaron Kelly had made DEAD SURE of that!

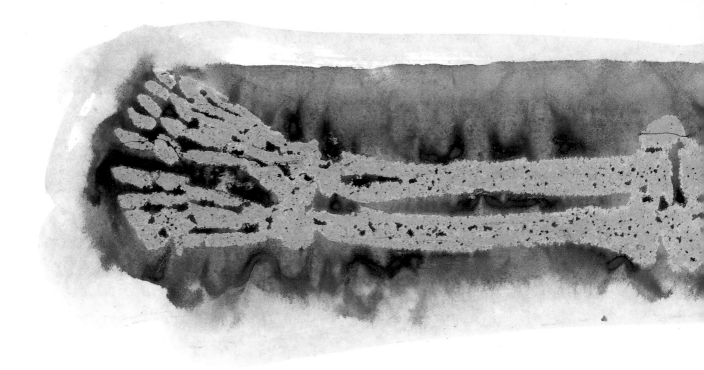

Dry Bones

TRADITIONAL

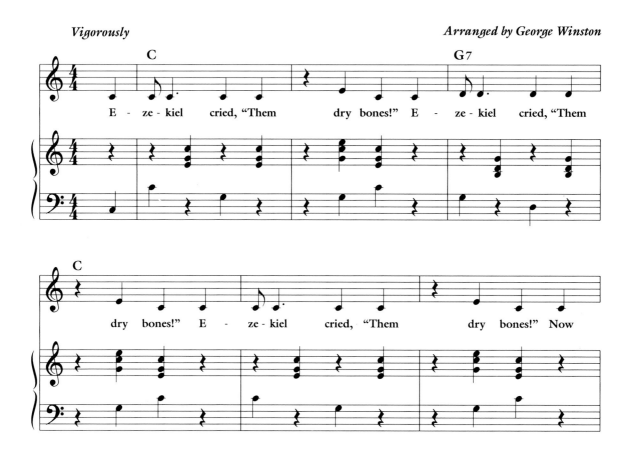

gradually getting faster

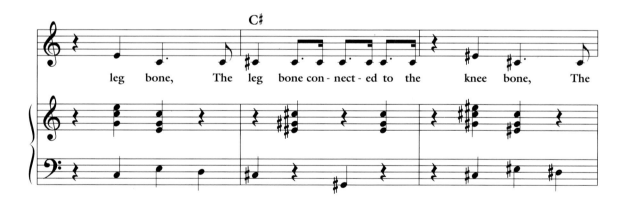

hear the word of the Lord. The foot bone con-nect-ed to the

leg bone, The leg bone con-nect-ed to the knee bone, The

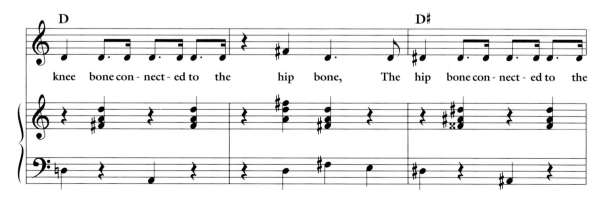

knee bone con-nect-ed to the hip bone, The hip bone con-nect-ed to the

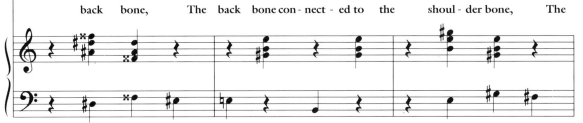

E

back bone, The back bone con-nect-ed to the shoul-der bone, The

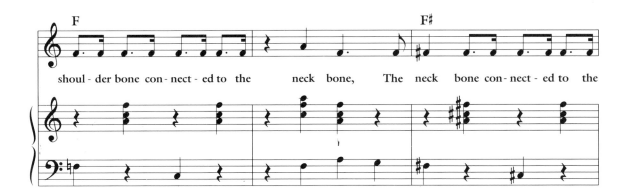

F   F#

shoul-der bone con-nect-ed to the neck bone, The neck bone con-nect-ed to the

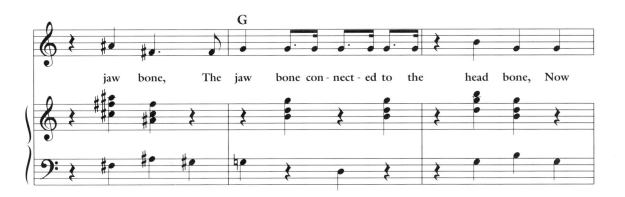

G

jaw bone, The jaw bone con-nect-ed to the head bone, Now

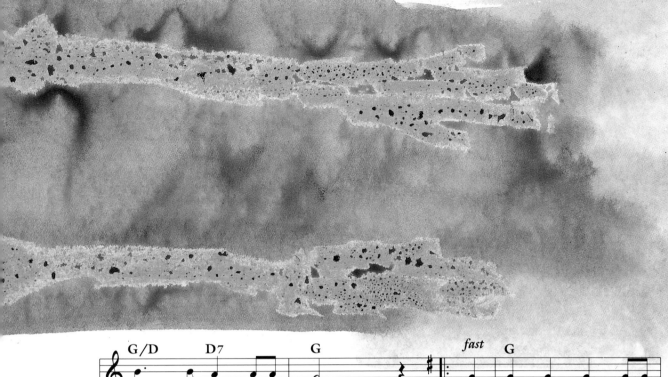

hear   the word   of the   Lord.   *fast*   Them bones, them bones gon - na

walk   a - round, Them   bones, them bones gon - na   walk   a - round, Them

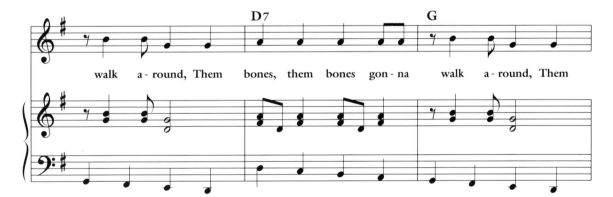

getting slower last time

bones, them bones gon - na   walk a - round, Now   hear   the word of the Lord.

The Ghost of Tom

WORDS AND MUSIC BY MARTHA GRUBB

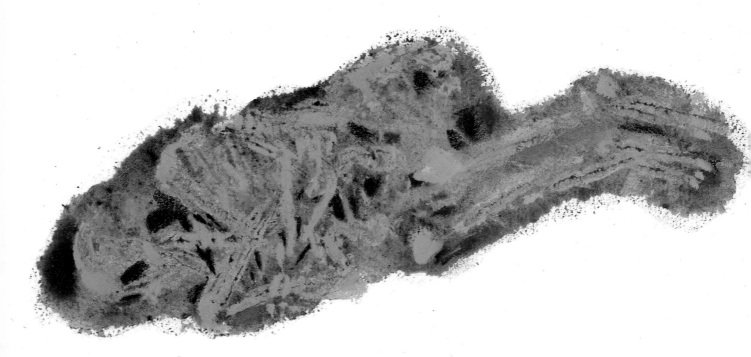

La Llorona, the Weeping Woman

RETOLD BY JOE HAYES

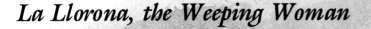

The story begins long ago, when the city we call Santa Fe was a little village called *La Villa Real de la Santa Fé de San Francisco de Asís.* That was a long name for a tiny village. And living in that village was one girl who was far prettier than any other. Her name was María.

People said María was certainly the prettiest girl in New Mexico. She might even be the most beautiful girl in the world. But because María was so beautiful, she thought she was better than everyone else.

María came from a hardworking family, and they had one of the finest homes in Santa Fe. They provided her with pretty clothes to wear. But she was never satisfied. She thought she deserved far better things.

When María became a young woman, she would have nothing to do with the youths from Santa Fe and the nearby village. She was too good for them.

Often as she was walking with her grandmother through the countryside surrounding Santa Fe, she would say to her grandmother, *"Abuelita,* when I get married, I'll marry the most handsome man in New Mexico."

The grandmother would just shake her head. But María would look out across the hillside and go on. "His hair will be as black and shiny as the raven I see sitting on that *piñon* tree. And when he moves, he will be as strong and graceful as the stallion *Abuelito* has in his corral."

"María," the old woman would sigh, "why are you always talking about what a man looks like? If you're going to marry a man, just be sure that he's a good man. Be sure he has a good heart in him. Don't worry so much about his face."

But María would say to herself, "These old people! They have such foolish old ideas. They don't understand."

Well, one day, a man came to Santa Fe who seemed to be just the man María was talking about. His name was Gregorio. He was a cowboy from the *llano*, the plain, east of the mountains.

He could ride anything. In fact, if he was riding a horse and it got well trained, he would give it away and go rope a wild horse. He thought it wasn't manly for him to ride a horse that wasn't half wild.

He was so handsome that all the girls were falling in love with him. He could play the guitar and sing beautifully. María made up her mind. That was the man she would marry.

But she didn't let on. If they passed on the street and Gregorio greeted her, she would look away. He came to her house and played his guitar and sang. She wouldn't even come to the window.

Before long, Gregorio made up *his* mind. "That haughty, proud girl María," he told himself. "That's the girl I'll marry. I can win her heart!" So things turned out just as María had planned.

María's parents didn't like the idea of her marrying Gregorio. "He won't make a good husband," they told her. "He's used to the wild life of the plains. He'll be gone on buffalo hunts and cattle drives, or drinking wine with his friends. Don't marry him."

Of course, María wouldn't listen to her parents. She married Gregorio. And for a time things were fine. They had two children.

But after a few years, Gregorio went back to his old ways. He would be gone for months at a time.

When he returned, he would say to María, "I didn't come to see you. I just want to visit my children." He would play with the children, and go off to the *cantina* to drink and gamble all night long. And he began to court other women.

As proud as María was, she became very jealous of those other women. And she began to feel jealous of her own children, as well, because Gregorio paid attention to them, but ignored her.

One evening, María was standing out in front of her house with her two children beside her when Gregorio came riding by in a hired carriage. Another woman sat on the seat beside him. He stopped and spoke to his children, but didn't even look at María. He just drove up the street.

At the sight of that, something just seemed to burst inside María. She felt such anger and jealousy! And it all turned against her children.

She seized her two children by their arms and dragged them along with her to the river. And she threw her own children into the water.

But as they disappeared with the current, María realized what she had done. She ran along the bank of the river, reaching out her arms, as though she might snatch her children back from the current. But they were long gone.

She ran on, driven by the anger and guilt that filled her heart. She wasn't paying attention to where she was going, and her foot caught on a root. She tripped and fell forward. Her forehead struck a rock. And she was killed.

The next day her parents looked all over town for her. Then someone brought the word that her body lay out on the bank of the river.

They brought María's body back into Santa Fe, but because of what she'd done, the priest wouldn't let her be buried in the *camposanto*, the holy graveyard. "Take her out and bury her on the bank of the river!" he commanded.

So her parents buried her there on the riverbank where she had been found. And many people in Santa Fe say they know exactly where she was buried, because a big building stands there today. It's called the New Mexico State Capitol!

But they also tell that the first night she was in the grave, she wouldn't rest at peace. She was up and walking along the bank of the river. They saw her moving through the trees, dressed in a long, winding white sheet, as a corpse is dressed for burial.

And they heard her crying through the night. Sometimes they thought it was the wind. But at other times they were sure they could hear the words she was saying: "*Aaaaaiii . . . mis hijos. . . . ¿Dónde están mis hijos?*"

"Where are my children?" she cried. She went all up and down the banks of the river, through all the *arroyos* to the base of the mountains and back down.

Night after night they saw her and heard her. Before long, no one spoke of her as María. They called her by a name every boy and girl in New Mexico knows — *La Llorona*, the weeping woman.

And they told the children, "When it gets dark, you get home! *La Llorona* is out looking for her children. She's so crazy, if she sees you, she won't know if it's you or her own child. She'll pick you up and carry you away! We'll never see you again."

The children heed that warning. They may play along the rivers and *arroyos* during the daytime, but when the sun sets, they hurry home!

Many tales are told of children who narrowly escaped being caught by *La Llorona*. One is about a boy who didn't believe she existed.

"Do you believe that nonsense?" he would ask his friends. "That's just a story parents made up to frighten children."

One evening the boys were playing out on the bank of the river, and it began to grow late. "It's getting dark," the other boys said. "We'd better get home."

But not that one boy. "No," he said. "I'm having fun. I'll stay out here a while longer."

The other boys couldn't believe what they were hearing. "Aren't you afraid of *La Llorona*?"

"*La Llorona!*" he laughed. "There's no such thing."

The other boys went home and left that one boy by himself. He had a good time throwing sticks into the river and hitting them with rocks as they floated past. It grew dark. The moon rose.

Suddenly, the boy felt cold all over, as though an icy wind were blowing through his clothes. And all around him there were dogs barking. He looked around and saw a white shape coming toward him through the trees.

He tried to run, but somehow his legs had no strength in them. He couldn't move. He sat there trembling as the shape drew nearer. And he could hear the high, wailing voice, "*Aaaaiiii . . . mis hijoooos . . .*"

Still he couldn't move. He crouched low, hoping she wouldn't see him. But suddenly she stopped. "*Mi 'jo!*" she cried, "my little boy!" And she came toward him.

His face was as white as the sheet that *La Llorona* was wearing! But still he couldn't run. She approached him and reached out her long fingers and took hold of his shoulders. When *La Llorona*'s fingers touched his shoulders, it felt like icicles were cutting into the flesh!

Just then, when *La Llorona* was about to pick him up and carry him away, back in Santa Fe the cathedral bell started ringing, calling the people to Mass. When the church bell started to ring, *La Llorona* looked over her shoulder furtively, dropped the boy, and disappeared into the trees.

The boy sat there for a long time, gathering his strength and courage together. Finally he was able to run home.

When he got home, his mother was furious. "Where have you been?" she demanded. "You should have been home hours ago!"

The boy stuttered and stammered, "M-M-Mamá . . . La Llorona!"

"Nonsense! Don't go making up stories about *La Llorona*. You should have been home a long time ago." She reached out to grab him. She was going to give him a good shaking.

But when she reached out to take hold of his shoulders, she noticed that on each shoulder there were five round, red marks — like five bloodstains. They had been left by *La Llorona*'s fingers!

Then she believed him. She took that shirt and washed it over and over. She tried every trick she knew. But she could never remove those stains.

She carried that shirt all around the neighborhood and showed it to the children. "Look here," she said. "You count these — one . . . two . . . three . . . four . . . five! Those stains were left by *La Llorona*'s fingers. *La Llorona can* carry children away. When it gets dark, you get home!"

And you can be sure that the children in that neighborhood got home when it got dark. But no one seems to know what became of the shirt, so who can say if the story is true?

Skin and Bones

TRADITIONAL

Deadpan and eerie   *Arranged by Marshall W. Barron*

pp

There was an old wom-an all

skin and bones, oo-oo-oo!____ She

lived down by the old grave-yard, oo-oo-oo!____ One
walked down by the old grave-yard, oo-oo-oo!____ She

Em   CMaj7   Em   Bm Am   Em

night   she thought she'd   take   a   walk,   oo - oo - oo!_____   She
saw   the   bones   a - lying   a - round,   oo - oo - oo!_____   She

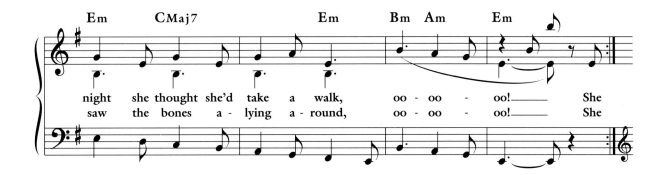

(Melody in left hand)

Em   7   A/G   C   Bm   Am

went   to   the   clos - et   to   get   a   broom,   oo - oo -

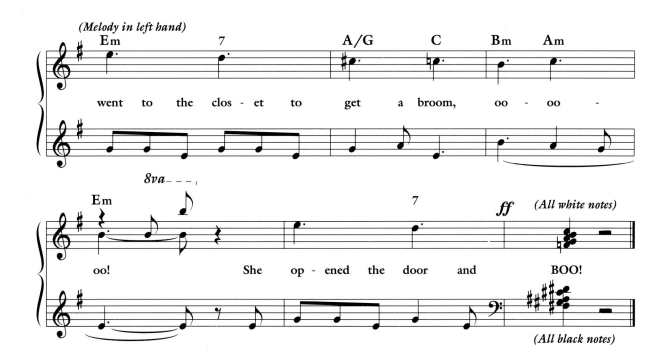

8va- - -

Em   7   **ff**   *(All white notes)*

oo!   She   op - ened   the   door   and   BOO!

(All black notes)

The Peculiar Such Thing

RETOLD BY VIRGINIA HAMILTON

A long time ago way off in the high piney woods lived a fellow all alone. He lived in a one-room log cabin. There was a big old fireplace, and that is where this fellow cooked his supper to eat it right in front of the fire.

One night, after the fellow had cooked and ate his supper, somethin crept through the cracks of the cabin logs. That somethin was the most peculiar such thing the fellow ever saw. And it had a *great, big, long tail.*

As soon as the fellow saw that somethin with its *great, big, long tail,* he reached for his axe. With a swoopin strike with it, he cut the somethin's tail clean off. The peculiar such thing crept away through the cracks between the logs, and was gone.

This fellow, like he had no sense, he cooked the *great, big, long tail.* Yes, he did. It tasted sweet and he ate it. Goodness! And then he went to bed, and in a little while he went off to sleep.

The fellow hadn't been asleep very long before he woke right up again. He heard somethin climbin up the side of his cabin. It sounded mighty like a cat. He could hear it scratchin and tearin away. And pretty soon he heard it say, *"Tailypo, tailypo. Give me back my tailypo."*

Now the fellow livin there all alone did have some dogs. Big one was Best, and the other two slight ones was All Right and Fair. And when that fellow heard somethin, he called his dogs, "Yuh! Dawgs! Come on!" like that. And his dogs come flyin out from under the cabin. And they chased the peculiar such thing away down a far piece. Then this fellow went on back to bed. He went to sleep.

It was deep in the middle of the next night when the fellow woke up. He heard somethin by his front door tryin to get in. He listened hard, and he could hear it scratchin and tearin away. And he heard it say, *"Tailypo, tailypo. Give me back my tailypo."*

Fellow sat up in his bed. He called his dogs, "Yuh! You, Best, you, All Right, you, Fair, come on in!" like that. And the dogs busted around the corner. And they caught up with the peculiar such thing at the gate, and they about broke they own tails tryin to catch it. This time they chased what it was down into the big hollow there. And the fellow, well, he went back to bed and went to sleep.

It was way long toward mornin, the fellow woke up and he hears somethin down in the big swamp. He had to listen. He heard it say, *"You know you got it. I know you know. Give me back my tailypo."*

That man sat up in bed. He called his dogs, "You, Best, you, All Right, and you, Fair. Yuh! Come on in here!"

Well, this time, the dogs never come. The thing down there in the hollow musta carried them off in there. It musta eaten the first one, says, *"That's best."* It eaten the other two, says, *"That ain't but all right and fair."*

And the fellow went back to bed. Don't see how he could sleep again. But he didn't know how bad off his dogs was by then.

Well, it was just daybreak. The fellow was awake. Scared, he didn't know why. Musta heard somethin. Somethin right there with him in the room. It sounded like a cat climbin up the covers at the foot of his bed. He listened. He could hear it, scratchin and tearin away.

The fellow look at the foot of his bed. He's seein two little pointy ears comin up over the edge of the bed. In another minute, he's seein two big, scary-red eyeballs lookin straight at him. He can't say nothin. He can't scream, he's too scared to death.

That peculiar such thing at the foot of the bed kept on creepin up, creepin up. By and by, it was right on top of the fellow. And it said in his face in a real low voice, *"Tailypo, tailypo. Give me back my tailypo."*

That man loses his voice, loses his power of speech. But finally, he can say it. Says, "I hasn't got it. I hasn't got your tailypo!"

And that somethin that was there, that peculiar such thing, says right back, *"Yes, you has!"* It jumped on that fellow and it was fierce. Its big teeth tore at him, made him ribbons. They say it got its tailypo back.

Fellow's cabin fall to ruin. It rot. It crumble and it disappear. Nothin left to it in the big woods but the place where it was.

And the folks that live near that place say that deep in the night, when the moon is goin down and the wind blows across the place just right, you can hear some peculiar such thing callin, *"Tailypo, tailypo . . ."* like that. And then, the sound of it do just fade away with the moonlight. Like it never even ever was.

Things That Go Bump in the Night

BY KATHRYN WINDHAM

Kathryn Windham, of Selma, Alabama, collects ghost stories. The stories she collects are true. They are told to her by the people to whom they happened, or by the friends and relatives and descendants of those to whom they happened. She also collects advice, the kind of age-old advice that comes in especially handy on dark and stormy nights.

"Put your shoes under the edge of the bed, with one toe pointing under the bed and one pointing the other way, and nothing bad will ever happen to you," she says.

"Sprinkle a line of salt all around your house, and no evil will ever enter. But, remember, it must be *plain* salt and not iodized salt.

"Make a bottle tree. Hang empty glass bottles of any kind on a low tree or shrub. Blue ones work best, though they're hard to find.

"Or take three mistletoe seeds and place them over the door facing. No evil will ever enter your home.

"Those are all pretty effective," says Ms. Windham, "but you can also carry a buckeye ball (the seed of the buckeye bush). It'll bring you good luck and protect you from evil, of course.

"Now, you can also keep witches out if you put a flour sifter at your front door at night. The witches will not come in. They have a phobia about counting things and they would have to count every hole in that sifter before they could enter your home. By the time they'd finish counting, it would be daylight and they'd have to go away.

"A little pile of sand works, too. The witches would have to count every grain before they could come in.

"Or try placing two crossed brooms outside your door. The witches would have to count the straws, and crosses always protect you."

The Woman with the Golden Arm

RETOLD BY MARK TWAIN

Once upon a time, a-way long ago, there was a man and his wife that lived all alone in a house out in the middle of a big lonesome prairie. There wasn't anybody or any house or any trees for miles and miles and miles around. The woman had an arm that was gold — just pure solid gold from the shoulder all the way down.

Well, by and by, one night, she died. It was in the middle of the winter, and the wind was a-blowing, and the snow was a-drifting, and the sleet was a-driving, and it was awful dark; but the man had to bury her; so he took her, and took a lantern, and went away off across the prairie and dug a grave; but when he was just going to put her in, he thought he would steal her golden arm, for he judged it couldn't ever be found out, and he was a powerful mean man.

So then he cut it off, and buried her, and started back home. And he stumbled along, and plowed along, and the snow and the sleet swashed in his face so he had to turn his head to one side, and could hardly get along at all; and the wind it kept a-crying, and a-wailing, and a-mourning, way off across the prairie, back there where the grave was, just so: *B-z-z-z-z-z-z.* It seemed to him like it was a ghost crying and worrying about some trouble or an-

other, and it made his hair stand up, and he was all trembling and shivering. The wind kept on going *B-z-z-z-z-z-z,* and all of a sudden he caught his breath and stood still, and leaned his ear to listen.

B-z-z-z-z-z-z goes the wind, but right along in the midst of that sound he hears some words, so faint and so far away off he can hardly make them out. *"W-h-e-r-e-'s*

342

m-y g-o-l-d-e-n a-a-a-arm? W-h-o's g-o-t m-y g-o-l-d-e-n a-a-a-arm?"

Down drops the lantern; and out it goes, and there he is, in that wide lonesome prairie, in the pitch-dark and the storm. He started along again, but he could hardly pull one foot after the other; and all the way the wind was a-crying, and the snow a-blowing, and the voice a-wailing, *"W-h-e-r-e's m-y*

g-o-l-d-e-n a-a-a-arm? W-h-o's g-o-t m-y g-o-l-d-e-n a-a-a-arm?"

At last he got home; and he locked the door, and bolted it, and chained it with a big log chain and put the chairs and things against it; and then he crept upstairs, and got into bed, and covered up his head and ears, and lay there a-shivering and a-listening.

The wind it kept a-going *B-z-z-z-z,* and there was that voice again — away, *ever* so far away, out in the prairie. But it was a-coming — it was a-coming. Every time it said the words it was closer than it was before. By and by it was as close as the pasture; next it was as close as the branch; next it was this side of the branch and right by the corncrib; next it was to the smokehouse; then it was right at the stile; then right in the yard; then it passed the ash hopper and was right at the door — right at the very door!

"W-h-e-r-e's m-y g-o-l-d-e-n a-a-a-arm?" The man shook, and shook, and shivered. He don't hear the chain rattle, he don't hear the bolt break, he don't hear the door move — still next minute he hear something coming *p-a-t, p-a-t, p-a-t,* just as slow, and just as soft, up the stairs. It's right at the door, now: *"W-h-e-r-e's m-y g-o-l-d-e-n a-a-a-arm?"*

Next it's right in the room: *"W-h-o's g-o-t m-y g-o-l-d-e-n a-a-a-arm?"*

Then it's right up against the bed — then it's a-leaning down over the bed — then it's down right against his ear and a-whispering soft, so soft and dreadful: *"W-h-e-r-e's m-y g-o-l-d-e-n a-a-a-arm? W-h-o's g-o-t m-y g-o-l-d-e-n a-a-a-arm?"*

"YOU GOT IT!"

Part 4

❧

IN OUR TIME

Folklore is being made even in our own
time. The events of our century will inspire
the stories our grandchildren will tell and
the songs they will sing in the years
to come.

❧

CHAPTER OPENING ILLUSTRATED BY JERRY PINKNEY

IN OUR TIME

Molly Bang

Marcia Brown

Barbara Cooney

Donald Crews

Leo and Diane Dillon

Richard Egielski

Trina Schart Hyman

Anita Lobel

Jerry Pinkney

John Schoenherr

Marc Simont

David Wiesner

Ed Young

The New Colossus

BY EMMA LAZARUS

ILLUSTRATED BY MARCIA BROWN

When the people of France gave the United States the Statue of Liberty to celebrate the centennial of the young nation, they gave a gift that has come to symbolize America the world over.

Not like the brazen giant of Greek fame,
With conquering limbs astride from land to land,
Here at our sea-washed, sunset gates shall stand
A mighty woman with a torch, whose flame
Is the imprisoned lightning, and her name
Mother of Exiles. From her beacon-hand
Glows world-wide welcome; her mild eyes command
The air-bridged harbor that twin cities frame.
"Keep ancient lands, your storied pomp!" cries she
With silent lips. "Give me your tired, your poor,
Your huddled masses yearning to breathe free,
The wretched refuse of your teeming shore.
Send these, the homeless, tempest-tost to me.
I lift my lamp beside the golden door!"

America! America!

BY WILLIAM JAY JACOBS
ILLUSTRATED BY ANITA LOBEL

Between 1890 and 1920 more than twenty million people immigrated to America. Most of them set foot on American soil for the first time on a tiny island in New York Harbor called Ellis Island, which housed the largest and busiest immigration center in the world.

March 27, 1907. A ship bringing newcomers to America steams slowly into New York Harbor.

People spill out onto the ship's deck.

Looming before them stands the Statue of Liberty. In her hand she holds high the torch of freedom.

Some passengers burst into tears at the sight. Some freeze in complete silence, as if in prayer. Others sing happily in the language of their own country.

At last they are in America.

For three weeks they were wedged together in the steerage area, the ship's bottom deck. Sometimes during the journey the first-class passengers stood above and looked at them, amused. They tossed down coins or oranges or nuts. Then they laughed to see the poor people scrambling for the prizes.

Some in steerage brought their own food. For others, there was nothing but black bread, boiled potatoes, watery soup. Many never left their bunks, even to go out onto their small deck.

The air inside was foul-smelling. There were few toilets for the more than nine hundred people in steerage. Nobody had been able to take a bath. Many were seasick from the steady rolling of the ship.

In the excitement of arriving in America, all of that is forgotten.

To the left of their boat, near the Statue of Liberty, they see the redbrick buildings of Ellis Island. It is there, they know, that they will be taken. They will be examined by doctors. They will be questioned. And they will be told whether they can stay in America. Having come so far, there is the fear — almost terror — that they still may have to leave.

On this day, March 27, 1907, 16,050 newcomers arrive. It is the greatest number for any one day in America's history. Before the year is over, more than a million will pass through the doors of Ellis Island.

In front of the castlelike main building of Ellis Island, guards quickly hustle the newcomers into line. Trudging beneath a large overhead canopy of heavy canvas, they enter a large hall.

Inside, they are greeted with a wave of sound. People speak in a babble of many languages, flailing their arms, shaking their fists. There is laughter, crying, screaming. Everywhere there is confusion.

The noise continues as they drop their bundles and baggage on the floor of the Baggage Room.

Then, once again, guards begin to shout and push them. This time they are prodded like cattle up a flight of steep stairs in twos and threes.

At the top they find themselves in the Great Hall of Ellis Island. It is a huge room, fifty-six feet high, with enormous arched windows. A large American flag is draped from a balcony overhead.

"Hurry up! Hurry up! This way!" demand the guards, leading them single file between rows of metal railings. At the end of each railing waits a doctor in the blue uniform of the United States Public Health Service.

The doctors examine each person. Through an interpreter they ask questions. They want to know whether the newcomer is deaf. They want to see how alert he may be. They look for skin rashes, infections, hernias.

In their hands, the doctors carry pieces of colored chalk. They mark letters on the coats of some newcomers: H for a heart problem, X for a possible mental defect, L for lameness.

An especially dreaded time is the eye examination. Doctors roll back people's eyelids with a small instrument. They are looking for a contagious eye disease called trachoma. Even if there is only a suspicion of eye disease, an E, for eyes, is marked on the front of a person's coat.

Those with chalk marks on their coats are separated from the others and put in wired-off areas called pens. There, other doctors examine them. People with certain diseases are sent back to their homelands on the next boat. No one who has typhoid fever, smallpox, or leprosy may be admitted.

A child of eight or nine may be found to have a disease. When that happens, the family must make a decision. Will everyone return with the child, or will just one adult go? It is a heartbreaking decision to have to make — and there is little time to think about it.

A child who is ten or older may be sent back alone, without an adult. But will such a child be able to make his way home alone from some port city in Europe?

For those who pass the medical examination, there is still one final test. Inspectors must ask each person a list of questions. Name? Married? Occupation? Ever been in prison? How will you earn a living in the United States? How much money do you have with you? Is anyone meeting you?

Most newcomers pass through Ellis Island in about four hours. About two out of every ten need more questioning or a longer medical exam. Only two of every one hundred are sent back home.

When they have passed inspection, they go to the Money Exchange. There they trade the currency of their home country for American dollars.

Next, those who are going to places outside of New York City go to the Railroad Room. After buying their railway tickets, they are ferried over on river barges to railroad terminals in New York or New Jersey.

Those who will stay in New York City simply walk down a corridor to a door marked PUSH. TO NEW YORK. Often on the other side of the door they see happy relatives and friends waiting for them behind a wire screen.

Now is the time to celebrate. The newcomers are free people in a free land. They are becoming "Americans."

Tramp Talk

BY AMY L. COHN

Just a few short years after many immigrants arrived in America from Europe, the Great Depression crippled the United States economy. Millions of people were out of work. Without the safety nets that exist today — unemployment insurance and Social Security — many found themselves without the money to maintain their homes. From New York to Oklahoma, from Boston to Burbank, thousands took to the road.

Many homeless men of that era were called hoboes. These men crisscrossed the country on freight trains, jumping on slow-moving freights when railroad guards were off duty or had their backs turned. And wherever they got off, they looked for work and food before moving on again.

Hoboes left secret messages for each other to help out one another and provide essential information. They wrote these messages in a special kind of picture writing, something like Egyptian hieroglyphs. The pictures, or hobo signs, said things like "You will get good food here" or "Stay away from this town!"

Hoboes left these messages, usually written in chalk or crayon, where others would find them — on a kitchen door, maybe, or on a sidewalk, fence, or wall.

It wasn't until the outbreak of the Second World War in 1941 that the Depression really ended. But that era lives on in our history books, in the memories of those who lived through it, and in these signs, which have become part of our nation's folklore.

The people here will take care of you if you are sick.

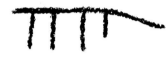

Police watching. This is a hostile town.

Train nearby.

Dangerous dog here.

These people give handouts to hoboes.

Doctor here will treat you for free.

Beware! Man who lives here owns a gun.

Handcuffs! If caught here you will be sent to jail.

A nice lady lives here.

Big Rock Candy Mountain

TRADITIONAL

ILLUSTRATED BY RICHARD EGIELSKI

Many hoboes congregated for fellowship and safety in "hobo jungles," encampments near railroad crossings in rural areas. This was their unofficial anthem.

Brightly

Arranged by Billy Joe Lafayette

1. In the Big Rock Can - dy Moun - tain There's a land that's fair and bright, Where the
2. In the Big Rock Can - dy Moun - tain All the cows have wood - en legs, And the

hand - outs grow on bush - es, And you sleep out ev - 'ry night; Where the
bull - dogs all are tooth - less, And the hens lay soft - boiled eggs, All the

box - cars all are emp - ty, And the sun shines ev - 'ry day. Oh, I'm
trees are full of ap - ples, And the barns are full of hay, There's a

bound to go where there is - n't an - y snow, Where the rain does - n't fall and the
lake of stew and — so - da pop, — too, You can pad - dle all a - round in a

Chorus

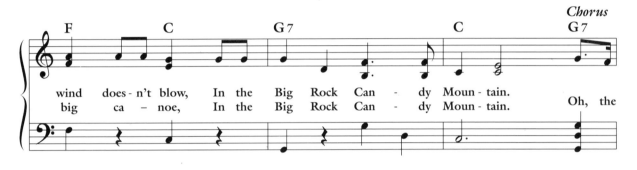

wind does-n't blow, In the Big Rock Can - dy Moun - tain.
big ca - noe, In the Big Rock Can - dy Moun - tain. Oh, the

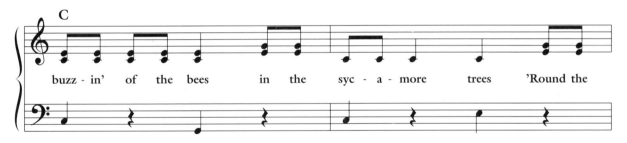

buzz - in' of the bees in the syc - a - more trees 'Round the

so - da wa - ter foun - tain, Where the lem - on - ade springs and the

blue - bird sings in the Big Rock Can - dy Moun - tain.

Gee, Mom, I Want to Go Home

ADAPTATION BY OSCAR BRAND
ILLUSTRATED BY BARBARA COONEY

When the United States entered the Second World War in December 1941, the country harnessed every ounce of its energy to defeat the fascist Axis Powers — Germany, Italy, and Japan. Unemployment vanished as the nation's factories and shipyards were swiftly retooled to produce planes, tanks, ships, and weapons. Millions of women went to work outside of the home for the first time, taking jobs usually held by the men now serving in the armed forces. And, at the same time the United States experienced this incredible industrial surge, the country mobilized the biggest military force in history. At peak strength, more than fifteen million men and women served in the armed forces. Here's one of their favorite songs.

Lively

Arranged by Douglas Townsend

They tell you in the Ar-my, The cof-fee's might-y fine; It's good for cuts and bruis-es, It

Chorus

tastes like tur - pen - tine.   I   don't want no more of Ar - my

life;   Gee, Mom,   I   want to go   home.

1. - 3.   4.

2. The biscuits that they give us,
   They say are mighty fine;
   Well, one fell off the table,
   And crushed a pal of mine.

   Chorus

3. The clothing that they give us,
   They say is mighty fine;
   Me and half my regiment
   Can all fit into mine.

   Chorus

4. The salary they pay us,
   They say is mighty fine;
   They pay you fifty dollars,
   And they take back sixty-nine.

   Chorus

A Shameful Chapter

BY BARBARA ROGASKY

ILLUSTRATED BY DAVID WIESNER

While America waged war to defend freedom abroad, at home our nation quietly stripped thousands of its residents and citizens of their freedom — simply because they were Japanese.

O n December 7, 1941, Japanese planes bombed the Pearl Harbor Naval Base in the Hawaiian Islands and destroyed most of the U.S. Pacific fleet. In a few days America was at war with Japan and her allies, Germany and Italy.

The lives of most people with German and Italian backgrounds who lived in America did not change much because of the war. The Japanese were not so lucky.

Nearly all 120,000 Japanese living on the West Coast spent the war years locked up behind barbed wire and under armed guard. Two thirds of them were American citizens.

The real reason seems simple. German Americans and Italian Americans were Caucasian. They were white. But the Japanese were not. That was enough to suspect each and every one of being a spy.

Racism against the Japanese had a long history here. The *Issei*, those born in Japan but living in the United States, were not allowed to own land. Nor were they ever permitted to become American citizens, no matter how long they lived here. They, and their American-born children, called *Nisei,* were stoned in the streets. Many restaurants refused to serve them, barbers would not cut their hair, homeowners would not sell or rent to them. Hand-painted signs announced JAPS KEEP MOVING — THIS IS A WHITE MAN'S NEIGHBORHOOD.

When the war started, rumors flew. Japanese were said to be radioing war planes about to bomb the coast. Japanese farmers burning brush were accused of lighting "arrows of fire," directing enemy aircraft to important targets. Japanese even were blamed for sabotaging power lines that were actually broken by cows scratching their backs on poles.

No evidence of spying or sabotage was ever found, then or at any time during the war. Yet, on February 19, 1942, President Franklin Roosevelt signed Executive Order 9066. It allowed the army to call sections of the country "military areas." Any person or group could be kept out of those areas if the army thought it necessary.

The West Coast was already officially a war zone. Lieutenant General John L. DeWitt, chief of the Western Defense Command, issued the first "Civilian Exclusion Orders." He intended to move out anyone he believed threatened the region's security. Soon all people of Japanese ancestry were forced to leave their homes.

The Japanese were given as little as one week's notice. They had to leave everything behind and sell what they could for whatever they could get. They were cheated in countless ways — by those who paid twenty-five dollars for a new car and three hundred dollars for a house, and by the U.S. Government, which promised to protect Japanese property but used it or disposed of it without offering compensation of any kind. The government promised to keep cars owned by the Japanese until the end of the war, and then took them for its own use without paying a penny.

No one told the Japanese where they were going. Loaded onto trains and buses, they were taken to "assembly centers." These were sometimes stockyards or stables, stinking and dirty. Each family was given a table, a chair, cots, and mattresses and straw to stuff them with. Everyone was kept under armed guard at all times.

In a few months the Japanese were moved again — this time to Camp Jerome in Arkansas, Camp Manzanar in the California desert, Camp Poston in Arizona, and to seven more camps miles from the West Coast. These were terrible places. It could get as hot as 120 degrees and as cold as below zero. The wind- and sandstorms were severe.

The Japanese found unfinished wooden barracks at the camps. Each barrack was divided into four or six rooms. Here, each family was given one twenty-by-twenty foot space, which contained a potbellied stove, one bare bulb hanging from the ceiling, cots, and blankets. That was all.

These places were called internment camps. They were really prisons. The Japanese were fenced in, the gates were locked, and they were watched twenty-four hours a day. According to American law, people may not be arrested and imprisoned unless there is some evidence of a crime. They are then considered innocent until proven guilty by a judge or jury using the evidence as proof. Then — and only then — may a resident or citizen be sentenced to a period of time under lock and key. The Japanese were denied these rights. The American government had broken its own law.

Ironically, in February 1943, the *Nisei* were allowed to be drafted into the army. Many eventually formed the 442nd Regimental Combat team. By the end of the war in Europe, this group of thirty-three thousand men had won more military honors than any other unit in the entire U.S. armed forces. Their families remained imprisoned.

The Japanese began to be released from the camps in January 1945. The war ended for good in August 1945, but the last internment camp was not closed until March 1946.

Gradually, several groups and individuals began pressuring the government to admit that it had violated the Constitution by interning the Japanese. In 1983, a government committee published a report called *Personal Justice Denied*. It admitted that the law had been broken and called for the government to apologize and make some payment to the Japanese who had been forced into camps.

Five years later, the government agreed. It would pay twenty thousand dollars to each person from the camps who was still alive. Every payment would come with a letter of apology from the president. By then, it was forty-six years after the camps had opened, and half of the original 120,000 had died.

The first payments were made on October 9, 1990. A personal letter of apology from President George Bush came with each check.

But are the money and the apology enough? No apology or payment can make what happened less wrong. Only one thing can begin to right this shameful chapter in our history. *We must remember it*. Because nothing like it must ever happen again.

Blowin' in the Wind

WORDS AND MUSIC BY BOB DYLAN
ILLUSTRATED BY LEO AND DIANE DILLON

This anthem of the antiwar and civil rights movement of the 1960s has become as familiar to Americans as any folk song.

Steadily

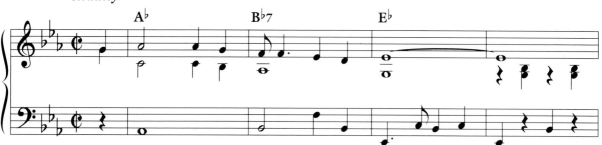

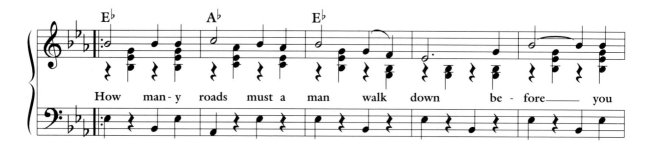

How man-y roads must a man walk down be-fore_____ you

call him a man?_____ Yes, 'n' How man-y seas must a

white dove sail be-fore_____ she sleeps in the sand? Yes, 'n'

2. How many times must a man look up
   before he can see the sky?
   Yes, 'n'
   How many ears must one man have
   before he can hear people cry?
   Yes, 'n'
   How many deaths will it take 'til he knows
   that too many people have died?

   Chorus

3. How many years can a mountain exist
   before it's washed to the sea?
   Yes, 'n'
   How many years can some people exist
   before they're allowed to be free?
   Yes, 'n'
   How many times can a man turn his head
   pretending he just doesn't see?

   Chorus

I Have a Dream

BY MARTIN LUTHER KING, JR.

ILLUSTRATED BY TRINA SCHART HYMAN

When we celebrate Martin Luther King Day every January, we celebrate the life of the great civil rights leader who believed that all Americans are equal, regardless of race, color, or creed, and must be given an equal opportunity to realize their dreams.

I say to you today, my friends, that in spite of the difficulties and frustrations of the moment, I still have a dream. It is a dream deeply rooted in the American dream. I have a dream that one day this nation will rise up and live out the true meaning of its creed: "We hold these truths to be self-evident — that all men are created equal." I have a dream that one day on the red hills of Georgia the sons of former slaves and the sons of former slave owners will be able to sit down together at the table of brotherhood. I have a dream that one day even the state of Mississippi, a desert state sweltering with the heat of injustice and oppression, will be transformed into an oasis of freedom and justice. I have a dream that my four little children will one day live in a nation where they will not be judged by the color of their skin but by the content of their character.

I have a dream today.

I have a dream that one day the state of Alabama, whose governor's lips are presently dripping with the words of interposition and nullification, will be transformed into a situation where little black boys and black girls will be able to join hands with little white boys and white girls and walk together as sisters and brothers.

I have a *dream* today.

I have a dream that one day every valley shall be exalted, every hill and mountain shall be made low, the rough places will be made plains, and the crooked places will be made straight, and the glory of the Lord shall be revealed, and all flesh shall see it together.

This is our hope. This is the faith I shall return to the South with. With this faith we will be able to hew out of the mountain of despair a stone of hope. With this faith we will be able to transform the jangling discords of our nation into a beautiful symphony of brotherhood. With this faith we will be able to work together, pray together, struggle together, go to jail together, stand up for freedom together, knowing that we will be free one day.

This will be the day when all of God's children will be able to sing with new meaning "My country 'tis of thee, sweet land of liberty, of thee I sing. Land where

my fathers died, land of the pilgrim's pride, from every mountainside, let freedom ring."

And if America is to be a great nation this must become true. So let freedom ring from the prodigious hilltops of New Hampshire. Let freedom ring from the mighty mountains of New York. Let freedom ring from the heightening Alleghenies of Pennsylvania. . . . But not only that; let freedom ring from Stone Mountain of Georgia. Let freedom ring from Lookout Mountain of Tennessee. Let freedom ring from every hill and molehill of Mississippi. From every mountaintop, let freedom ring.

When we let freedom ring, when we let it ring from every village and every hamlet, from every state and every city, we will be able to speed up that day when all of God's children, black men and white men, Jews and Gentiles, Protestants and Catholics, will be able to join hands and sing in the words of the old Negro spiritual, "Free at last! Free at last! Thank God almighty, we are free at last!"

In the early part of the twentieth century, most of the immigrants who came to America to find a new and better life were from different parts of Europe. But since 1960, most are from diverse places around the globe — the Caribbean, Asia, and the Near East. And when these immigrants come, they bring favorite stories with them.

El Gallo de Bodas: The Rooster on the Way to the Wedding

RETOLD BY LUCÍA M. GONZÁLEZ
ILLUSTRATED BY MOLLY BANG

This is one of the oldest and best-known stories in all Cuban folklore, one as familiar to Cuban-American children as Goldilocks and the Three Bears.

There was once a bossy little rooster, *un gallito mandón*, who was on his way to the wedding of his uncle the parrot, *su tío el perico*. He looked very elegant and clean. As he walked along, he spotted two kernels of corn, so shiny and gold, very near a puddle of mud. The little *gallito* stopped and thought:

> If I eat
> *¿Pico o no pico?*

I'll dirty my beak
> *Si pico me ensucio el pico*
and I won't be able to go
> *y no podré ir*
to the wedding of my Tío Perico
> *a la boda de mi Tío Perico.*

But he could not resist, ate the corn, and dirtied his beak.

Just then he saw the grass to the side of the road. He went to the grass and ordered:

> "Grass, clean my *pico*
> so that I can go
> to the wedding of my Tío Perico!"

But the grass said: "I will not."

The little *gallito* then saw a goat and he ordered:

> "Goat, eat the grass
> who won't clean my *pico*
> so that I can go
> to the wedding of my Tío Perico!"

But the goat, who didn't like to be bossed around, said: "I will not."

The little *gallito* went to a stick and said:

"Stick, hit the goat
 who won't eat the grass
 who won't clean my *pico*
 so that I can go
 to the wedding of my Tío Perico!"

But the stick said: "I will not."

Then the little *gallito* saw a fire burning in the nearby bushes, and he told the fire:

"Fire, burn the stick
 who won't hit the goat
 who won't eat the grass
 who won't clean my *pico*
 so that I can go
 to the wedding of my Tío Perico!"

But the fire said: "I will not."

Then the little *gallito* went to the river and told the water:

"Water, quench the fire
 who won't burn the stick
 who won't hit the goat
 who won't eat the grass
 who won't clean my *pico*
 so that I can go
 to the wedding of my Tío Perico!"

But the water said: "I will not."

Then the little *gallito* looked at his friend the Sun — *el Sol* — and said:

"*Sol,* dry the water
 who won't quench the fire
 who won't burn the stick
 who won't hit the goat
 who won't eat the grass
 who won't clean my *pico*
 so that I can go
 to the wedding of my Tío Perico!"

And the Sun said: "With pleasure, my friend! *¡Con gran placer!*"

The water, who had heard the Sun's reply, said: "Pardon me, but I will quench the fire."

And the fire said: "Pardon me, I will burn the stick."

And the stick said: "Pardon me, I will hit the goat."

And the goat said: "Pardon me, I will eat the grass."

And the grass said: "Pardon me, I will clean your *pico*."

And so it did.

The little *gallito* thanked his good friend *el Sol* with a long *¡QUI-QUI-RI-QUÍ!* — COCK-A-DOODLE-DOO! — and rushed the rest of the way to get to the wedding on time.

Bye-Bye

COLLECTED BY DIANE WOLKSTEIN
ILLUSTRATED BY DONALD CREWS

Diane Wolkstein first heard this tale in Haiti from a girl of about nineteen named Michelle, who worked as a seamstress.

All the birds were flying from Haiti to New York. But Turtle could not go, for he had no wings.

Pigeon felt sorry for Turtle and said, "Turtle, I'll take you with me. This is what we'll do. I'll hold in my mouth one end of a piece of wood and you hold on to the other end. But you must not let go. No matter what happens, do not let go or you'll fall into the water."

Pigeon took one end of a piece of wood and Turtle the other end. Up into the air Pigeon flew and Turtle with him, across the land and toward the sea.

As they came near the ocean, Turtle and Pigeon saw on the shore a group of animals who had gathered together to wave good-bye to the birds who were leaving. They were waving steadily until they noticed Turtle and Pigeon. Turtle? They stopped waving and a great hubbub broke out.

"Look!" they cried to each other. "Turtle is going to New York. Even Turtle is going to New York!"

And Turtle was so pleased to hear everyone talking about him that he called out the one English word he knew:

"Bye-bye!"

Uh-oh. Turtle had opened his mouth, and in opening his mouth to speak, he let go of the piece of wood and fell into the sea.

For that reason there are many pigeons in New York, but Turtle is still in Haiti.

The Raven and the Star Fruit Tree

**RETOLD BY TRAN VAN DIEN
AND WINABELLE GRITTER
ILLUSTRATED BY JOHN SCHOENHERR**

This is one of the most beloved of all Vietnamese folktales, one that has traveled with Vietnamese immigrants to their new home in America.

Once upon a time, there was a very rich man who lived in a village. When he died, he left his two sons a huge fortune.

But the two brothers were entirely different. The elder was greedy, but the younger was very kind. The elder claimed all the fortune and left his younger brother only a star fruit tree, a *cay khe*. The younger brother took good care of his *cay khe*. He watered it every day and hoped it would give him a lot of fruit, so he could make a living by selling it.

The elder brother, on the other hand, had nothing to worry about.

Unfortunately for the younger brother, when the fruit was ripe, a raven, a *con qua*, flew by and stopped in the tree to eat it. The younger brother was very sad to see this happen day after day, but he did not know what to do. So one day, he stood beneath the tree and spoke to the *con qua*.

"*Con qua*, please don't eat my fruit," he called. "This *cay khe* is my only fortune. If you eat all the fruit, my family will starve."

"Don't worry," the *con qua* answered. "I'll pay you back in gold. Make yourself a bag two feet long to keep the gold in."

Hearing those words, he was very excited and told his wife to make the bag. The next day, the *con qua* came as he had promised. He landed by the gate, let the younger brother sit on his back, and took off for a place filled with gold. There, the younger brother filled the bag with gold. Then he flew back home on the back of the *con qua*.

And, so, he became very rich. But he still loved and respected his elder brother.

One day he told his wife to prepare a good meal for his brother and his family. But when he invited his brother, the latter refused to come at first. The brother only accepted after his younger brother had begged him again and again. When the elder brother arrived at the house, he was surprised to see it all changed. It was no

longer the poor house that he had seen before. He asked his younger brother the reason. The latter told him everything that happened. After he heard it all, the elder brother offered to trade all his fortune for the *cay khe*. The kind brother gladly agreed.

The *con qua* came as usual. The greedy brother spoke to the *con qua* the same words as his brother, and received the same answer. But he was so greedy that he got a bag much larger than the two-foot one.

The next day, the *con qua* came to take the elder brother to the place of gold. After he had filled the bag, he filled all his pockets, too, before he climbed onto the back of the *con qua* to go home. But the load was so heavy that when they flew over the sea, the *con qua* spread his tired wings and dropped the elder brother off into the sea.

His wife and younger brother waited and waited, but did not see him come back. So they decided to ask the *con qua* and, from him, they learned the truth.

This Land Is Your Land

WORDS AND MUSIC BY WOODY GUTHRIE
ILLUSTRATED BY MARC SIMONT

Confidently

Arranged by James Rooker

Chorus: This land is your land. This land is my land. From Cal - i-
1. As I was walk - ing that rib - bon of high - way, I saw a-

for - nia to the New York is - land; From the red - wood for - est
bove me that end - less sky - way. I saw be - low me

to the Gulf Stream wa - ters; This land was made for you and me.
that gol - den val - ley, This land was made for you and me.

2. I've roamed and rambled and I followed my
   footsteps
   To the sparkling sands of her diamond deserts,
   And all around me a voice was sounding,
   "This land was made for you and me."

   Chorus

3. When the sun comes shining and I was strolling
   And the wheat fields waving and the dust clouds
   rolling,
   As the fog was lifting a voice was chanting,
   "This land was made for you and me."

   Chorus

Earth
  always
  endures.

— MANDAN AND HIDATSA INDIANS

ILLUSTRATED BY ED YOUNG

A Note to Readers

~

The notes and comments that follow provide additional historical and cultural information about the selections in *From Sea to Shining Sea*. They also provide information about the literary or musical background of a selection. Some notes include suggestions to help tell a story or sing a song more effectively. Some, or all, of the following also appear: ethnic origin, geographic region, and the term generally used to classify the type of story or song.

At the end of each chapter is a section called Read More About It. Combine the books listed in these sections, the Suggestions for Further Reading, and the sources cited in the Acknowledgments to gain a broad range of references. Ask a librarian, storyteller, teacher, or bookseller for more information.

Glossary of Terms

~

Ballad   A song that tells a story, often about an actual event.

Call and Response   Singing that involves both a leader and a chorus. The chorus responds after the leader sings. "Shanties" (see Shanty) are an example of call-and-response singing.

Cante (CAHN-teh) Fable   A story that features a repeated refrain or song.

Folktale   A story told by the average person rather than created by a published author. Folktales often feature talking animals, superhuman men and women, and unexpected, unexplainable, or outrageous incidents.

Hand Clap   A chant used in conjunction with specific hand motions or clapping rhythms.

Hymn   A song praising a sacred being.

Jump Tale or Jump Song   A story or song that builds up to a climactic moment to make listeners jump in surprise.

Legend   A story that may or may not be true, told about a person who actually lived.

Lullaby   A soothing song to help children sleep.

Myth   A story rooted in a set of spiritual beliefs to help explain natural events such as thunder or the existence of the stars.

Narrative Poem   A poem that tells a story, written by a known author.

Nonsense Song   A song that uses meaningless sounds in place of actual words, or a song about a silly subject.

Noodlehead Tale   A story about a fool or numskull.

Occupational Tale   A tall tale about work and workers.

Popular Song   A song written by either a known composer or lyricist, or both.

Pourquoi (pour-KWAH) Story   *Pourquoi* is the French word for "why." This kind of story, told to entertain, usually features a talking animal character, a very specific setting, a trickster element, humor, and a clear conclusion describing why a species of animal or a type of person behaves in a certain way.

Prayer   A poem, song, or statement offered to a god or gods in thanks or to make a request.

Riddle   A tricky question often posed in a verse.

Shanty   A traditional song sung aboard ships to keep time while sailors performed tasks. A leader, called a shantyman, sang the verses, and the entire crew joined in on the chorus. Some spell shanty *chantey* to reflect the French verb *chanter*, to sing.

Spiritual   A song incorporating religious themes to express hope. It is most closely associated with the slaves of African descent who lived in the United States in the time before the Civil War.

Tall Tale   An imaginative, humorous story filled with exaggeration, told with a straight face as if true, and often called a windy, a stretcher, or a whopper. Short tall tales are called tall talk.

Trickster Tale   A story in which one character tricks another, using his or her wits instead of his or her fists, often acting out of self-protection.

Work Song   Any song developed to accompany a specific task.

NOTES ABOUT THE BOOK

✦

PART 1   IN THE BEGINNING

IN THE BEGINNING

These Native-American myths explain how the land that came to be called North America and its dwellers were created.

The Creation (Iroquois; Central New York State; Myth). Iroquois isn't the name of one tribe but the collective name used for six tribes — the Cayuga, the Seneca, the Onondaga, the Oneida, the Mohawk, and the Tuscarora — that united in a loose federation to stop intertribal warfare. The turtle is sacred to the Iroquois. It represents the earth and the special relationship between the Iroquois and the land.

Raven Brings Fresh Water (Regional Tribes of the Pacific Northwest, Including the Haida, the Kwakiutl, the Tlinglit, and the Tsimshian; Alaska, Washington State, and British Columbia; Myth). Raven is the hero of many tales of the Indians of the Pacific Northwest. He can act like a rascal, tricking others for his own amusement. But sometimes he helps humans, as he does in this story.

Grandmother Spider Steals the Sun (Cherokee; Northern Georgia, Western North Carolina, and Eastern Tennessee, Later Oklahoma; Myth). Grandmother Spider's journey had far better results than an actual journey taken by the Cherokee during the early nineteenth century. When European settlers came to the United States, their way of life clashed with that of the people who already lived here. This conflict led to the systematic removal of the Cherokee from their ancestral lands. In 1785, the Cherokee nation signed a treaty with the young American government that guaranteed its independence. But when Andrew Jackson became president in 1828, he allowed settlers to move into Cherokee territory. Then, in 1835, he ordered government troops to uproot sixteen hundred Cherokee and relocate them west to land set aside for Indians in present-day Oklahoma. Five hundred Cherokee lost their lives during this forced march, which came to be called "The Trail of Tears."

Dream Song (Chippewa; Upper Midwest). The Chippewa, or Ojibwa, lived west of the Great Lakes, in the area we now call Wisconsin, Minnesota, and Michigan. The Chippewa didn't farm. Instead, they traveled in large bands to gather wild plants, especially wild rice, and to hunt and fish.

Coyote Helps Decorate the Night (Hopi; Arizona and New Mexico; Myth). Coyote, like Raven, is a mischief maker and a helper. It seems natural for Coyote to be a hero to American Indian groups in the western United States since this intelligent animal was once common there.

Sedna, the Sea Goddess (Native Alaskans and Arctic-Circle Dwellers; from Alaska East to Greenland; Myth). Sedna's story is the most important of all myths told by the Arctic dwellers. It describes how the animals that supplied people with food and materials for clothing and shelter were created.

Song for Smooth Waters (Haida; Queen Charlotte Island, British Columbia; Prayer). Those who braved the sea in small, fragile boats appealed to the mercy of the gods for protection.

The Gods Made Man (Navajo; New Mexico and Arizona; Myth). Traditional Navajo beliefs state that human beings originated underground and were led to the earth's surface by gods, who fashioned them from materials common to their region.

Song of Happiness (Navajo Inspired; Arizona and New Mexico). Navajo people often dance as they sing. The strong beat of "Song of Happiness" lends itself to that custom.

READ MORE ABOUT IT

Bierhorst, John, editor. *In the Trail of the Wind: American Indian Poems and Ritual Orations.* New York: Farrar, Straus & Giroux, Inc., 1971.
Bierhorst, John. *The Mythology of North America.* Illustrated with maps. New York: William Morrow & Co., Inc., 1985.
Caduto, Michael, and Joseph Bruchac. *Keepers of the Earth.* Golden, Colorado: Fulcrum, Inc., 1988.

PART 2   FROM SEA TO SHINING SEA

COMING TO AMERICA

In the three hundred years following the first of Christopher Columbus's four voyages to what came to be called the New World, many different groups from Europe and Africa came to North America to begin new lives or seek their fortunes. Some came freely. Others came against their wills.

The Mezcla Man (Spanish/Mexican American; Texas; Legend). From approximately 1500 to 1850, Spain, and later Mexico, controlled much of North America from Florida in the east to California in the west, from Texas in the south to Wyoming in the north. Although this legend was probably told first at the end of this period, if not later, the story reflects Spanish culture and institutions.

The Other 1492 (Historical Essay). Although the author implies that the first Jews came to the Americas in the seventeenth century, it is believed that the very first European to step on the soil of the New World was Luis De Torres, a Jew who sailed with Columbus in 1492 as the expedition's interpreter.

The Debate in Sign Language (Traditional Jewish Tale; Contemporary Retelling; Trickster Tale/Noodlehead Tale). For thousands of years, Jews have been forced to leave their countries. Tales similar to "The Debate in Sign Language" have been found in texts dating from the tenth century.

The First Thanksgiving (New England; Contemporary Retelling Based on Primary Source Documents). Samoset and Massasoit, guests at the First Thanksgiving, were Wampanoag. Although the Wampanoag and the settlers lived in peace for fifty years, war broke out between them in 1676. Massasoit's son, Metacom, known as King Philip because he wore European clothes, joined with his Indian neighbors to stop the expanding settlements and destruction of the land. King Philip's War was a disaster for the Wampanoag. Many were killed; many were captured; many became slaves, an ironic and tragic fate for the descendants of those whose skills and cooperation made the survival of the first European settlers in New England possible.

Simple Gifts (Shaker; Primarily New York State and New England; Hymn). The Shakers, a Christian sect, were founded by Ann Lee. She emigrated from England to America in 1774. Shakers did not believe in private property or traditional family life and used dance and music in their religious services. "Simple Gifts," first heard around 1848, was such a song. Adapted from an English folk song, the tune was later incorporated by the twentieth-century U.S. composer Aaron Copland in his *Appalachian Spring*.

Sarasponda (Dutch; Colonial New York State; Work Song). In 1626, Peter Minuet, governor of New Amsterdam, the Dutch colony in North America, bought Manhattan Island with a handful of beads and baubles from the local Indian people who had no concept of the private ownership of land. The Dutch settled most of the region that became New York City and established towns along the Hudson River north to the present-day city of Albany and beyond. Dutch colonial women sang "Sarasponda" at their spinning wheels. The nonsense words imitate the sounds of spinning and alleviated the tedium of operating the spinning wheel. The "boom da's" supplied the steady rhythm necessary to keep the wheel moving efficiently.

AFRICAN RHYTHMS IN AMERICA: **Juba This and Juba That; Hambone** (African American/Gullah; Coast and Offshore Islands in South Carolina, Georgia, and North Florida; Hand Claps). Both "Juba" and "Hambone" were chanted and sung in the Gullah region, where a unique culture flourished. When Africans were brought to the remote region, they had little contact with those living in the rest of the American South. As a result, much of their indigenous culture and language was preserved. The term *Gullah* refers both to the people and to the language many of them speak — a mixture of seventeenth-century English and African dialects. The clapping patterns of "Juba" appear in many playground games; the last portion of the "Hambone" clap, or pat, is familiar to some as the southern folk song "Frog Went a-Courtin'." Here's how to do the pats:

Juba This and Juba That

L: Slap your left thigh with your left hand.
LB: Raise your left hand, and slap the back of it with your right hand.
L: Slap your left thigh with your left hand.
R: Slap your right thigh with your right hand.
RB: Raise your right hand, and slap the back of it with your left hand.
R: Slap your right thigh with your right hand.

Now fit the pat to the verse.

L LB L R   RB R L   LB L R RB   R L LB L
Ju-ba this and Ju- ba that and Ju-ba killed a yel-low cat

R   RB R L LB L R RB   R L LB L R RB R etc.
And get o- ver doub-le troub- le Ju-ba

"Juba" can be performed both by yourself and in a group, with one person leading the chanting and the other person — or people — patting along as fast as they can.

Hambone

1. Slap the side of your thigh with the palm of your hand in an upward brushing motion.
2. Continuing the upward brushing, strike your side or your chest with the palm of your hand.
3. Strike your thigh downward with the back of your hand.
4. Do this series twice, then slap your thigh three times.

Now fit the pat to the verse. First chant each line and then follow with the "Hambone" pat. Remember to repeat it after each line of the rhyme, and while you're chanting the rhyme, lightly pat your thigh on the second of every two beats.

Three Pennsylvania Dutch Riddles (Amish; Pennsylvania; Riddles). The Amish, known as Pennsylvania Dutch, don't speak Dutch at all but a dialect of German. When asking these riddles, try to pronounce the *w*'s as *v*'s for a more authentic sound.

Why Alligator Hates Dog (Cajun; Louisiana; Pourquoi Story/ Trickster Tale). Because the Cajun people once lived in a relatively isolated area in Canada called Acadie, they speak a form of French that more closely resembles the kind spoken in seventeenth-century France than that spoken in France today. Cajun French was also influenced by others who lived in southwest Louisiana in the eighteenth century, including Spanish-speaking people from the Caribbean, Native Americans (especially the Choctaw), and African Americans.

'Tit Galop pour Mamou (Louisiana). Cajun music blends musical styles from many cultures, including the Native American, Scots, Irish, Spanish, German, English, Creole, Caribbean, and French. Cajun musicians play three main instruments: accordion, 'teefer (a small triangle), and fiddle.

READ MORE ABOUT IT

Fritz, Jean. *Who's That Stepping on Plymouth Rock?* Illustrated by J. B. Handelsman. New York: Putnam & Grosset, 1975.
Irving, Washington. *Rip Van Winkle.* Illustrated by N. C. Wyeth. New York: Books of Wonder/William Morrow & Co., Inc., 1987.
O'Dell, Scott. *The King's Fifth.* Illustrated by Samuel Bryant. Boston: Houghton Mifflin Co., 1966.

THE SHOT HEARD 'ROUND THE WORLD

The title of this chapter is from Ralph Waldo Emerson's poem "Concord Hymn," which commemorates the Battles of Lexington and Concord fought at the beginning of the American Revolution. This "shot" inspired people elsewhere to overthrow tyrants and form democratically elected governments.

Revolutionary Tea (New England; Ballad). "Taxation without representation is tyranny!" was one of the battle cries of the American Revolution. The tea tax described here symbolizes the conflict between England and the thirteen American colonies.

Paul Revere's Ride. Longfellow's description of events of April 18 and 19, 1775, is exciting and dramatic. But it is not quite accurate. Paul Revere was a member of the Sons of Liberty, which harassed the British Army in Boston and kept a close eye on all its activities. On the night of April 18, 1775, the British prepared to march from Boston to Concord to destroy a cache of weapons and ammunition stockpiled there by the colonists. Revere rowed across the Mystic River to Charlestown where William Dawes and Dr. Samuel Prescott waited with horses so that all three could gallop to Concord and warn the militia. Revere arrived in Lexington but was captured before he reached Concord. Dawes was thrown from his horse and captured. Prescott did reach Concord and sounded the alarm. In the battle that followed, 273 British regulars and 93 colonists died.

Yankee Doodle (New England; Popular Song). This well-known song has a colorful beginning. In 1756, men from the Connecticut Colony were asked to form a brigade to fight alongside the British in the French and Indian War. When the recruits arrived at Brigade Commander Thomas Fitch's home in Norwalk, the colonel's sixteen-year-old sister and a group of young women gathered feathers for the soldiers from the family's chicken yard. According to legend, Elizabeth Fitch insisted that each man put a feather in his hat band. When the Connecticut cavalry swung into British headquarters, it is said that Dr. Richard Shuckburgh exclaimed, "Why, stab my vitals, they're macaronis!" (People of that time used the word *macaroni* to describe someone who dressed outlandishly while trying to look fashionable). Shuckburgh began to sing a little jingle he made up on the spot, set to the tune of an English folk song. Twenty years later, the Continental Army made "Yankee Doodle" its theme song. A musical cousin of "Yankee Doodle" called "Doodle Dandy" appears below.

Brightly

Doo - dle, doo - dle, doo - dle dan - dy, corn-stalks, rum, and home - made bran - dy, In - dian pud - ding and a pump-kin pie, and that - 'll make the Yan - kees fly, and ev - 'ry Yan - kee will have on his back a great big pump-kin in a sack, a lit - tle mo - las - ses and a piece of pork, and a - way we'll march straight for New York.

The Tory's Conversion (Pennsylvania; Legend). In England during the time of the American Revolution, the Conservative Party, whose members were nicknamed "Tories," was loyal to King George III and supported his policies in North America. Tory was also the term derisively used for colonists who aided the British during the Revolutionary War. The army encampment described is the one at Valley Forge, Pennsylvania, where the Continental forces spent the freezing winter of 1777–1778.

Johnny Has Gone for a Soldier (Irish American; New England; Ballad). Music historians believe this song was first sung in Ireland in 1691 when young men left home for a war in Europe. In America, the lyrics changed to express the feelings of women who watched their men leave home to fight in the Revolution. This melodic lament is especially powerful when sung without instrumental accompaniment.

Clever Mistress Murray (New York City; Legend). Mistress Murray and her daughters probably detained General Howe, Commander of British troops, in August 1776. Howe had won the Battle of Long Island, and was chasing General Washington's army. Washington's men escaped unscathed, thanks to these quick-thinking women.

Jennie Jenkins (Colonial America; Nonsense Song). Children will enjoy improvising new lyrics to this song. They can name as many colors as they know and create other rhyming couplets to sing.

Concord Hymn. Ralph Waldo Emerson was among the most famous nineteenth-century essayists and poets. He lived most of his life in Concord, Massachusetts, site of the Battle of Con-

cord. The "embattled farmers" were the Minutemen, farmer-soldiers ready to drop their plows and pick up their weapons at a moment's notice.

READ MORE ABOUT IT

Collier, Christopher, and James Lincoln Collier. *My Brother Sam Is Dead.* New York: Four Winds Press, 1984.
Fritz, Jean. *Early Thunder.* Illustrated by Lynd Ward. New York: Coward McCann, 1967.
McGovern, Ann. *The Secret Soldier: The Story of Deborah Sampson.* New York: Scholastic Inc., 1990.

BRIDGING THE GAP

Appalachia is a small region consisting of pieces of Kentucky, Tennessee, North Carolina, South Carolina, Virginia, and West Virginia. People from Great Britain and America moved to the area in increasing numbers after the end of the Revolutionary War. Because the region was difficult to reach, people lived in relative isolation and developed a rich folk tradition filled with unique stories, songs, and turns of phrase.

The Wilderness Road. This brief excerpt from a book about Nancy Hanks, mother of Abraham Lincoln, describes the road pioneers in the late eighteenth and early nineteenth centuries traveled to go beyond the mountains to a place they hoped would have rich farmland and provide bountiful hunting, fishing, and trapping.

Cumberland Gap (Appalachia; Comic Ballad). Contemporary country music has its roots in songs like this. Shout out the "Hey!" in the middle of the song, just as a cowboy would shout "Yee-ha!"

Bewildered Boone (Appalachia; Legend/Tall Tale). Daniel Boone and Davy Crockett (see below) are known now as frontiersmen, rugged individuals who lived by their own rules and called themselves "ring-tailed roarers" and "half-horse/half-alligator" to show how tough they were. Daniel Boone defied the British ban against settling the lands beyond the southern Appalachian Mountains. In the 1770s, he led others through the Cumberland Gap from Pennsylvania. By 1815, so many had moved that three new states were formed: Tennessee, Ohio, and Kentucky.

Strong but Quirky: The Birth of Davy Crockett (Tennessee; Legend/Tall Tale). Davy Crockett's action-packed life ended in 1836 when he died at the Alamo in San Antonio, Texas, during the war for Texas's independence. Crockett's exploits were made famous in a series of almanacs that were published between 1835 and 1856.

Ol' Dan Tucker (Popular Song). Daniel Emmett spent a long career as a songwriter for the popular minstrel shows of the nineteenth century. Minstrel shows were comedy-variety revues in which whites performed in black makeup — blackface — to appear as though they were people of color. This practice was accepted in its day but is now considered demeaning and insulting. Emmett also composed "Dixie," the unofficial anthem adopted by the Confederacy. Ironically, he was from Ohio.

Jack and the Two-Bullet Hunt (Appalachia and the Ozarks; Tall Tale). Stories about an easygoing hero named Jack have been told for generations in both Appalachia and the Ozark region. Jack is a regular, ordinary fellow to whom extraordinary things happen, and he is certainly related folklorically to the Jack in the English tale "Jack and the Beanstalk." Like his English cousin, American Jack knows how to turn unexpected events to his advantage.

Groundhog (Appalachia; Comic Ballad). In addition to being a realistic account of groundhog (or woodchuck) hunting, this is also a clogging tune. Irish in origin, clogging is a dance style enjoyed in Appalachia. Cloggers wear heavy wooden shoes, or clogs, as they jig in time to music. Clog along to "Groundhog" by stamping your feet on the offbeat as you sing.

Gol' in the Chimley (Appalachia and the Ozarks; Cante Fable). Many stories share similar motifs or characteristics with other stories. One of the motifs that appears in "Gol' in the Chimley" concerns the bad sister and the good sister. The bad sister treats those who might help her with scorn and derision and is eventually punished. The good sister responds to each request graciously and is rewarded. Stories featuring this same motif include "The Talking Eggs" (Creole); "Mufaro's Beautiful Daughters" (Zimbabwe); "Mother Hulda" (Germany); and "Little Sister and the Month Brothers" (Russia).

Hush, Little Baby (Appalachia; Lullaby). Parents everywhere lull their youngsters to sleep with repetitive, dreamlike songs. "Hush, Little Baby" contains a series of generous promises to reward the child who settles into sleep.

READ MORE ABOUT IT

Chase, Richard. *Grandfather Tales*. Boston: Houghton Mifflin Co., 1973.
Chase, Richard. *Jack Tales*. Boston: Houghton Mifflin Co., 1943.
Rylant, Cynthia. *Appalachia: The Voices of Sleeping Birds*. Illustrated by Barry Moser. San Diego: Harcourt Brace Jovanovich Inc., 1991.

WATER, WATER EVERYWHERE

Long before railroad tracks and superhighways crossed the nation, people traveled and traded on oceans, rivers, lakes, and canals. Those who worked along these waterways developed their own folklore.

Blow, Ye Winds, in the Morning (New England; Capstan Shanty). A capstan, or windlass, is a hauling or lifting machine consisting of a drum or cylinder wound with a rope and turned by a crank. As a sailing ship left the harbor and headed for open sea, the men sang capstan shanties as they used that device to hoist and secure, or set, the sails for efficient travel. "Blow, Ye Winds" refers to the New Bedford, Massachusetts, area, home port in the mid-nineteenth century for half the U.S. whaling fleet.

With a Way, Hey, Mister Stormalong (New England; Occupational Tale). Because the soil was poor and difficult to farm, many New Englanders turned to the sea for a living. Fishing, trading, whaling, and shipbuilding were important industries. Stormalong, the legendary hero of the men who worked on or around merchant ships, shares characteristics, such as his size and the unknown place of his burial, with other tall-tale heroes.

The Sailor's Alphabet (New England; Shanty/Forecastle Song). A ship's forecastle (pronounced "fo'c'sle" or FOK sul) is located forward, or aft, below deck. Goods could be stored there, but more frequently sailors lived there. Forecastle songs like "The Sailor's Alphabet" (presented here as a poem) were sung for entertainment and relaxation. Many groups of workers, such as miners and lumberjacks, crafted alphabet songs specific to their own industries.

Blow, Boys, Blow (New England; Halyard Shanty). Halyard shanties have strong beats at precise intervals to help sailors with jobs requiring cooperative efforts such as pulling on the halyards, or lines, to raise a sail.

The Salem Ghost Ship (Massachusetts; Legend). Wherever there are ships and sailors, there are tales of phantom, or ghost, ships that mysteriously appear and vanish. Many such tales were told around Salem, Massachusetts, one of the nation's busiest ports in the early decades of the nineteenth century.

Clinton's Ditch: Digging the Erie Canal (Historical Essay). The task of building the 363-mile-long Erie Canal fell, in large part, to Irish immigrants. Accustomed to working for a dime per day in Ireland, many eagerly accepted a wage of fifty cents per day plus "found" — room and board.

The Erie Canal (New York State; Work Song). Mules pulled the boats and barges that traveled the canal. Led by mule drivers, the beasts walked along a towpath, tied to the vessels they hauled with long ropes. Many of the bridges spanning the canal were quite low. When the drivers sang out, "Low bridge, everybody down!" passengers had better duck quickly or risk injury.

Sally Ann Thunder Ann Whirlwind Crockett Meets Mike Fink, Snappin' Turkle (Mississippi River Region; Tall Tale). History tells us that Davy Crockett married twice — first to Polly Finley in 1806 and then, following her death, to Elizabeth Patton. But storytellers insist Crockett married only once, to Sally Ann Thunder Ann Whirlwind. He won Whirlwind in a contest when he "danced her down." After dancing all night to at least two hundred fiddle tunes, Crockett was the only suitor standing after Sally Ann collapsed with exhaustion. (Some say she would have married him anyway.)

Steamboats on the Mississippi: Sounding Calls. Traders on all river routes before the age of steam faced the same problem: How to return home? Floating downstream with the current was easy enough. Fighting the current to go upstream depended on the strength of a person's back and arms or the vagaries of the wind. In the early nineteenth century, inventor Robert Fulton used a steam engine to power a boat. It was so successful that soon steamboats regularly traveled the nation's rivers, including the Mississippi. But the Mississippi twisted and turned. Underwater obstacles littered its great length. Steamboat pilots learned to "sound" or measure the river to be sure they had enough "draw" or depth to continue.

As a young man, Samuel Clemens trained to be a steamboat pilot and chose his pen name from the sounding call for safe water: "Mark Twain." For a vivid description of sounding on the Mississippi, read Chapter XII, "Sounding," in Mark Twain's memoir *Life on the Mississippi*.

Shenandoah (Missouri River Region; River Shanty). Although most shanties are associated with oceangoing vessels, "Shenandoah" is a river shanty, originally sung aboard boats plying inland waterways. "Shenandoah" has many meanings. One of the most beautiful is the translation from the Algonquian: "daughter of the stars."

READ MORE ABOUT IT

Avi. *The True Confessions of Charlotte Doyle*. Illustrated by Ruth E. Murray. New York: Orchard Books, 1990.
Latham, Jean L. *Carry On, Mr. Bowditch*. Illustrated by John O. Cosgrove. Boston: Houghton Mifflin Co., 1955.
Twain, Mark. *The Adventures of Huckleberry Finn*. New York: Scholastic Inc., 1987, paperback; and various editions.

LET MY PEOPLE GO

In 1619, a group of Africans was brought by European traders to the Virginia colony of Jamestown to work as slaves. Two hundred forty-four years later, President Abraham Lincoln signed the Emancipation Proclamation, which freed all Africans held in bondage in the United States. In the long years that separate these two events, black Africans in America endured misery and hardship, captured forever in memory and in these stories and songs, which express the omnipresent longing of the enslaved to be free.

Go Down, Moses (African American; American South; Spiritual). Because slave owners converted enslaved Africans to Christianity, slaves began to use Biblical imagery in songs and stories. Here, they compare their plight to that of the ancient Hebrews held in bondage in pharoah's Egypt.

How the Slaves Helped Each Other (African American; American South; Family Story). Because slaves were not permitted to learn to read and write, much of the history of Africans in this country was passed down from generation to generation through stories families told.

I Got Shoes (African American; American South; Spiritual). In slavery, few adults had shoes; for many, shoes became a symbol of freedom.

High John the Conqueror (African American; American South; Legend). Some say High John the Conqueror, or High John de Conquer, was a real person who came to America with the first Africans. Others say he was a supernatural being who came later, flying across the ocean when he heard about the misery his black brothers and sisters endured. Zora Neale Hurston, noted folklorist, wrote: "High John de Conquer came to be a man, and a mighty man at that. But he was not a natural man in the beginning. First off, he was a whisper, a will to hope, a wish to find something worthy of laughter and song. Then the whisper put on flesh. His footsteps wandered across the world in a low but musical rhythm as if the world he walked on was a singing drum. The black folks had an irresistible impulse to laugh. High John de Conquer was a man in full, and had come to live and work on the plantations, and all the slave folks knew him in the flesh." (From Hughes, Langston, and Arna Bontemps, editors, *The Book of Negro Folklore*, New York: Dodd, Mead, 1966, page 93.)

Long John (African American; American South; Call and Response). Songs like "Long John" helped workers to mark time on jobs that required rhythmic, physical movements.

The Sad Tale of Three Slavers (Ohio; Legend). This story undoubtedly took place after the passage of the Fugitive Slave Act in 1850. After the act was passed, slave owners were permitted to "reclaim their property" in the free states. Suddenly, blacks weren't safe when they escaped, even if they had found homes and jobs. People who concealed or helped fugitives became subject to harsh fines and imprisonment.

Follow the Drinkin' Gourd (African American; American South; Spiritual). By the 1840s, a loosely organized group of free blacks, slaves, and white abolitionists formed a secret network to hide escaped slaves on their dangerous journey to freedom. The network is known as the Underground Railroad (see "Harriet Tubman" below). Peg Leg Joe, a free black, was a pivotal part of this effort. He hired himself out at various plantations as a worker and taught the slaves the simple song "Follow the Drinkin' Gourd." Including the additional verse noted below, the song is a kind of oral map describing the route north for escaping blacks. The "drinkin' gourd" is the Big Dipper, which points to the North Star. "When the sun comes back and the first quail calls" meant spring, when travel was less dangerous. As the runaways followed the stars north, they looked for marks Peg Leg Joe made in mud or in charcoal on dead trees — a left foot, for example — and would know they were headed in the right direction. The river that "ends in between two hills" is the Tombigbee River in Alabama. The "little river" is the Tennessee, and the "great big river," the Ohio, which divided the slave state of Kentucky from the free state of Ohio. Additional verse: "When the great big river meets the little river, / Follow the drinkin' gourd. / For the old man's waitin' for to carry you to freedom. / If you follow the drinkin' gourd."

Harriet Tubman (Narrative Poem). Harriet Tubman escaped from slavery in 1849. For the next fifteen years she risked her life again and again and returned to the South to help more than three hundred others to freedom. Slave owners offered a reward of forty thousand dollars for her arrest, but never captured her.

The People Could Fly (African American; American South; Legend). Human flight has long been a metaphor for escape, appearing in tales as ancient as the Greek myth of Daedalus and as contemporary as Faith Ringgold's picture book *Tar Beach* (New York: Crown Publishers, Inc., 1991).

Swing Low, Sweet Chariot (African American; American South; Spiritual). The image of flight as escape also appears in this spiritual. Although the tone of many spirituals, including this one, is sorrowful, the songs are sung with great gusto. The vitality of the music conveys the fundamental determination of the human spirit to endure.

READ MORE ABOUT IT

Hamilton, Virginia. *Anthony Burns: The Defeat and Triumph of a Fugitive Slave.* New York: Alfred A. Knopf, Inc., 1988.

Myers, Walter Dean. *Now Is Your Time! The African-American Struggle for Freedom.* Illustrated with black-and-white photographs. New York: HarperCollins Publishers, 1991.

Turner, Ann. *Nettie's Trip South.* Illustrated by Ronald Himler. New York: Macmillan Publishing Co., 1987.

I'VE BEEN WORKING ON THE RAILROAD

The first railroad was built in Great Britain in 1825, but by the 1840s there were twice as many miles of track in the United States as in all of Europe. Communities at major railway junctions surged into prominence while those passed over by the railroad withered. In 1869, a dream was realized when the Atlantic and Pacific coasts were linked by a rail network.

John Henry (African American; American South; Ballad). Did John Henry really live? It's hard to say. Legend insists the forty-four-pound baby finished his first meal and headed out the door in search of work. He found it as a steel driver with the Chesapeake and Ohio (the C & O) Railroad, helping to tunnel through mountains. Steel drivers hammered long steel pins that made holes in the rock face. Blasting charges were placed in the holes to explode rough tunnels through rock walls. Shakers, who helped the steel drivers, held the bit steady and twisted it a quarter turn after every blow of the sledgehammer. It was long, slow, hot, tedious, exhausting, and dangerous work, requiring prodigious strength and superhuman endurance.

Building the Transcontinental Railroad (Historical Essay). Convinced that a transcontinental railroad was in the best interest of the United States, the government granted large amounts of money and gave land to the directors of two companies, the Union Pacific and the Central Pacific. The workers of the Union Pacific moved west from Omaha, Nebraska, while those of the Central Pacific built tunnels and railbeds east from Sacramento, California. The workers of both crews were driven hard, for every mile of track meant additional government money. The two groups met at Promontory Point, Utah, on May 10, 1869. The linking of the nation by rail was a significant event. The memory of the Union's fragility was still alive soon after the end of the Civil War, and the completed rail network became a symbol of the nation's present and future unity.

Drill, Ye Tarriers (Irish American; Plains States; Work Song). Many Irish immigrated to the United States in the first half of the nineteenth century, and many of those immigrants served in the Union forces during the Civil War. After the war, many Irish veterans made their way to Omaha rail yards to work on the Union Pacific. These Irishmen were nicknamed "Tarriers." Some say the nickname was inspired by the full mustaches many of them wore, which made them look like terrier dogs. Others say the name came about because they were urged not to waste time, not to be "Tarriers" in the competition with the Chinese, who were building tracks and blasting through mountains for the rival Central Pacific on their way east from Sacramento, California. (See "The Iron Moonhunter.")

Death of the Iron Horse (Cheyenne; Plains States; Legend).

By the time the railroad came to the western plains, the Cheyenne were locked in a struggle with settlers to preserve their nomadic way of life. The Cheyenne roamed freely over the plains on horseback, following the buffalo that supplied them with food and materials for housing and clothing. But settlers believed in land ownership, and the discovery of gold and silver encouraged miners, farmers, and ranchers to claim Indian hunting grounds for themselves. The conflict over land led to years of war between the U.S. Army and the original inhabitants of the region. These wars eventually decimated the Cheyenne nation.

The Iron Moonhunter (Chinese American; California; Legend). While the Tarriers labored laying rails for the Union Pacific Railroad, Chinese workers struggled across the Sierra Nevada Mountains for the Central Pacific Railroad. Charles Crocker, one of the four founders of the Central Pacific, had the vision to hire Chinese workers. He had trouble with U.S. workers, many of whom accepted free passage to California and then deserted. The Chinese were nicknamed "Crocker's Pets" because they enjoyed the boss's enthusiastic support. Most of these workers were between fourteen and twenty years old.

A Gust of Fall Wind (Chinese American; California; Musical Lament). Although there is no factual evidence that the Chinese who participated in building the transcontinental railway network sang "A Gust of Fall Wind," the sadness expressed about the coming winter seems to reflect the sorrow of those toiling long hours far from their homes in China. The song uses the Chinese five-tone scale rather than the Western seven-tone scale.

Casey Jones, Railroad Man (American South; Legend/Occupational Tale). When Casey Jones was killed in 1903 in the most famous of all railway collisions, the United States had more than 193,000 miles of track and hundreds of railway lines. Although some said Casey's negligence — or maybe his drinking — caused the crash, he is considered a hero for urging his fireman to jump and save himself.

The Rock Island Line (African American; American South; Probably Work Song). "The Rock Island Line" was made famous in this century by the folk singer Huddie Ledbetter, known as Leadbelly. Unlike many folk songs, this one has a rolling blues beat, characteristic of the sound most closely associated with the Mississippi Delta and African-American musicians. Why would Southerners sing about a railroad with its headquarters in Illinois? The first route on the Rock Island Line ran only forty miles, from Chicago to Moline, Illinois; in time, the line stretched east, west, north, and then south from Illinois to the Delta, where Casey is said to have crashed.

READ MORE ABOUT IT

McKissack, Patricia, and Fredrick McKissack. *The Long Hard Journey: The Story of the Pullman Porters*. Illustrated with photographs. New York: Walker & Co., 1990.

Weitzman, David. *Superpower: The Making of a Steam Locomotive*. Boston: David R. Godine, Publishers, Inc., 1987.

Wilder, Laura Ingalls. *By the Shores of Silver Lake*. Illustrated by Garth Williams. New York: HarperCollins Publishers, 1953.

O PIONEERS!

From the moment gold was discovered on January 24, 1848, at John Sutter's sawmill in Coloma, California, the trickle of settlers moving west of the Mississippi River became a torrent. Not all sought gold. Some planned to farm. Others wanted to establish businesses. All hoped to find better lives.

Handcart Song (Mormon; Utah; Hymn). The Mormons, members of the Church of Jesus Christ of Latter-day Saints, established in 1830 in Fayette, New York, by Joseph Smith, experienced life-threatening prejudice in almost every community in which they lived because of their nontraditional beliefs.

In the late 1840s, Brigham Young, the new church leader, decided to move the group from Nauvoo, Illinois, when they were driven out, to the Great Salt Lake area in Utah Territory. The first settlers arrived in Conestoga wagons. Later, others traveled as far as the railroad would take them, then walked across the plains and deserts pulling rough-hewn handcarts to their new homes.

Febold Feboldson, First Citizen of Nebraska (Nebraska; Occupational Tale). Farming the prairie wasn't all popcorn balls and miracles during pioneer days, even though Febold Feboldson's story might make you think so. It was backbreaking work. Foot-thick sod had to be turned, or tilled, before planting. Many crops failed because of extreme summer temperatures, lack of water, and bitter-cold winters. Hordes of grasshoppers devoured everything in sight from crops to laundry. And the isolation from other families and established communities was more than many could bear.

Oh, Susannah (Popular Song). Although Stephen Collins Foster probably wrote the nonsense lyrics most sing along to his tune ("It rained so hard the day I left, / The weather was bone dry, / The sun so hot I froze to death, / Susannah, don't you cry...."), the lyrics here were made up by the thousands who arrived in California in 1849 to seek their fortunes in the goldfields.

The First Woman to Vote in the State of California (California; Legend). After Charlotte Parkhurst fled from a New England orphanage, she donned boys' clothing, changed her name to Charley, and eventually headed to gold country in 1849, where she became one of the best and toughest drivers to ever hold the reins on a Wells, Fargo stagecoach.

Sweet Betsy from Pike (California; Ballad). The slow, steady rhythms of this song were just right for singing hour after hour as a wagon swayed first left, then right, then left again, mile after endless mile over the prairies and mountains on the way to California. No one is quite sure where "Pike" is. Some say Missouri; others say Arkansas; still others claim Illinois or northern Texas.

The Darning Needle (Oregon; Legend). The temperate climate, plentiful water, and fertile soil of Oregon Territory made it a pioneer's paradise. The journey to the region was tough. Pioneers left from St. Joseph or Independence, Missouri, and headed west on the Oregon Trail. They traveled through areas occupied for centuries by various Native-American tribes, including the Pawnee, the Sioux, the Cheyenne, the Arapaho, the Shoshone, and the Nez Percé, all of which quickly learned to be suspicious of the newcomers. There were countless water crossings followed by long stretches where no fresh water could be found. Hundreds died along the way. Finally, the successful travelers pushed and pulled their wagons over one last obstacle — the Cascade Mountains — to settle in the Willamette Valley.

Acres of Clams (Washington State; Ballad). Thousands who poured into California hoping to strike it rich discovered little more than dirt, rocks, and hardship in the goldfields. Some headed north to Washington Territory, where digging for clams proved somewhat more profitable — and easier — than panning for gold. The terms referred to in the song's first verse — tunneled, hydraulicked, and cradled — are all different methods of extracting gold.

Dakota Dugout. To encourage the population of the western states, the U.S. Congress passed the Homestead Act in 1862. Under its provisions, pioneers could receive 160 acres of land if they built a structure on the property and remained to farm for at least five years. Wood was in short supply on the plains, so pioneers cut great blocks of sod — grass-covered soil held together by dense masses of roots — and built with it as if it were brick. Some dug soddies directly into the hillsides of the rolling plains.

By'm Bye (Possibly African American; Texas; Lullaby). Music historians believe this lullaby has its roots in Texas and may have been sung first during the time of slavery by African Americans. Its tender, wistful tone captures the vast loneliness of the prairies.

READ MORE ABOUT IT

Conrad, Pam. *Prairie Songs*. Illustrated by Darryl S. Zudeck. New York: HarperCollins Publishers, 1985.

Fleischman, Sid. *By the Great Horn Spoon!* Illustrated by Eric Von Schmidt. Boston: Joy Street/Little, Brown & Co., Inc., 1988 (reissue).

Freedman, Russell. *Children of the Wild West*. Illustrated with black-and-white photographs. New York: Clarion Books, 1983.

PART 3 ONLY IN AMERICA

Part 3 presents six chapters that introduce American interpretations of some of the great themes of world folklore: trickster tales, tall tales, humor, nonsense, animal stories, and ghost stories. And, of course, no book about this nation's folklore and traditions would be complete without a chapter about baseball.

TRICKSTERS, ON TWO FEET, FOUR — OR MORE

Tricksters are wily characters who use their wits to dupe their stronger, more powerful opponents. Sometimes these sly characters triumph; sometimes they are outwitted by faster-thinking foes. But whatever the outcome, tales about tricksters celebrate the triumph of brains over brawn or brag.

Tía Miseria (Puerto Rican American; Trickster Tale). Matching wits against the devil, or Death, is a popular theme the world over. This tale comes from the island of Puerto Rico, although another version has also been found in the European country of Portugal. Some traditional tales set in the continental United States about outwitting death include "Wicked John and the Devil" and "Soldier Jack."

The Devil's Questions (Appalachia; Ballad). The oldest known version of "The Devil's Questions" was collected in Oxford, England, in the fifteenth century. It may have been brought to this country by British immigrants who settled Appalachia following the Revolutionary War. Telling and solving riddles has always been part of the folk tradition. If you could win a riddling contest with the devil, some said you would be safe from him forever. Consider singing this song in two voices, or in two groups of voices, one taking the devil's part, one the human's.

Iktome and the Ducks (Sioux; Great Plains; Trickster Tale). Spider Iktome is the vain and bumbling trickster hero of many stories told by the Sioux of the Great Plains. Although the Sioux traditionally wore full-length leggings, here Iktome is pictured wearing short ones, which make him appear as foolish and as silly as he is.

Glooskap and Wasis (Abnaki; Northeast; Trickster Tale). Glooskap dominates the stories told by the Abnaki, the people who once lived throughout the region stretching north and east from Cape Cod, Massachusetts, to the Bay of Fundy in the Maritime Provinces of Canada. Abnaki, or Abenaki, is an umbrella term for a group of tribes including the Maliseet, the Passamaquoddy, and the Penobscot who are linked by geography and language. Glooskap is considered the Abnaki "culture hero." He is part benefactor, part friend, part trickster, and part god.

Brer Rabbit in Mr. Man's Garden (African American; American South; Trickster Tale). The stories about Brer Rabbit and his friends and foes were told for entertainment and amusement. The subtext of these tales was serious, for it describes the victory of the powerless slave over the all-powerful master. Joel Chandler Harris, a newspaperman with the *Atlanta Constitution* in the latter part of the nineteenth century, was the first to write down the Brer Rabbit stories. Harris collected the tales from blacks, chose the version of the story he thought best, and then tried to reproduce the sound and style of the oral telling in print. He created an imaginary former slave called Uncle Remus who "told" the stories to a young white boy. In later years, Uncle Remus was considered a stereotype, a symbol of the continued subservience of blacks despite the abolition of slavery. Because of the associations with the Uncle Remus character, the tales became unpopular for many years. Only now are they enjoying a healthy revival as contemporary tellers separate the stories from their negative stereotypes.

Oh, John the Rabbit (African American; American South; Call and Response). "Oh, John" offers a good example of the way a folk song can begin: Leaning on an established song type, it describes an everyday activity using exact, concrete details as it tells a humorous story.

The Connecticut Peddler (New England; Trickster Tale). Before the days of department stores and mail-order catalogs, people purchased goods from itinerant merchants called peddlers. Many peddlers hailed from New England because it was the first region of the country to develop industries that manufactured goods people needed.

Sharing the Crops (African American; American South; Trickster Tale). When the Civil War ended, former slaves had neither money nor property, and many of the benefits promised during Reconstruction were not fulfilled. Southern planters didn't have much money, but they did have property. To meet the needs of those with land and those without, sharecropping began. Workers planted crops on an owner's property, and the two parties shared the harvest. These arrangements were often unfair, favoring the landowner over the laborer, as "Sharing the Crops" shows. This story is sometimes told with animal characters like Brer Rabbit. And sometimes High John the Conqueror is the wily " 'cropper" who tricks "the man" out of his profits.

READ MORE ABOUT IT

Bang, Molly. *Wiley and the Hairy Man*. New York: Macmillan Publishing Co., 1976.

Goble, Paul. *Iktome and the Boulder*. New York: Orchard Books, 1988.

Harris, Joel Chandler. *Jump! The Adventures of Brer Rabbit*. Retold by Van Dyke Parks. Illustrated by Barry Moser. San Diego: Harcourt Brace Jovanovich Inc., 1986.

NO-SENSE NONSENSE

Nonsense is anything silly or humorous meant for fun and enjoyment. These comic tales represent different jokes and humor enjoyed by a variety of culture groups in the United States. At the same time, they also reflect something about the locale of each story.

The Talking Mule (African American; Florida; Nonsense Tale). Few people did more to preserve the cultural heritage of African Americans than Zora Neale Hurston. A trained anthropologist educated at Barnard College in the 1920s, she traveled to her hometown, Eatonville, Florida, and other places in the South to record the old tales before those who told them best passed away. She was the first African-American researcher to collect tales from her own people.

Keemo Kyemo (Appalachia; Nonsense Song). Both the traditional lyrics to "Keemo Kyemo" and the new lyrics below the music staffs are full of word play and tongue twisters. Try making up your own verses.

THREE TALL TIDBITS: 'Twas Midnight. The upside-down, inside-out poem, " 'Twas Midnight," is a good example of folk poetry — a rhyme of unknown origins that was passed from person to person either in casual conversation or as part of a game. **The Split Dog** (Appalachia; Tall Talk). "The Split Dog" is a first-class example of a windy, an improbable tale the listener is expected to believe. Variants of the story appear all over the world. **The Sad Tale of Tom the Catfish** (Midwest; Tall Talk). The tale of poor Tom the catfish is, like "The Split Dog," a small-scale tall tale in which an impossible event seems merely, if not fully, improbable.

The Boy Who Ate Too Much (Arctic-Circle Dwellers; Tall Tale). For a listener or reader to believe a tall tale, the details surrounding the action must be precise and accurate. This requirement is realized masterfully here. Much of what we know about igloos is incorporated into the story without impeding the action or slowing down the telling.

Mrs. Murphy's Chowder (Composer Unknown; Vaudeville Song/Nonsense Song). Vaudeville shows featured entertainers of all kinds — singers, dancers, acrobats, and comedians — for the price of a single admission and were popular from about 1890 to 1940.

Juan Bobo and the Buñuelos (Puerto Rican American; Noodlehead Tale). Juan Bobo, noodlehead and fool, has relatives the world over. In Guatemala, Juan Bobo is called Juan Primo. Yiddish stories abound about the noodleheads of a town in Poland called Chelm. The English tell about the silly people of the made-up village of Gotham. In the Cajun country of Louisiana, tales are told about a fool called Jean Sot. Amish living in the Lancaster, Pennsylvania, area enjoy stories about bumbling Till Eulenspiegel, who is also a popular folk figure in Germany.

The Twist-Mouth Family (New England; Noodlehead Tale). All true folktales were told aloud before they appeared in print, and "The Twist-Mouth Family" is no exception. The descriptions that appear in the text of each family member's attempt to blow out a candle provide a guide for the teller. Imitate the descriptions when you tell the story.

Michael Finnegan (Unknown Origin; Nonsense Song/Round). Have you ever read or told a circular story? That's a story in which a particular statement or phrase forces you back to the beginning. Here's an example: "It was a dark and stormy night. Some soldiers were sitting around a campfire when somebody asked someone to tell a story. The captain obliged. He stood up and began. 'It was a dark and stormy night. Some soldiers were sitting around a campfire when somebody asked someone to tell a story. The captain obliged. He stood up and began. "It was a dark and stormy night . . ."'" "Michael Finnegan" is a circular song. Once you get started there's no way to stop. To add to the fun, try singing it as a round.

READ MORE ABOUT IT

Lyons, Mary E. *Sorrow's Kitchen: The Life and Folklore of Zora Neale Hurston.* Illustrated with black-and-white photographs. New York: Charles Scribner's Sons, 1990.

Schwartz, Alvin, collector. *And the Green Grass Grew All Around: Folk Poetry from Everyone.* Illustrated by Sue Truesdell. New York: HarperCollins Publishers, 1992.

Schwartz, Alvin, collector. *Flapdoodle: Pure Nonsense from American Folklore.* Illustrated by John O'Brien. New York: HarperCollins Publishers, 1980.

FEATHERS AND FUR, SCALES AND TAILS

As long as there have been people, there have been storytellers and tales about animals. Sometimes these tales reveal an animal's habits or nature. More often than not, they reveal something about human beings.

Wake, Snake (Texas; Wake-Up Song). We learn many lullabies, but very few wake-up songs. According to Alan Lomax, an expert on American folk music, "Wake, Snake" may have first been sung as "Wake-Up, Jacob," in the cattle country of Texas south of San Antonio (where peas and hoecakes were standard breakfast fare for cowboys). Make the song your own by improvising rhythms or by substituting the name of a friend or family member for the word *snake*.

Brer Possum's Dilemma (African American; American South; Trickster Tale). Brer Rabbit isn't the only animal to take a leading role in tales told by blacks in the South. The slaves who worked the fields of the rural South observed the small animals who lived around them and made up stories about Brer Fox, Brer Skunk, Brer Wolf, and others. "Brer" is a form of the word *brother*.

Turtle Makes War on Man (Iroquois; Central New York State; Trickster Tale). Turtle tricks the Iroquois who trap him in much the same way Brer Rabbit tricks Brer Fox in the famous Tar Baby story ("Whatever you do, don't throw me into that Briar Patch!"). How could two stories from two very different ethnic groups have such similar plot details? Some believe there may have been contact between Africans living in North America and different Native Americans, and the two groups may have shared stories. Others believe that the stories have a common source. Still others hypothesize that basic similarities occur in stories that have superficial differences because people, no matter where or how they live, are essentially the same.

The Travels of a Fox (New England; Trickster Tale). Like Iktome and Glooskap, Fox is a trickster who is outwitted by a character more clever than he.

The Fox, the Goose, and the Corn (Riddle). Telling riddles, or puzzlers, is a traditional part of folklore. Children enjoy challenging others, especially adults, to solve them.

The Cat's Purr (Montserrat, the Leeward Islands of the West Indies; Pourquoi Story). Ashley Bryan retold "Why Cat Eats Rat" from a story fragment collected in Montserrat by Elsie Clews Parsons early in the twentieth century. Anyone who puts a traditional story into his or her own words is a reteller.

Bought Me a Cat (Ozarks; Nonsense Song). "Bought Me a Cat" is known by many different names, including "Fiddle-I-Fee," "The Barnyard Song," and "I Had a Cat." It may remind singers of "Old MacDonald Had a Farm."

Owl (Haitian; Cante Fable). Diane Wolkstein, collector and reteller of folktales, gathered and recorded Haitian stories that she reshaped and retold for publication. Here's the tune for the song Owl sings.

With spirit

Dong ga da, Dong ga da, Dong ga da, Dong.

Dong ga da, Dong. Eh - ee - oh.

All the Pretty Little Horses (American South; Lullaby). This gentle, poignant lullaby has been sung throughout the South. This version was arranged by John A. Lomax and Alan Lomax, father and son, who traveled the length and breadth of the United States collecting songs from people in all walks of life to preserve the nation's musical history and heritage.

READ MORE ABOUT IT

Bierhorst, John. *Doctor Coyote: A Native-American Aesop's Fables.* Illustrated by Wendy Watson. New York: Macmillan Publishing Co., 1987.

Kesey, Ken. *Little Tricker the Squirrel Meets Big Double the Bear.* Illustrated by Barry Moser. Viking Kestrel, 1990.

Schwartz, Alvin, collector. *Kickle Snifters and Other Fearsome Critters.* Illustrated by Glen Rounds. New York: HarperCollins Publishers, 1976.

AMERICAN GIANTS ON THE JOB

Here is a gathering of stories and songs about the legendary and the flesh-and-blood men and women who helped the nation grow. The stories also catalog some of the first industries.

When I First Came to This Land (Pennsylvania Dutch; Nonsense Song). From the earliest years of the seventeenth century, many Americans have earned their livings by farming the land. "When I First Came to This Land" celebrates the eternal optimism of farmers even as it gently pokes fun at their experiences.

Johnny Appleseed! Johnny Appleseed! (Midwest; Legend). Johnny Appleseed was a real person, although many of the tales told about him are probably not true. As with all legends, no one is quite sure where he was born; the Massachusetts towns of Boston, Leominster, and Essex all claim to be his birthplace. Some of the eccentric behavior ascribed to John Chapman is an outgrowth of his religious beliefs. He was a devout follower of Emanuel Swedenborg, a Swedish philosopher who believed that humans should live simply and in harmony with the natural world.

Strong as Annie Christmas (New Orleans; Legend; Occupational Tale). In the nineteenth century, the Mississippi River was a major commercial lifeline. Annie Christmas may have been a New Orleans dockworker who loaded and unloaded the keelboats and steamboats. Or she may have been a keelboat pilot, responsible for poling the flat-bottomed boats upriver after floating them down.

Paul Bunyan, the Mightiest Logger of Them All (From Maine West to Washington State; Tall Tale/Occupational Tale). Sometimes what we consider folklore did not develop in the traditional way. Stories about Paul Bunyan were neither invented nor recounted by men who made their livings as lumbermen. Instead, they were the invention of James L. Stephens, an advertising copywriter in Austin, Minnesota, who used stories about Paul to attract business to his company. He set his tales about Paul from Maine to Washington State, following the trail blazed by the lumberjacks themselves. The stories were so widely told that they have, over the years, come to be considered folklore.

The Frozen Logger (Ballad). James L. Stephens (see "Paul Bunyan, the Mightiest Logger of Them All") also wrote the words and music to this tongue-in-cheek ballad.

Ride 'em, Round 'em, Rope 'em: The Story of Pecos Bill (Texas and the American Southwest; Occupational Tale). The Spanish *conquistadores* brought both horses and cattle to the New World, providing Pecos Bill with two requirements for his work as a cowboy. Bill, who was not a real person, supposedly "invented" the cattle drive. In reality, the drives began when Texas ranchers decided to ship their cattle east by rail because beef prices were seven to eight times higher there. To reach the railroads in Kansas, Missouri, and Nebraska, cowboys drove their herds one thousand miles or more from Texas. Contrary to the images presented in movies, at least one third of the cowhands driving herds in the 1880s were Mexicans and African Americans.

Git Along, Little Dogies (Texas; Work Song). Cowboys sang this song on long trail drives to pass the time and to reassure restless calves. Dogies (DOUGH-gees) are calves deserted by their mothers and forced as a result to eat grass before they were quite able to digest it. This condition led to acute discomfort, perhaps alleviated by the singing.

I Hear America Singing. When Walt Whitman lived in New York City during the nineteenth century, he watched a metropolis being born. He wrote about the "numberless crowded streets" and the "immigrants arriving, fifteen or twenty thousand a week," and "the teeming nation of nations." "I Hear America Singing" celebrates the workers — and the work — that forged not only a new city but a new nation.

READ MORE ABOUT IT

Kellogg, Steven. *Mike Fink.* New York: William Morrow & Co., Inc., 1992.

Osborne, Mary Pope. *American Tall Tales.* Illustrated by Michael McCurdy. New York: Alfred A. Knopf, Inc., 1991.

Rounds, Glen. *Ol' Paul, the Mighty Logger.* New York: Holiday House, Inc., 1936, 1949, 1976.

TAKE ME OUT TO THE BALL GAME

For more than a century baseball has been considered our national pastime, and the game has inspired a body of folklore all its own. Historians disagree about who first played baseball and set down the rules, but its earliest origins may lie with the British game "rounders."

Take Me Out to the Ball Game. During the seventh-inning stretch, fans at many major league ballparks, from Boston's Fenway to Oakland's Coliseum, stand up, stretch, and sing "Take Me Out to the Ball Game." According to legend, neither composer nor lyricist had ever seen a baseball game when they wrote, in 1908, what would become the anthem of our national sport.

How It All Began (Historical Essay). When baseball was first organized into professional leagues, the teams were located east of the Mississippi. As the country grew and railroad transportation gave way to travel by air, teams were established in southern and western cities.

Jackie Robinson Breaks the Color Barrier (Historical Essay). The Baseball Hall of Fame now recognizes the contribution of the Negro Leagues with an extensive exhibit about the highlights of black baseball and by inducting outstanding players into the Hall of Fame.

A Baseball Lexicon. Almost every profession develops its own special language, but none seems as colorful and extensive as the language of baseball and the nicknames of its players.

THREE FOR THE BOOK: Say It Ain't So, Joe. In 1919, the Chicago White Sox were considered shoo-ins to win the World Series. The odds were so strongly in favor of the Sox that a group of gamblers paid various players to throw the series. The Sox lost, but the plot was uncovered, and all the players involved were banished from major league baseball forever. **The Babe Calls His Shot** (Legend). In 1920, George Herman Ruth, the "Babe," hit fifty-four homers during his first year with the New York Yankees and transformed the game of baseball. Before Ruth began belting balls out of parks, teams scored runs by putting together singles, sacrifice flies, bunts, and stolen bases, as they still do. But now teams also want home-run hitters who can put games away with one swing of the bat. **Willie Mays's Miraculous Catch.** Willie Mays dazzled fans with his explosive hitting, daring baserunning, and electrifying fielding. He is one of the greatest center fielders ever to play baseball. His nickname, the "Say-Hey Kid," was given to him during his early days with the New York Giants. Supposedly, he was too shy to speak up and started his answers to questions with "Say hey?"

The Bad News. Little League Baseball is played all over the world, and every year the North American champions meet the championship team from another part of the world at the Little League World Series in Williamsport, Pennsylvania. There are no records of games played in heaven.

Who's on First? Bud Abbott and Lou Costello were a comedy team popular in the 1930s and 1940s in vaudeville and the movies. Their baseball routine is a comedy classic, and the phrase "Who's on first?" is now part of popular culture.

Casey at the Bat: A Ballad of the Republic, Sung in the Year 1888 (Narrative Poem). "Casey at the Bat" was published first with little fanfare in the *San Francisco Examiner* on Sunday, June 3, 1888. But after a theatrical performer recited it with great success to a group of major league ball players, the poem was reprinted repeatedly in papers throughout the country. Though many claimed to be the real Casey, in fact, "Casey" never lived. Ernest Lawrence Thayer made up the whole thing.

READ MORE ABOUT IT

Berler, Ron. *The Super Book of Baseball*. Illustrated with full-color and black-and-white photographs. New York: Sports Illustrated Books for Kids/Little, Brown & Co., Inc., 1991.

Morrison, Lillian, compiler. *At the Crack of the Bat*. Illustrated by Steve Cieslawski. New York: Hyperion Press Inc., 1992.

Sullivan, George. *Sluggers: Twenty-seven of Baseball's Greatest*. Illustrated with full-color and black-and-white photographs. New York: Atheneum Publishers, 1991.

SCARY, CREEPY, SPOOKY GHOST STORIES

Why are there so many scary folktales? One reason might be that people have always been interested in the supernatural and have tried, through stories, to solve mysteries. Another reason may be that when it comes to entertainment, nothing beats a good ghost story.

The Ghost of Jean Lafitte (New Orleans and Gulf Coast Region; Legend). The numerous channels, bays, and estuaries of the U.S. Gulf Coast made ideal havens for pirates like Jean Lafitte. Lafitte made a good living smuggling goods into the country and by capturing merchant ships and stealing cargo. He was usually on the wrong side of the law, but during the War of 1812 he helped U.S. forces win the Battle of New Orleans.

The Dancing Skeleton (African American; South Carolina Coast; Ghost Story). John Bennett, a doctor in Charleston, South Carolina, collected stories from many of the African Americans he knew. "Daid Aaron," his title for "The Dancing Skeleton," was one of them. Cynthia C. DeFelice's retelling is a good example of the folk process at work. A contemporary teller reshapes a tale in his or her own style but maintains the flavor and integrity of the original.

Dry Bones (African American; American South; Spiritual). Based on a famous story from the Old Testament about the prophet Ezekiel, "Dry Bones" is an African-American spiritual sung well before the Civil War. When you sing, try the following motions: Hold palms upward at shoulder level and shrug each time you come to the words *dry bones* or *them bones*. Tap each body part as it is mentioned four times (on the beat) with both hands. When you reach the phrase *walk around* at the end of the song, wiggle the hips loosely, as a skeleton might.

The Ghost of Tom (Kentucky). Try singing this ghostly song as a round. Divide into two groups. The first sings the first two measures ("Have you seen the ghost of Tom?") alone. The other group then joins in, starting from the beginning of the song. To increase the mood, add any musical instrument or noisemaker that rattles, creaks, or chimes.

La Llorona, the Weeping Woman (American Southwest; Ghost Story). The story of La Llorona (pronounced la yo-ROW-na) is told all over the Southwest. Its origins are undoubtedly in Mexico, which once controlled the land stretching from Texas to California.

Skin and Bones (Appalachia; Narrative Song/Jump Song). Jean Ritchie collected this ominous, ghostly song in Kentucky many years ago. Begin singing at an average volume. Lower your voice steadily, verse after verse, until you are practically whispering. When the time comes for the final "BOO!" shout it out. As a play, one can be the old woman and another, the ghost. The other singers stand up straight, then gradually crouch lower and lower until they are almost on the ground. At the final "BOO!" they spring up for the dramatic conclusion.

The Peculiar Such Thing (African American; American South; Ghost Story/Jump Tale). "The Peculiar Such Thing" is called "Tailypo" by other storytellers and folklorists. It may remind readers of the English nursery tale "The Teeny Tiny Woman." If you learn to tell this story, practice building up the intensity. Each time the creature asks for its tailypo, speak a bit louder with more urgency. By the time you reach its last request, the listeners will be on the edge of their collective seat.

Things That Go Bump in the Night (Folk Wisdom). Kathryn Windham is a collector of folk stories, sayings, and instructional tidbits of all kinds about ghosts and ghostly behavior. Collectors like Windham speak directly with people, record exactly what they say, and present it in an unchanged form.

The Woman with the Golden Arm (African American; American South; Ghost Story/Jump Tale). Mark Twain is considered by many to be one of the best of all American authors. During his lifetime he also worked as an entertainer — reading aloud, telling stories, and talking about his life. "The Woman with the Golden Arm," his version of a ghost story told with slight variations throughout the world, was one of his favorites. It's a jump tale. If you learn to tell it, don't forget to pounce on the nearest listener when you say, "You got it!" and watch him or her jump!

READ MORE ABOUT IT

Leach, Maria. *The Thing at the Foot of the Bed and Other Scary Tales*. Illustrated by Kurt Werth. New York: Dell Publishing Co., 1981.

Lyons, Mary E., selector. *Raw Head, Bloody Bones: African American Tales of the Supernatural*. New York: Charles Scribner's Sons, 1992.

Schwartz, Alvin, collector and reteller. *Scary Stories 3: More Tales to Chill Your Bones*. Illustrated by Stephen Gammell. New York: HarperCollins Publishers, 1991.

PART 4 IN OUR TIME

IN OUR TIME

Folklore is being made even in our own time, the twentieth century. Pivotal events inspire poets, writers, and songwriters to create work that becomes part of our national experience. In time, we may share these songs, phrases, and stories with our grandchildren and they, in turn, may share them with theirs.

The New Colossus. Since 1886 the Statue of Liberty has stood in New York Harbor. Designed by French sculptor Frédéric-Auguste Bartholdi, its full name is Liberty Enlightening the World. Liberty holds a lamp in her upraised right arm to welcome those who come to the United States. She holds a tablet in her left hand inscribed with the date of the Declaration of Independence. The poem is inscribed on the base of the statue.

America! America! (Historical Essay). Because it was no longer needed, the immigration center at Ellis Island was closed in 1954. In 1976, the historical importance of the site was recognized by the U.S. Congress. Through the efforts of individuals in the public and private sectors, the Ellis Island Immigration Museum opened in 1990 to honor those who came to the country through New York City.

Tramp Talk (Historical Essay). The Great Depression lasted from the failure of the New York Stock Market in 1929 until the Second World War in 1941. During those years, more than two million people were homeless. Many lived on the road and many lived in makeshift encampments, "Hoovervilles," named for Herbert Hoover who was president when the Depression began.

Big Rock Candy Mountain (Twentieth-Century Popular Song). In keeping with the folk tradition, the lyrics of this song have changed frequently over the years. Originally, the words captured the anger and frustration of those men forced by the wholesale unemployment of the 1930s to wander the country trying to find work. Later, when the song became part of popular culture, the lyrics became less harsh and more upbeat. Start the song with this introduction:

Gee, Mom, I Want to Go Home. Originally known as "I Don't Want No More of Army Life," this song sprang up spontaneously among troops serving in the armed forces during the Second World War.

A Shameful Chapter (Historical Essay). In recent times, efforts have been made to learn more about the Second World War from the viewpoint of the people of Japan. Recommended children's books on the subject include *Sadako and the Thousand Paper Cranes* by Eleanor B. Coerr; *Hiroshima No Pika*, written and illustrated by Toshi Maruki; *The Miracle Tree* by Christobel Mattingly; and *Faithful Elephants* by Yukio Tsuchiya.

Blowin' in the Wind. After the Second World War and throughout the 1960s, young people from all over the country flocked to New York City's Greenwich Village to perform and listen to popular music that used the melodies and motifs of traditional folk music. Some songwriters wrote protest songs that questioned the policies of the government and the social norms of previous generations. Bob Dylan's "Blowin' in the Wind" became the unofficial anthem of the civil rights movement.

I Have a Dream (Delivered on August 28, 1963). Many people believe that society changes only through violent means. Like the Massachusetts writer and philosopher, Henry David Thoreau, and Mahatma Gandhi, the leader of the independence movement in India, Martin Luther King, Jr., believed an individual could promote change through nonviolent means — demonstrations, letter-writing campaigns, marches, and sit-ins. King worked to provide equality under the law for all who faced prejudice and discrimination.

TALES OF NEW AMERICANS. In the 1980s, more than ten million people from other countries came to the United States. Here are just three of the countless number of stories brought along. **El Gallo de Bodas: The Rooster on the Way to the Wedding** (Cuban American; Florida; Cante Fable). In the late 1950s, many Cubans fled to nearby Florida after Fidel Castro, Cuba's Communist leader, came to power. **Bye-Bye** (Haitian; Pourquoi Story). In the early nineteenth century, Haiti was the second democracy established in the Western Hemisphere, but over the decades the country has been ruled by many different dictators. In recent years many Haitians have come to live in the United States. **The Raven and the Star Fruit Tree** (Vietnamese American). When the Vietnam conflict ended in 1975, many Vietnamese immigrated to the United States, and a large number now live in California's Orange County.

This Land Is Your Land (Twentieth-Century Popular Song). Oklahoma, where Woody Guthrie was born and brought up, was one of the areas hit hardest during the Great Depression. Thousands, including Guthrie, abandoned their homes and dust-caked farms, loaded all they had onto vehicles of every description or on their backs, and headed west to California, Oregon, and Washington State, where jobs were said to be available. Guthrie's songs described these people and their experiences. "This Land Is Your Land," one of his most popular songs, was written after the Second World War ended.

Earth Always Endures (Mandan and Hidatsa; Traditional). The Mandan lived on the high plains in the present-day states of North and South Dakota. Their lodgings, dress, and way of life were typical of the seminomadic Indians of the region. After a disastrous smallpox epidemic killed thousands in the mid-nineteenth century, thirty survivors joined a handful of Hidatsa and Arikara on a small reservation in South Dakota. The poem echoes the reverence and respect these First Americans felt for the land.

READ MORE ABOUT IT

Haskins, James. *The Life and Death of Martin Luther King, Jr.* Illustrated with black-and-white photographs. New York: Beech Tree Books, 1977, 1992.

Stanley, Jerry. *Children of the Dust Bowl: The True Story of the School at Weedpatch Camp.* Illustrated with black-and-white photographs. New York: Crown Publishers, Inc., 1992.

Stevenson, James. *Don't You Know There's a War On?* New York: Greenwillow Books, 1992.

MOLLY BANG made her own rendition of a classic American motif — "a patchwork quilt of sorts," as she describes it, by using old magazine cutouts for collage art. In addition to the animal models Ms. Bang found in her books, she was fortunate enough to have one live model — a groundhog. Unfortunately, he demanded a high price for his labor — all the fresh vegetables in her backyard garden!

Molly Bang has worked on several continents as an Education and Public Health Consultant and a translator, in addition to illustrating more than fifteen books for children. Both *The Grey Lady and the Strawberry Snatcher* (1981) and *Ten, Nine, Eight* (1984) were selected as Caldecott Honor Books. She lives in Falmouth, Massachusetts. (Medium: Collage with Construction Paper, Magazine Cutouts, and Elmer's Glue)

MARCIA BROWN hails from New England and loves to visit old whaling towns in Maine and Massachusetts where some clipper ships still remain. "I used to love to go to Europe by ship," she says. "And I remember one trip on a banana boat in the West Indies when we got caught in a hurricane. But when the storm subsided, we were rewarded with the most spectacular skies." Of the many books she has illustrated for children, Ms. Brown was awarded three Caldecott Medals for *Cinderella* (1955), *Once a Mouse* (1962), and *Shadow* (1983), and six Caldecott Honors for *Stone Soup* (1948), *Henry Fisherman* (1950), *Dick Whittington and His Cat* (1951), *Skipper John's Cook* (1952), *Puss in Boots* (1953), and *The Steadfast Tin Soldier* (1954). In 1992, she was honored with the Laura Ingalls Wilder Award for her lifetime body of distinguished works in children's literature. She lives in West Redding, Connecticut. (Medium: Watercolor and Acrylic)

BARBARA COONEY researched "O Pioneers!" by looking at hundreds of pictures of the plains and prairies of the Great West, as well as photographs from trips she has taken over the years. "I've been back and forth across the United States many times now," she says. "I'm always amazed what a vast country this is."

Strongly influenced by her artist mother, Ms. Cooney studied art and art history at Smith College and later furthered her studies at the Art Students League in New York City. Illustrator of over one hundred books for children, she was twice awarded the Caldecott Medal, first in 1959 for *Chanticleer and the Fox*, and again in 1980 for *Ox-Cart Man*. She lives in Damariscotta, Maine, with her husband. (Medium: Acrylic on Gesso with Colored Pencil)

DONALD CREWS was surprised when he was chosen to illustrate "No-Sense Nonsense," since he has never thought of himself as a humorous artist. But as he read and reread the stories, and listened to the music, he soon entered into the spirit of the work. "I had to stretch to something broader, something different from what I'd done before. Something more spontaneous."

After graduating from New York City's Cooper Union, Mr. Crews worked as a designer, and an art director, served eighteen months in the military in Germany, and then illustrated the children's book *We Read: A to Z* as a piece for his portfolio. His career as a children's book artist followed, as did his two Caldecott Honor books, *Freight Train* (1979) and *Truck* (1981). Mr. Crews lives in Brooklyn, New York, with his wife, the noted author and illustrator, Ann Jonas. (Medium: Transparent Dyes)

LEO and DIANE DILLON meticulously researched the various North American Indian tribes appearing in "In the Beginning" in order to accu-

rately portray each different culture. "We didn't try to imitate the Native American art, but rather we used it as inspiration for our own style." The Dillons, who have collaborated for over thirty-five years, began their career together illustrating adult book jackets, album covers, and advertising material. Their more than twenty award-winning books for children, which reflect a wide-ranging variety of locales and cultures (African, Alaskan, Japanese, Egyptian, and Native American), include their two Caldecott Medal books, *Why Mosquitoes Buzz in People's Ears* (1976) and *Ashanti to Zulu* (1977). The Dillons live in Brooklyn, New York.
(Medium: Mixed Media on Three-Ply Strathmore)

RICHARD EGIELSKI, while working on "Coming to America," reminisced about both of his grandfathers who emigrated from Poland in the early twentieth century. "One was recruited by a coal mining company that showed up in his hometown; the other had a more nerve-racking experience at Ellis Island. He lied about his age for fear that only young immigrants would be accepted."

Mr. Egielski attended Pratt Institute and Parsons School of Design, where he studied with Maurice Sendak. It was Mr. Sendak who first inspired him to pursue a career in children's book illustration, and through him that he accidentally met his collaborator, the author Arthur Yorinks. Together, they have created several popular picture books, including *Hey Al*, the winner of the 1987 Caldecott Medal. Mr. Egielski lives in Milford, New Jersey, with his wife and young son.
(Medium: Watercolor)

TRINA SCHART HYMAN was delighted by "Tricksters, on Two Feet, Four — or More" because she considers herself "a trickster by nature." She wanted to do something with the illustrations that was distinctly American, and after considering various techniques, she finally hit on the idea of using a medium that is the most American of all art materials — Crayola crayons. "They are still as much fun to color with as they were when I was in the third grade. And it was encouraging to learn that I'm still pretty good at staying in the lines." Ms. Hyman received her art training at the Philadelphia College of Art and the Boston

Museum School. The illustrator of more than seventy books, she won a Caldecott Medal for *Saint George and the Dragon* (1985), and Caldecott Honors for *Little Red Riding Hood* (1984) and *Hershel and the Hanukkah Goblins* (1990). She lives in Lyme, New Hampshire.
(Medium: Crayola Crayons, Acrylics, and India Ink)

ANITA LOBEL, whose work contains all of the intensity and richness of opera, posed and staged her figures the way one would a tableau. "The characters are close to the action," she says. "I wanted to create a feeling of solidity and vigor. These must have been sturdy, heroic people going through something very unifying. . . ."

Ms. Lobel was born in Krakow, Poland, and studied art in New York and Sweden. She also studied French, Italian, Japanese, acting, singing, stained glass design, and literature in New York City where she currently lives and works. "I love the eighteenth century," she says, "and I love America." Ms. Lobel, who began her career as a textile designer, has illustrated many highly acclaimed books for children over the years, including her Caldecott Honor book *On Market Street* (1982).
(Medium: Gouache)

JERRY PINKNEY's fascination with the way spirituals relate to African-American history inspired his work for "Let My People Go." "If we think of how Harriet Tubman is referred to as Moses, and of the way the slaves communicated through songs, we can understand the symbolisms, codes, and connections between a song, for instance, like 'Go Down, Moses,' and the Underground Railroad."

Mr. Pinkney is a native of Philadelphia. He and his wife, Gloria, a writer, have four children and three grandchildren, and now live in Croton-on-Hudson, New York. He has illustrated over fifty books for children, and has won numerous awards for his outstanding illustrations, including his two Caldecott Honors for *Mirandy and Brother Wind* (1989) and *The Talking Eggs* (1990).
(Medium: Sepia Prisma-Color Pencil on Paper with Watercolor Wash)

JOHN SCHOENHERR and his wife live on an old farm in Stockton, New Jersey, where their neighbors are mostly opossums, foxes, skunks, snakes, owls, geese, turtles, and bears. "I've always been concerned with drawing them realistically, so these stories offered a welcome change, and a chance for some unpredictable results." Despite using his animal neighbors as models, Mr. Schoenherr also has traveled extensively throughout the western United States and Canada to research his subjects. He began formal art training at the Art Students League when he was only thirteen, and later went on to study at Pratt Institute. He has been illustrating children's books for over thirty years and was awarded the Caldecott Medal in 1988 for *Owl Moon*.
(Medium: Pen and Ink and Watercolor)

MARC SIMONT kept all his old sketch books from his days working for *Sports Illustrated*, and from them he modeled his work for "Take Me Out to the Ball Game." Born in Paris of Catalan parents, he wasn't exposed to baseball until he came to this country at age eleven.

Mr. Simont is a portrait painter, a caricature artist, an author, and a translator, in addition to being an award-winning children's book illustrator. He was awarded the Caldecott Medal in 1957 for *A Tree Is Nice*, and he received a Caldecott Honor in 1950 for *The Happy Day*. He lives with his wife in West Cornwall, Connecticut.
(Medium: Watercolor and Charcoal)

CHRIS VAN ALLSBURG looked at both old photos from a clipping file and his own mirrored expressions in order to match the faces of the tall-tale characters to his own artistic vision. "The process of creating spaces and characters from imagination is a very time-consuming one. I have this theory that, drawing from my imagination, I am likely to leave a lot of small details out and create a drawing that ultimately has a touch of the surreal." Mr. Van Allsburg began his career as a sculptor after completing the Master of Fine Arts

program at the Rhode Island School of Design. Among his thirteen award-winning picture books are his two Caldecott Medal winners, *Jumanji* (1982) and *The Polar Express* (1986), and his first book, *The Garden of Abdul Gasazi* (1980), which won a Caldecott Honor. He lives in Providence, Rhode Island, with his wife, Lisa, and their daughter, Sophia.
(Medium: Pen and Ink)

DAVID WIESNER no longer has the big Lionel train sets that were such a memorable part of his childhood. Fortunately, his brother-in-law took numerous photographs for him on a recent trip to Durango, Colorado, where a working steam train still exists. "The photographs were a tremendous help because in many of the historical photographs I had been looking at, it was difficult to detect the train's intricate workings." David Wiesner has won numerous awards for illustration in the twelve years since he was graduated from the Rhode Island School of Design, including a Caldecott Medal in 1991 for *Tuesday* and a Caldecott Honor in 1989 for *Free Fall*. He lives with his wife, Kim, and young son, Kevin, in Philadelphia, Pennsylvania.
(Medium: Watercolor)

ED YOUNG was born in Tientsin, China, was raised in Shanghai, and attended high school in Hong Kong before coming to college in the United States. The interrelationship of words and pictures is very important to him. He prefers to illustrate only stories that have "inner meaning . . . timelessness, and a universal quality." A superb draftsman, he allows the story to dictate the medium, using charcoal, watercolor, pastel, collage, or whatever best suits the particular text. Ed Young has illustrated over fifty books for children, six of which he has also written. He received a Caldecott Medal in 1990 for *Lon Po Po: A Red Riding Hood Story from China*, and *Seven Blind Mice* was named a Caldecott Honor Book in 1992. He and his wife live in Hastings-on-Hudson, New York.
(Medium: Tempera and Oil Pastel)

ACKNOWLEDGMENTS

PART 1 IN THE BEGINNING

IN THE BEGINNING

"The Creation" retold by Joseph Bruchac. Copyright © 1979 by Joseph Bruchac. Reprinted by permission of Joseph Bruchac.

"Raven Brings Fresh Water" retold by Fran Martin. Reprinted from *Raven-Who-Sets-Things-Right* by Fran Martin. Copyright © 1975 by Frances M. Martin. Reprinted by permission of HarperCollins Publishers.

"Dream Song" reprinted from *Songs of the Chippewa* edited by John Bierhorst. Copyright © 1974 by John Bierhorst. Reprinted by permission of Farrar, Straus and Giroux, Inc.

"Coyote Helps Decorate the Night" retold by Harold Courlander. Copyright © 1970 by Harold Courlander. Reprinted by permission of Harold Courlander.

"Sedna, the Sea Goddess" retold by Helen Caswell. Reprinted by permission of AMS Press, Inc., New York, from *Intellectual Culture of the Iglulik* by Knud Johan Victor Rasmussen.

"The Gods Made Man" by Natalia Belting. From *Our Fathers Had Powerful Songs* by Natalia Belting. Copyright © 1974 by Natalia Belting. Used by permission of Dutton Children's Books, a division of Penguin Books USA Inc.

PART 2 FROM SEA TO SHINING SEA

COMING TO AMERICA

Adaptation of "The Mezcla Man" retold by J. Frank Dobie, from *Tales of Old-Time Texas* by J. Frank Dobie. Copyright © 1928, 1930, 1931, 1943, 1955 by J. Frank Dobie. By permission of Little, Brown and Company, Inc. Edited and abridged for *From Sea to Shining Sea* by Amy L. Cohn and Suzy Schmidt.

"The Other 1492" by Norman H. Finkelstein. Adapted with permission of Charles Scribner's Sons, an imprint of Macmillan Publishing Company, from *The Other 1492* by Norman H. Finkelstein. Copyright © 1989 by Norman H. Finkelstein.

"The Debate in Sign Language" retold by Syd Lieberman. Copyright © 1988 by Syd Lieberman. Reprinted by permission of Syd Lieberman. Edited and abridged for *From Sea to Shining Sea* by Amy L. Cohn.

"The First Thanksgiving" by Marcia Sewall. Reprinted with permission of Atheneum Publishers, an imprint of Macmillan Publishing Company, from "Menfolk" in *The Pilgrims of Plimoth* by Marcia Sewall. Copyright © 1986 by Marcia Sewall.

"Simple Gifts" arranged by Marilyn Davidson and Nathaniel Fenmore. Arrangement copyright © 1985 by Silver Burdett Company. Used by permission of Silver Burdett and Ginn, Inc. All rights reserved.

"Why Alligator Hates Dog" retold by J. J. Reneaux. Copyright © 1990 by J. J. Reneaux. Reprinted by permission of J. J. Reneaux.

"'Tit Galop pour Mamou" words and music by Dewey Balfa. Lyrics and music transcribed by Ann Allen Savoy. Copyright © by Flat Town Music. Used by permission of Flat Town Music.

THE SHOT HEARD 'ROUND THE WORLD

"Revolutionary Tea" arranged by Ruth and Norman Lloyd. Copyright © 1969 by American Heritage, a division of Forbes, Inc. Reprinted from *American Heritage Songbook*, by permission of Forbes, Inc.

"Yankee Doodle" words by Dr. Richard Shuckburgh, arranged by William Ward. Arrangement copyright © 1985 by Silver Burdett Company. Used by permission of Silver Burdett and Ginn, Inc. All rights reserved.

"Johnny Has Gone for a Soldier" arranged by Ruth and Norman Lloyd.

Copyright © 1969 by American Heritage, a division of Forbes, Inc. Reprinted from *American Heritage Songbook*, by permission of Forbes, Inc.

"Clever Mistress Murray" retold by M. A. Jagendorf. From *The Ghost of Peg Leg Peter and Other Stories of Old New York* by M. A. Jagendorf. Copyright © 1965 by M. A. Jagendorf. Reprinted by permission of Vanguard Press, a division of Random House, Inc. Edited and abridged for *From Sea to Shining Sea* by Amy L. Cohn.

"Jennie Jenkins" arranged by Darrell Peter. Arrangement copyright © 1985 by Silver Burdett Company. Used by permission of Silver Burdett and Ginn, Inc. All rights reserved.

BRIDGING THE GAP

"The Wilderness Road" by Meridel LeSueur. Reprinted from *Nancy Hanks of Wilderness Road* by Meridel LeSueur. Copyright © 1949 by Meridel LeSueur. Reprinted by permission of Alfred A. Knopf, Inc.

"Strong but Quirky: The Birth of Davy Crockett" retold by Irwin Shapiro. From *Yankee Thunder* by Irwin Shapiro. Copyright © 1972, 1974 by Irwin Shapiro. Used by permission of the publisher, Julian Messner, a division of Simon and Schuster, Inc., New York.

"Gol' in the Chimley" reprinted from *Old Greasybeard* collected by Leonard Roberts, by permission of Mrs. Edith Roberts. Edited and abridged for *From Sea to Shining Sea* by Amy L. Cohn.

"Hush, Little Baby" arranged by Allan Miller. From *The Fireside Book of Children's Songs* by Marie Winn and Allan Miller. Copyright © 1966 by Marie Winn and Allan Miller. Reprinted by permission of Simon and Schuster, Inc.

WATER, WATER EVERYWHERE

"Blow, Ye Winds, in the Morning" arranged by Jerome Epstein, reprinted from a Revels, Inc. recording, by permission of Revels, Inc.

"The Erie Canal" arranged by Denes Agay. From *Best Loved Songs of the American People* by Denes Agay. Copyright © 1975 by Denes Agay. Used by permission of Doubleday, a division of Bantam Doubleday Dell Publishing Group, Inc.

"Sally Ann Thunder Ann Whirlwind Crockett Meets Mike Fink, Snappin' Turkle" retold by Caron Lee Cohen. From *Sally Ann Thunder Ann Whirlwind Crockett*. Copyright © 1985 by Caron Lee Cohen. Reprinted by permission of Greenwillow Books, a division of William Morrow and Company, Inc.

"Shenandoah" arranged by Denes Agay. From *Best Loved Songs of the American People* by Denes Agay. Copyright © 1975 by Denes Agay. Used by permission of Doubleday, a division of Bantam Doubleday Dell Publishing Group, Inc.

LET MY PEOPLE GO

"Go Down, Moses" arranged by Theodore Raph. From *The American Song Treasury* edited by Theodore Raph. Copyright © 1964 by Theodore Raph. Reprinted by permission of Dover Publications, Inc.

"How the Slaves Helped Each Other" retold by William J. Faulkner. Permission granted by Marie Brown Associates from *The Days When the Animals Talked* by William J. Faulkner. Copyright © 1977 by William J. Faulkner. Edited and abridged for *From Sea to Shining Sea* by Amy L. Cohn.

"I Got Shoes" arranged by Darrell Peter. Arrangement copyright © 1985 by Silver Burdett Company. Reprinted by permission of Silver Burdett and Ginn, Inc. All rights reserved.

"High John the Conquerer" by Steve Sanfield. From *The Adventures of High John the Conquerer* by Steve Sanfield. Copyright © 1989 by Steve

Sanfield. Reprinted by permission of the publisher, Orchard Books, a division of Franklin Watts, Inc.

"Long John" arranged by James Rooker. Copyright © 1985 by Silver Burdett Company. Used by permission of Silver Burdett and Ginn, Inc. All rights reserved.

"The Sad Tale of Three Slavers" retold by M. A. Jagendorf. From *Sand in the Bag and Other Folk Stories of Ohio, Indiana, and Illinois* by M. A. Jagendorf. Copyright © 1952 by M. A. Jagendorf and renewed 1980 by M. A. Jagendorf. Reprinted by permission of Vanguard Press, a division of Random House, Inc. Edited and abridged for *From Sea to Shining Sea* by Amy L. Cohn.

"Follow the Drinkin' Gourd" arranged by Carl Miller. From *I Hear America Singing! Great Folk Songs from the Revolution to Rock* compiled by Hazel Arnett. Copyright © 1975 by Hazel Arnett. Reprinted by permission of Henry Holt and Company, Inc.

"Harriet Tubman" by Eloise Greenfield. From *Honey, I Love* by Eloise Greenfield. Copyright © 1978 by Eloise Greenfield. Reprinted by permission of HarperCollins Publishers and Marie Brown Associates.

"The People Could Fly" retold by Virginia Hamilton. From *The People Could Fly* by Virginia Hamilton. Copyright © 1985 by Virginia Hamilton. Reprinted by permission of Alfred A. Knopf, Inc.

"Swing Low, Sweet Chariot" arranged by Theodore Raph. From *The American Song Treasury* edited by Theodore Raph. Reprinted by permission of Dover Publications, Inc. Copyright © 1964 by Theodore Raph.

I'VE BEEN WORKING ON THE RAILROAD

"John Henry" arranged by Elizabeth Poston. Copyright © 1964 by Elizabeth Poston. Used by permission of Ludlow Music, Inc.

"Building the Transcontinental Railroad" from Adele Nathan. From *The Building of the First Transcontinental Railroad* by Adele Nathan. Copyright © 1950 by Adele Nathan. Reprinted by permission of Random House, Inc. Edited and abridged for *From Sea to Shining Sea* by Amy L. Cohn and Suzy Schmidt.

"Death of the Iron Horse" retold by Paul Goble. Reprinted with permission of Bradbury Press, an affiliate of Macmillan Publishing Company, from *Death of the Iron Horse* by Paul Goble. Copyright © 1987 by Paul Goble.

"A Gust of Fall Wind" arranged by Georgette LeNorth. Arrangement copyright © 1985 by Silver Burdett Company. Used by permission of Silver Burdett and Ginn, Inc. All rights reserved.

"The Rock Island Line" new words and music by Huddie Ledbetter. TRO copyright © 1959 renewed by Folkways Music Publishers, Inc., New York, New York. Used by permission. This arrangement by Florence White. From *Songs to Grow On* by Beatrice Landeck. Copyright © 1950 by Edward B. Marks Music Company. Copyright renewed. International copyright secured. Used by permission of Edward B. Marks Music Company and Hal Leonard Music Publishing Company.

O PIONEERS!

"Handcart Song" arranged by Darrell Peter. Arrangement copyright © 1964, 1971 by Silver Burdett Company. Used by permission of Silver Burdett and Ginn, Inc. All rights reserved.

"Oh, Susannah" arranged by Ruth and Norman Lloyd. Copyright © 1969 by the American Heritage, a division of Forbes, Inc. Reprinted from *American Heritage Songbook* by Ruth and Norman Lloyd, by permission of Forbes, Inc.

"The First Woman to Vote in the State of California" by Carolyn Polese. Copyright © 1990 by Carolyn Polese. Used by permission of Carolyn Polese.

"The Darning Needle" by Eric A. Kimmel. Copyright © 1993 by Eric A. Kimmel. Reprinted by permission of Eric A. Kimmel.

"Acres of Clams" arranged by Denes Agay. From *Best Loved Songs of the American People* edited by Denes Agay. Copyright © 1975 by Denes Agay. Reprinted by permission of Doubleday, a division of Bantam Doubleday Dell Publishing Group, Inc.

"Dakota Dugout" by Ann Turner. Reprinted with permission of Macmillan Publishing Company from *Dakota Dugout* by Ann Turner. Copyright © 1985 by Ann Turner.

"By'm Bye" arranged by Allan Miller. From *The Fireside Book of Children's Songs* edited by Marie Winn and Allan Miller. Copyright © 1966 by Marie Winn and Allan Miller.

PART 3 ONLY IN AMERICA

TRICKSTERS ON TWO FEET, FOUR — OR MORE

"Tía Miseria" retold by Olga Loya. Reprinted by permission of Olga Loya. Edited and abridged for *From Sea to Shining Sea* by Amy L. Cohn.

"Iktome and the Ducks" retold by Lame Deer. From *The Sound of Flutes and Other Indian Legends* by Richard Erdoes. Copyright © 1976 by Richard Erdoes. Reprinted by permission of Pantheon Books, a division of Random House, Inc.

"Glooskap and Wasis" retold by Alan Garner. From *The Hamish Hamilton Book of Goblins* by Alan Garner. Copyright © 1969 by Alan Garner.

"Brer Rabbit in Mr. Man's Garden" retold by Julius Lester. From *The Tales of Uncle Remus by Julius Lester*. Copyright © 1987 by Julius Lester. Used by permission of Dial Books for Young Readers, a division of Penguin Books USA Inc. and The Bodley Head, United Kingdom. "Brer Rabbit and the Little Girl" and "Brer Rabbit Goes Back to Mr. Man's Garden" combined and retitled "Brer Rabbit in Mr. Man's Garden" for *From Sea to Shining Sea*.

"The Connecticut Peddler" retold by Maria Leach. Copyright © 1958 by Maria Leach and renewed 1986 by Macdonald H. Leach. Reprinted by permission of Macdonald H. Leach.

"Sharing the Crops" retold by Harold Courlander. Copyright © 1957, 1985 by Harold Courlander. Reprinted by permission of Harold Courlander.

NO-SENSE NONSENSE

"The Talking Mule" collected by Zora Neale Hurston. From *Mules and Men* by Zora Neale Hurston. Copyright © 1935 by Zora Neale Hurston, renewed 1963 by John C. Hurston and Joel Hurston. Reprinted by permission of HarperCollins Publishers. Edited and abridged for *From Sea to Shining Sea* by Amy L. Cohn.

"Keemo Kyemo" arranged by Allan Miller. From *The Fireside Book of Fun and Game Songs* by Marie Winn and Allan Miller. Copyright © 1974 by Marie Winn and Allan Miller. Reprinted by permission of Simon and Schuster, Inc.

"The Split Dog" retold by Richard Chase from *American Folk Tales and Songs* edited by Richard Chase, published by Dover Publications, Inc. Edited and abridged for *From Sea to Shining Sea* by Amy L. Cohn.

"The Sad Tale of Tom the Catfish" retold by M. A. Jagendorf. From *Sand in the Bag and Other Folk Stories of Ohio, Indiana, and Illinois* by M. A. Jagendorf. Copyright © 1952 and renewed 1980 by M. A. Jagendorf. Reprinted by permission of Vanguard Press, a division of Random House, Inc.

"The Boy Who Ate Too Much" retold by Edward L. Keithahn. From *Igloo Tales* by Edward L. Keithahn, edited by Kenneth Gilbert. Copyright © 1974 by Mrs. E. L. Keithahn. Reprinted by permission of GTE Discovery Publications, Inc., Bothell, Washington.

"Mrs. Murphy's Chowder" arranged by Allan Miller. From *The Fireside Book of Fun and Games Songs* by Marie Winn and Allan Miller. Copyright © 1974 by Marie Winn and Allan Miller. Reprinted by permission of Simon and Schuster, Inc.

"Juan Bobo and the Buñuelos" a Puerto Rican folktale adapted and translated by Lucía M. González. Used by permission of Lucía M. González.

"Michael Finnegan" arranged by Allan Miller. From *The Fireside Book of Fun and Game Songs* by Marie Winn and Allan Miller. Copyright © 1974 by Marie Winn and Allan Miller. Reprinted by permission of Simon and Schuster, Inc.

FEATHERS AND FUR, SCALES AND TALES

"Brer Possum's Dilemma" retold by Jackie Torrence. From the repertoire of Jackie Torrence. Used by permission of Jackie Torrence/Traditional Arts Services.

"Turtle Makes War on Man" retold by Joseph Bruchac. Reprinted by permission of Joseph Bruchac.

SUGGESTIONS FOR FURTHER READING

~

Here are some interesting and helpful books with which to begin learning more about American folklore, history, and culture. Combine these titles with the sources listed in the Acknowledgments and those cited at the end of each chapter in the Notes About the Book for a broad base of materials from which to begin reading.

FOLKTALES

Abrahams, Roger. *Afro-American Folktales*. New York: Pantheon Books Inc., 1985.

Battle, Kemp P., compiler. *Great American Folklore: Legends, Tales, Ballads, and Superstitions from All Across America*. New York: Doubleday & Co., 1986.

Bierhorst, John. *The Girl Who Married a Ghost and Other Tales from the North American Indians*. Illustrated by Robert Andrew Parker. New York: Four Winds Press, 1984.

Bierhorst, John. *The Naked Bear: Folktales of the Iroquois*. Illustrated by Dirk Zimmer. New York: William Morrow & Co., Inc., 1987.

Botkin, B. A., editor. *A Treasury of American Folklore*. New York: Crown Publishers, Inc., 1944.

Dorson, Richard. *America in Legend*. New York: Pantheon Books Inc., 1973.

Emrich, Duncan. *Folklore on the American Land*. Boston: Little, Brown, 1972.

Erdoes, Richard, and Alfonso Ortiz. *American Indian Myths and Legends*. New York: Pantheon Books Inc., 1985.

Goode, Diane. *The Diane Goode Book of American Folk Tales & Songs*. New York: E. P. Dutton Inc., 1989.

Haviland, Virginia, compiler and editor. *North American Legends*. New York: Putnam & Grosset, 1979.

Leach, Maria. *The Rainbow Book of American Folk Tales and Legends*. Illustrated by Marc Simont. Cleveland: World Publishing Company, 1958.

Lester, Julius. *Black Folktales*. New York: Baron, 1969.

Lester, Julius. *The Knee-High Man and Other Tales*. Illustrated by Ralph Pinto. New York: Dial Books for Young Readers, 1972.

Malcolmson, Anne. *Yankee Doodle's Cousins*. Illustrated by Robert McCloskey. Boston: Houghton Mifflin Co., 1941, 1968.

Smith, Jimmy Neil, editor. *Homespun: Tales from America's Favorite Storytellers*. New York: Crown Publishers, Inc., 1988.

Stoutenberg, Adrian. *American Tall Tales*. Illustrated by Richard M. Powers. New York: Puffin Books, 1976.

Yep, Laurence. *The Rainbow People*. Illustrated by David Wiesner. New York: HarperCollins Publishers, 1989.

FOLK SONGS

Bryan, Ashley. *All Night, All Day: A Child's First Book of African-American Spirituals*. New York: Atheneum Publishers, 1991.

Burgie, Irving. *Caribbean Carnival: Songs of the West Indies*. Illustrated by Frané Lessac. New York: Tambourine Books, 1992.

Hart, Jane, editor. *The Singing Bee!: Favorite Children's Songs*. Illustrated by Anita Lobel. New York: Lothrop, Lee & Shepard Books, 1983.

Krull, Kathleen, collector and arranger. *Gonna Sing My Head Off! American Folk Songs for Children*. Illustrated by Allan Garns. New York: Alfred A. Knopf, Inc., 1992.

Langstaff, John, selector and editor. *Climbing Jacob's Ladder: Heroes of the Bible in African-American Spirituals*. Illustrated by Ashley Bryan. New York: Margaret K. McElderry Books, 1991.

Langstaff, John. *What a Morning!: The Christmas Story in Black Spirituals*. New York: Margaret K. McElderry Books, 1987.

Seeger, Ruth Crawford, selector and editor. *American Folk Songs for Children*. Illustrated by Barbara Cooney. New York: Doubleday & Co., 1948.

HISTORY AND CULTURE

Bierhorst, John. *The Mythology of North America*. New York: William Morrow & Co., Inc., 1985.

Blumberg, Rhoda. *The Great American Gold Rush*. Illustrated with period photographs and prints. New York: Bradbury Press, 1990.

Blumberg, Rhoda. *The Incredible Journey of Lewis & Clark*. Illustrated with period photographs and prints. New York: Lothrop, Lee & Shepard Books, 1987.

Conrad, Pam. *Prairie Visions: The Life and Times of Solomon Butcher*. New York: HarperCollins Publishers, 1990.

Davis, Kenneth C. *Don't Know Much About History: Everything You Need to Know About American History but Never Learned*. New York: Crown Publishers, Inc., 1990.

Fisher, Leonard Everett. *The Oregon Trail*. Illustrated by the author and with black-and-white photographs. New York: Holiday House, Inc., 1990.

Freedman, Russell. *Buffalo Hunt*. Illustrated with period photographs and prints. New York: Holiday House, Inc., 1988.

Freedman, Russell. *Franklin Delano Roosevelt*. Illustrated with black-and-white photographs. New York: Clarion Books, 1990.

Freedman, Russell. *Indian Chiefs*. Illustrated with black-and-white photographs. New York: Holiday House, Inc., 1987.

Katz, William Loren. *Black Indians: A Hidden Heritage*. New York: Atheneum Publishers, 1986.

Katz, William Loren. *Breaking the Chains: African-American Slave Resistance*. Illustrated with black-and-white photographs. New York: Atheneum Publishers, 1990.

Lester, Julius. *To Be a Slave*. Illustrated by Tom Feelings. New York: Dial Books for Young Readers, 1968.

Lyons, Mary E. *Letters from a Slave Girl*. New York: Charles Scribner's Sons, 1992.

Ross, Willma S. *Fabulous Facts About the 50 States*. New York: Scholastic Inc., 1991.

Winter, Jeanette. *Follow the Drinking Gourd*. New York: Alfred A. Knopf, Inc., 1988.

Wolfson, Evelyn. *From Abenaki to Zuni: A Dictionary of Native American Tribes*. Illustrated by William Sauts Bock. New York: Walker & Co., 1988.

RHYMES AND RIDDLES

Bierhorst, John, editor. *The Lightning Inside You and Other Native American Riddles*. Illustrated by Louise Brierly. New York: William Morrow & Co., Inc., 1992.

Cole, Joanna, and Stephanie Calmenson, compilers. *Anna Banana: 101 Jump-Rope Rhymes*. Illustrated by Alan Tiegreen. New York: William Morrow & Co., Inc., 1989.

Cole, Joanna, and Stephanie Calmenson, compilers. *Miss Mary Mack and Other Children's Street Rhymes*. Illustrated by Alan Tiegreen. New York: William Morrow & Co., Inc., 1990.

Withers, Carl. *A Rocket in My Pocket: The Rhymes and Chants of Young Americans*. Illustrated by Susanne Suba. New York: Henry Holt & Co., Inc., 1948.

RECORDINGS

MUSIC

Cassidy, Nancy. *KidsSongs 1, KidsSongs 2*, and *KidsSongs Jubilee*. Palo Alto, California: Klutz Press, 1986, 1988, and 1990.

Cowboy Songs on Folkways. Assorted recording artists. Washington, D.C.: Smithsonian/Folkways Recordings, 1991.

Folk Classics: Roots of American Folk Music. Assorted recording artists. New York: CBS Records, 1989.

Holt, David. *Grandfather's Greatest Hits*. Fairview, North Carolina: High Windy Audio, 1991.

Jones, Bessie. *So Glad I'm Here*. Cambridge, Massachusetts: Rounder Records, 1987.

Jones, Bessie. *Step It Down: Games for Children*. Cambridge, Massachusetts: Rounder Records, 1988.

Langstaff, John. *Let's Make Music*. Cambridge, Massachusetts: Revels Records, 1986.

Langstaff, John. *Songs for Singing Children*. Cambridge, Massachusetts: Revels Records, 1986.

Seeger, Mike, and Peggy Seeger. *American Folk Songs for Children, Part 1 and Part 2*. Cambridge, Massachusetts: Rounder Records, 1987.

Songs of the Working People: From the American Revolution to the Civil War. Assorted recording artists. Chicago, Illinois: Flying Fish Records, 1988.

Sweet Honey in the Rock. *All for Freedom*. Redway, California: Music for Little People, 1989.

Watson, Doc. *Songs for Little Pickers*. Durham, North Carolina: Sugar Hill Records, 1990.

The Weavers. *The Best of the Weavers*. Universal City, California: MCA Records, 1983.

STORIES

Davis, Donald. *Jack Tales: More Than a Beanstalk*. Weston, Connecticut: Weston Woods, 1985.

The Folktellers (Freeman, Barbara, and Connie Regan). *Tales to Grow On*. Weston, Connecticut: Weston Woods, 1982.

Hayes, Joe. *Coyote & Native American Folk Tales*. Santa Fe, New Mexico: Trails West Publishing, 1983.

Hayes, Joe. *A Heart Full of Turquoise: Pueblo Indian Tales*. Santa Fe, New Mexico: Trails West Publishing, 1988.

Hayes, Joe. *Tales of the Southwest*. Weston, Connecticut: Weston Woods, 1984.

Holt, David. *Hairy Man*. Fairview, North Carolina: High Windy Audio, 1981.

Holt, David. *Taily Bone*. Fairview, North Carolina: High Windy Audio, 1985.

Jones, James Earl, and Virginia Hamilton. *The People Could Fly: American Black Folktales*. New York: Alfred A. Knopf, Inc., 1987.

Reneaux, J. J. *Gumbo Ya-Ya: Cajun Songs and Stories*. Comer, Georgia: Story Theater South, 1989.

Torrence, Jackie. *Brer Rabbit Stories*. Weston, Connecticut: Weston Woods, 1984.

Torrence, Jackie. *Country Characters*. Chicago, Illinois: Earwig Music Company, 1986.

Torrence, Jackie. *Legends from the Black Tradition*. Weston, Connecticut: Weston Woods, 1982.

Torrence, Jackie. *Mountain Magic: Jack Tales 1*. Chicago, Illinois: Earwig Music Company, 1984.

OTHER RESOURCES

August House Publishers, P.O. Box 3223, Little Rock, Arkansas 72203; 501-372-5450; 800-284-8784. Publishers of a number of books about the folklore of different regions of the United States and ethnic groups living there.

Center for Folklife Programs and Cultural Studies at the Smithsonian Institution, 955 L'Enfant Plaza, Suite 2600, Washington, D.C. 20560; 202-287-3424. Sponsors an annual festival, publishes monographs, educational materials, recordings, films, and videos about enduring American folk traditions.

Journal of American Folklore. Published by the American Folklife Society, Library of Congress, American Folklife Center, Washington, D.C. 20540; 202-707-6590. A quarterly journal containing folklore of all kinds collected throughout North America. The American Folklife Center provides information about traditional American folk culture.

The National Association for the Preservation and Perpetuation of Storytelling, P.O. Box 309, Jonesborough, Tennessee 37659; 615-753-2171. For general information about storytelling and information about specific festivals, classes, and workshops. Sponsors of an annual storytelling festival.

Rounder Records, 1 Camp Street, Cambridge, Massachusetts 02140; 617-354-0700. Producers of numerous recordings of American folk music, including the Smithsonian/Folkways recordings.

Weston Woods, Weston, Connecticut 06883. Publishers of audio- and videotapes by many different American storytellers.

Author and Title Index

GENERAL SUBJECT GUIDE

~

The stories, songs, poems, and essays in *From Sea to Shining Sea* take on an added meaning when seen through particular contexts. This General Subject Guide contains these four major headings: Ethnic and Religious Groups, Geographical Regions, Song Types, and Story Types.

CHRONOLOGY

~√~

The stories, songs, poems, and essays in *From Sea to Shining Sea* take on added meaning when considered in terms of American history. The following chronology places many of the selections in a more precise historical context than provided by the Contents.

Editor-in-Chief: Jean Feiwel

Executive Editor: Dianne Hess

Art Director: Claire Counihan

Designer: Kathleen Westray

Production Director: Nancy J. Smith

Production Editor: Joan L. Giurdanella

Music Editor: Rachel Miller

Music Note-Setter: Randa Kirshbaum

Assistant Editor: Tracy Mack

Rights and Permissions: Alan Barnes and Ann Sandhorst

Manufacturing Manager: Angela Biola

Managing Editor: Pamela Nelson

~/~

The book is printed on eighty-pound
Cartiera di Sarego Nature Matt

The text type is set in Galliard
by Monotype Composition Company, Inc.,
Baltimore, Maryland.
The display type is Isadora.

Separations, printing, and binding
by New Interlitho, S.p.A., Milan, Italy.